ELEMENTARY MATHEMATICS

FROM AN ADVANCED STANDPOINT

GEOMETRY

FELIX KLEIN

ELEMENTARY MATHEMATICS
FROM AN ADVANCED STANDPOINT

GEOMETRY

TRANSLATED FROM THE THIRD GERMAN EDITION BY

E. R. HEDRICK   AND   C. A. NOBLE
VICE PRESIDENT AND PROVOST   PROFESSOR OF MATHEMATICS, EMER-
THE UNIVERSITY OF CALIFORNIA   ITUS, THE UNIVERSITY OF CALIFORNIA

WITH 141 FIGURES

DOVER PUBLICATIONS, INC.

Library of Congress Catalog Card Number: A48-5461

Manufactured in the United States of America

Dover Publications, Inc.
180 Varick Street
New York 14, N.Y.

PREFACE TO THE FIRST EDITION

In the preface to Part I of these lectures (Arithmetic, Algebra, Analysis) I expressed a doubt as to whether Part II, devoted to geometry, could appear very soon. Nevertheless it has been possible to complete it, thanks to the diligence of Mr. Hellinger.

Concerning the origin and purpose of this series of lectures I have nothing especial to add to what was said in the foreword to Part I. However, a word seems necessary concerning the new form which this second part has assumed.

This form is, in fact, quite unlike that of Part I. I made up my mind to give, above all, a *comprehensive view* of the field of geometry, of such a range as I should wish every teacher in a higher school to have; the discussions about geometric *instruction* were pushed into the background and were placed in connected form at the end, insofar as there was room.

The choice of this new order was motivated partly by the desire to avoid a stereotyped form. There were, however, weightier and deeper reasons. In geometry we possess no unified textbooks corresponding to the general level of the science, such as exist in algebra and analysis, thanks to the model French Cours. We find, rather, a single page here, another there, of an extensive subject, just as it has been developed by one or another group of investigators. In contrast to this, it seemed to be demanded by the pedagogic and the general scientific purpose which I am pursuing that I attempt a more unified presentation.

I close with the wish that the two complementary parts of my *Elementary Mathematics from an Advanced Standpoint* which are herewith completed may find the same friendly reception in the teaching world as the lectures on the organization of mathematical instruction by Mr. Schimmack and myself, which appeared last year.

Göttingen, Christmas, 1908

Klein

PREFACE TO THE THIRD EDITION

In accord with the comprehensive plan for the new edition of my mimeographed lectures, which I developed in the preface to the third edition of the first volume, the text and presentation of this, the second volume, have remained unaltered, except for small changes in detail and a few insertions.[1]

---

[1] Newly added remarks are indicated by square brackets.

The two supplements, which concern literature of a scientific and pedagogic character which was not considered in the original text, were prepared by Mr. Seyfarth after repeated conferences with me. He assumed again the major portion of the burden entailed by the publication. Messrs. Hellinger, Vermeil, and Walther assisted him in the proof reading. Mr. Vermeil undertook the preparation of the two indexes. I feel under obligation to these gentlemen, and also to the firm of Julius Springer, which showed on all occasions a willing spirit of accommodation.

Göttingen, May, 1925

Klein

TRANSLATORS' PREFACE

The favorable reception given to the English translation of volume one of Klein's three-volume work entitled *Elementary Mathematics from an Advanced Standpoint* seems to justify the appearance of the present book, which is a translation of volume two. Professor Courant of New York University, who, while he was a professor at Göttingen, suggested the English translation of Klein's books, has been generously helpful in smoothing the way for the printing of volume two in the United States.

The Translators

CONTENTS

Part Two: Geometric Transformations

Part Three: Systematic Discussion of Geometry and Its Foundations

ELEMENTARY MATHEMATICS FROM AN ADVANCED STANDPOINT—GEOMETRY

INTRODUCTION

Gentlemen! The course of lectures which I now begin will be an immediate continuation of, and a supplement to, my course of last Winter.[1] My purpose now, as it was then, is to gather together all the mathematics that you studied during your student years, insofar as this could be of interest for the future teacher, and, in particular, to show its bearing in the business of school instruction. I carried out this plan, during the winter semester, for *Arithmetic, Algebra,* and *Analysis.* During the current semester, attention will be given to geometry, which was then left to one side. In this course, comprehension of our considerations will be independent of a knowledge of the preceding course of lectures. Moreover, I shall give the whole a somewhat different tone: In the foreground I shall place, let me say, the *encyclopedic ideal*—you will be offered a *survey of the entire field of geometry* into which you can arrange, as into a rigid frame, all the separate items of knowledge which you have acquired in the course of your study, in order to have them at hand when occasion to use them arises. Only afterward shall I emphasize that *interest in mathematical instruction* which was always my starting point last winter.

I am glad to refer to a *vacation course* for teachers of mathematics and physics which was given here in Göttingen during the Easter vacation in 1908. In it I gave an account of my winter lectures. In connection with this, and also with the address of Professor Behrendsen of the local gymnasium, there arose an interesting and stimulating discussion concerning the reorganization of school instruction in arithmetic, algebra, and analysis, and more particularly about the introduction of differential and integral calculus into the schools.[2] Those who took part showed an extremely gratifying interest in these questions and, in general, in our efforts to bring the university into living touch with the schools. I hope that my present lectures also may exert an influence in this direction. May they contribute their part

---

[1] [Appeared as Part I of these lectures on *Elementary Mathematics from an Advanced Standpoint,* Berlin, 1924, 3rd edition. The quotation "Part I" refers to the third edition.]

[2] See the report by R. Schimmack, *Ueber die Gestaltung des mathematischen Unterrichts im Sinne der neueren Reformideen,* Zeitschrift für mathematischen und naturwissenschaftlichen Unterricht, vol. 39, pp. 513–527, 1908 (also printed separately, Leipzig, 1908).

1

toward the elimination of the old complaint which we have had to hear continually—and often justly—from the schools: University instruction provides, indeed, much of a special nature, but it leaves the beginning teacher entirely without orientation as to many important general things which he could really use later.

Concerning now the *material of these lectures*, let me say that, as in the preceding course, I shall now and then have to presuppose knowledge of important theorems from all of the fields of mathematics which you have studied, in order to lay emphasis upon a *general survey of the whole*. To be sure, I shall always try to assist your memory by brief statements, so that you can easily orient yourself in the literature. On the other hand, I shall draw attention, more than is usually done, as I did in Part I, to the *historical development of the science*, to the accomplishments of its great pioneers. I hope, by discussions of this sort, to further, as I like to say, your *general mathematical culture:* alongside of knowledge of details, as these are supplied by the special lectures, there should be a grasp of subject-matter and of historical relationship.

Allow me to make a last general remark, in order to avoid a misunderstanding which might arise from the nominal separation of this "geometric" part of my lectures from the first arithmetic part. In spite of this separation, I advocate here, as always in such general lectures, a tendency which I like best to designate by the phrase *"fusion of arithmetic and geometry"*—meaning by arithmetic, as is usual in the schools, the field which includes not merely the theory of integers, but also the whole of algebra and analysis. Some are inclined, especially in Italy, to use the word *"fusion"* as a catchword for efforts which are restricted to geometry. In fact it has long been the custom in the schools as well as the university, first to study geometry of the plane and then, entirely separated from it, the geometry of space. On this account, space geometry is unfortunately often slighted, and the noble faculty of space perception, which we possess originally, is stunted. In contrast to this, the "fusionists" wish to treat the plane and space together, in order not to restrict our thinking artificially to two dimensions. This endeavor also meets my approval, but I am thinking, at the same time, of a still more far-reaching fusion. Last semester I endeavored always to enliven the abstract discussions of arithmetic, algebra, and analysis by means of figures and graphic methods, which bring the things nearer to the individual and often make clear to him, for the first time, why he should be interested in them. Similarly, I shall now, from the very beginning, accompany space perception, which, of course, will hold first place, with analytic formulas, which facilitate in the highest degree the precise formulation of geometric facts.

You will most easily see what I mean if I turn at once to our subject and consider first a series of simple geometric fundamental forms.

PART ONE

THE SIMPLEST GEOMETRIC MANIFOLDS

I. LINE–SEGMENT, AREA, VOLUME AS RELATIVE MAGNITUDES

You will notice by this chapter heading that I am following the intention announced above, of examining simultaneously the corresponding magnitudes on the straight line, in the plane, and in space. At the same time, however, we shall take into account the principle of fusion by making use at once of the *rectangular system of coordinates* for the purpose of analytic formulation.

If we have a *line-segment*, let us think of it as laid upon the x axis. If the abscissas of its endpoints are x_1 and x_2, its *length* is $x_1 - x_2$, and we may write this difference in the form of the determinant

$$(1, 2) = x_1 - x_2 = \frac{1}{1}\begin{vmatrix} x_1 & 1 \\ x_2 & 1 \end{vmatrix}.$$

Similarly, the *area of a triangle* in the xy plane which is formed by the three points 1, 2, 3, with coordinates (x_1, y_1), (x_2, y_2), (x_3, y_3), will be

$$(1, 2, 3) = \frac{1}{1 \cdot 2}\begin{vmatrix} x_1 & y_1 & 1 \\ x_2 & y_2 & 1 \\ x_3 & y_3 & 1 \end{vmatrix}.$$

Finally, we have, for the *volume of the tetrahedron* made by the four points 1, 2, 3, 4, with coordinates $(x_1, y_1, z_1), \cdots, (x_4, y_4, z_4)$, the formula

$$(1, 2, 3, 4) = \frac{1}{1 \cdot 2 \cdot 3}\begin{vmatrix} x_1 & y_1 & z_1 & 1 \\ x_2 & y_2 & z_2 & 1 \\ x_3 & y_3 & z_3 & 1 \\ x_4 & y_4 & z_4 & 1 \end{vmatrix}.$$

We say ordinarily that the length, or, as the case may be, the area or the volume, is equal to the *absolute value* of these several magnitudes, whereas, actually, our formulas furnish, over and above that, a *definite sign*, which depends upon the order in which the points are taken. We shall make it a fundamental rule always to take into account in geometry the signs which the analytic formulas supply. We must accordingly inquire as to the *geometric significance of the sign in these determinations of content.*

It is important, therefore, how we choose the *system of rectangular coor-*

3

dinates. Let us, then, at the outset, adopt a convention, which is, of course, arbitrary, but which must be binding in all cases. In the case of *one dimension*, we shall think of the positive *x* axis as always pointing to the right. In the plane, the positive *x* axis will be directed toward the right, the positive *y* axis upward (see Fig. 1). If we were to let the *y* axis point downward, we should have an essentially different coordinate system, one which would be a reflection of the first and not superimposable upon it by mere motion in

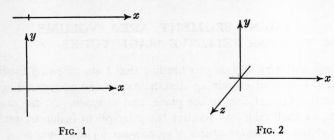

FIG. 1   FIG. 2

the plane, i.e., without going out into space. Finally, the *coordinate system in space* will be obtained from the one in the plane by adding to the latter a *z* axis directed positively to the *front* (see Fig. 2). A choice of the *z* axis pointing positively to the rear would give, again, an essentially different coordinate system, one which could not be made to coincide with ours by any movement in space.[1]

If we always adhere to these conventions, we shall find the *interpretation of our signs in simple geometric properties of the succession of points as these are determined by their numbering.*

For the *segment* (1, 2) this property is obvious: *The expression $x_1 - x_2$ for its length is positive or negative according as point 1 lies to the right or to the left of point 2.*

In the case of the *triangle*, we obtain: *The formula for area has the positive or the negative sign according as a circuit about the triangle from the vertex 1 to 3 via 2 turns out to be counterclockwise or the reverse.*

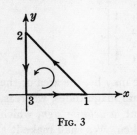

FIG. 3

We shall prove this by taking, first, a conveniently placed special triangle, evaluating the determinant which expresses its area, and then, through consideration of continuity, passing to the general case. We consider that triangle which has, as its first vertex, the unit point on the *x* axis ($x_1 = 1, y_1 = 0$), as its second, the unit point on the *y* axis ($x_2 = 0$, $y_2 = 1$), and as its third the origin ($x_3 = 0$, $y_3 = 0$). According to our agreement about the system of coordinates,

---

[1] These two systems are distinguished as "right-handed" and "left-handed" because they correspond respectively to the position of the first three fingers of the right and left hand. (See Part I, p. 64.)

we must traverse the boundary of this triangle in the counterclockwise sense (see Fig. 3), and our formula for its area yields the positive value:

$$\frac{1}{2}\begin{vmatrix} 1 & 0 & 1 \\ 0 & 1 & 1 \\ 0 & 0 & 1 \end{vmatrix} = +\frac{1}{2}.$$

Now we can bring the vertices of this triangle, by continuous deformation, into coincidence with those of any other triangle traversed in the same sense, and we can do this in such a way that the three vertices of the triangle shall at no time be collinear. In this process, our determinant changes value continuously, and since it vanishes only when the points 1, 2, 3 are collinear, it must always remain positive. This establishes the fact that the area of any triangle whose boundary is traversed in counterclockwise sense is positive. If we interchange two vertices of the original triangle, we see at once that every triangle which is traversed *in clockwise sense* has negative area.

We can now treat the *tetrahedron* in analogous fashion. We start, again, with a conveniently placed tetrahedron. As first, second, and third vertices, we choose, in order, the unit points on the x, y, and z axes, and as fourth vertex, the origin. Its volume is therefore

$$\frac{1}{6}\begin{vmatrix} 1 & 0 & 0 & 1 \\ 0 & 1 & 0 & 1 \\ 0 & 0 & 1 & 1 \\ 0 & 0 & 0 & 1 \end{vmatrix} = +\frac{1}{6}.$$

It follows, as before, that every tetrahedron which can be obtained from this one by continuous deformation during which the four vertices are never complanar (i.e., during which the determinant never vanishes), has positive volume. But one can characterize all these tetrahedrons by the sense in which the one face (2, 3, 4) is traversed when it is looked at from the vertex 1. In this way we obtain the result: *The volume of the tetrahedron* (1, 2, 3, 4) *which our formula yields is positive if the vertices* 2, 3, 4, *looked at from vertex* 1, *follow one another in counterclockwise sense; otherwise it is negative.*

We have thus, from our analytic formulas, actually deduced geometric rules which permit us to assign a definite sign to any segment, any triangle, any tetrahedron, if the vertices are given in a definite order. Great advantages are thus gained over the ordinary elementary geometry which considers length and contents as absolute magnitudes. Indeed, we can mention general simple theorems where elementary geometry must distinguish numerous cases according to the appearance of the figure.

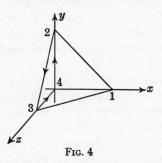

FIG. 4

Let me begin with a very primitive example, the *ratio of the segments* made by three points on a line, say the x axis. Denoting the three points by 1, 2, and 4 (see Fig. 5), as is convenient in view of what is to follow, we see that the ratio in question will be given by the formula $S = (x_1 - x_2)/(x_1 - x_4)$, and it is clear that this quotient is positive or negative according as the point 1 lies outside or inside the segment (2, 4). If, as is customary in elementary presentations, we give only the absolute value

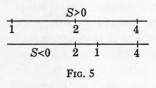

FIG. 5

$|S| = |x_1 - x_2|/|x_1 - x_4|$, we must always either refer to the figure, or state in words whether we have in mind an inside or an outside point, which is, of course, more complicated. *The introduction of the sign thus takes account of the different possible orders of the points on the line*, a fact to which we shall often have to refer in the course of these lectures.

If we now add a fourth point 3, we can set up the *cross ratio* of the four points, that is,

$$D = \frac{x_1 - x_2}{x_1 - x_4} : \frac{x_3 - x_2}{x_3 - x_4} = \frac{(x_1 - x_2)(x_3 - x_4)}{(x_1 - x_4)(x_3 - x_2)}.$$

This expression has again a definite sign, and we see at once that $D < 0$ when the pair of points 1 and 3, on the one hand, and the pair 2 and 4, on the other hand, mutually separate one another; and that $D > 0$ in the opposite case, i.e., when 1 and 3 lie both outside or both inside the segment 2, 4. (See Figs. 6 and 7.) Thus there are always two essentially different

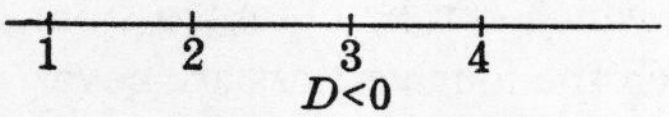

$D<0$

FIG. 6

$D>0$

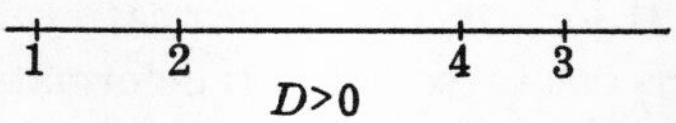

FIG. 7

arrangements which yield the same absolute value D. If this absolute value alone is given, we must give the arrangement also. For example, if we define harmonic points by the equation $D = 1$, as is still the custom, unfortunately, in the schools, one must include in the definition the demand that the two pairs of points separate each other, whereas in our plan the *one* statement $D = -1$ is sufficient. This practice of taking account of the sign is especially useful in *projective* geometry, in which, as you know, the cross ratio plays a leading role. There we have the familiar theorem that four points on a line have the same cross ratio as the four points which arise when we project the given points from a center upon another line (perspective). If we now consider the cross ratio as a relative magnitude, affected by a sign, the converse of this theorem holds without exception: If each of two sets of four points lies on one of two lines, and if they have the same cross ratio, they can be derived one from the other by projection, either single or repeated. For example, in Fig. 8, the sets 1, 2, 3,

4, and 1″, 2″, 3″, 4″ are in perspective to 1′, 2′, 3′, 4′ if we use the centers P and P'. If, however, we know only the absolute value of D, the corre-

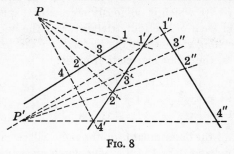

FIG. 8

sponding theorem does not hold in this simple form; we should have to make a special assumption about the arrangement of the points.

We have a more fruitful field if we consider *applications of our triangle formula*. Let us first select any point 0 in the interior of a triangle (1, 2, 3) and let us join 0 to each of the vertices (see Fig. 9). Then the sum of the areas of the three partial triangles, thought of in the elementary sense as absolute magnitudes, is equal to the area of the original triangle. Thus we may write $| (1, 2, 3) | = | (0, 2, 3) | + | (0, 3, 1) | + | (0, 1, 2) |$. The figure shows that, in all the triangles, the order of the vertices, as they appear in the above equation, is counterclockwise. Hence the areas (1, 2, 3), (0, 2, 3), (0, 3, 1), (0, 1, 2), are all positive in the sense of our general definition, so that we may write our formula in the form

$$(1, 2, 3) = (0, 2, 3) + (0, 3, 1) + (0, 1, 2).$$

Now I assert *that the same formula also holds when 0 lies outside the triangle, and, further, when 0, 1, 2, 3 are any four points whatever in the plane.* If we take Fig. 10, for example, we see that the boundaries of (0, 2, 3) and

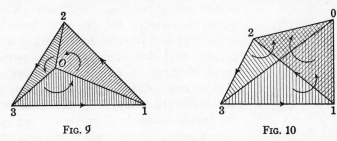

FIG. 9   FIG. 10

(0, 3, 1) are traversed in counterclockwise sense, but that of (0, 1, 2) is traversed in the clockwise sense, so that our formula for the absolute areas would give $| (1, 2, 3) | = | (0, 2, 3) | + | (0, 3, 1) | - | (0, 1, 2) |$. The figure verifies the correctness of this equation.

We shall give a general proof of our theorem by means of the *analytic*

definition, whereby we shall recognize in our formula a well known theorem of the theory of determinants. For convenience, let us take the point O as our origin $x = 0$, $y = 0$, which is obviously no essential specialization, and let us substitute for each of the four triangle areas the appropriate determinant. Then, omitting everywhere the factor $\frac{1}{2}$, we are to prove that, for arbitrary $x_1, \cdots, y_3$, the following relation holds:

$$\begin{vmatrix} x_1 & y_1 & 1 \\ x_2 & y_2 & 1 \\ x_3 & y_3 & 1 \end{vmatrix} = \begin{vmatrix} 0 & 0 & 1 \\ x_2 & y_2 & 1 \\ x_3 & y_3 & 1 \end{vmatrix} + \begin{vmatrix} 0 & 0 & 1 \\ x_3 & y_3 & 1 \\ x_1 & y_1 & 1 \end{vmatrix} + \begin{vmatrix} 0 & 0 & 1 \\ x_1 & y_1 & 1 \\ x_2 & y_2 & 1 \end{vmatrix}$$

The value of each of the determinants on the right will remain unchanged if we replace the second and third 1 of the last column by zeros, since these elements enter only those minors which are multiplied by zero when we develop according to the top row. If we now make a cyclic interchange of rows in the last two determinants, which is permissible in determinants of the third, or, in fact, of any odd order, we can write our equation in the following form:

$$\begin{vmatrix} x_1 & y_1 & 1 \\ x_2 & y_2 & 1 \\ x_3 & y_3 & 1 \end{vmatrix} = \begin{vmatrix} 0 & 0 & 1 \\ x_2 & y_2 & 0 \\ x_3 & y_3 & 0 \end{vmatrix} + \begin{vmatrix} x_1 & y_1 & 0 \\ 0 & 0 & 1 \\ x_3 & y_3 & 0 \end{vmatrix} + \begin{vmatrix} x_1 & y_1 & 0 \\ x_2 & y_2 & 0 \\ 0 & 0 & 1 \end{vmatrix}$$

But this is an identity, for on the right there are only the minors of the last column of the first determinant, so that we have merely the well known development of this determinant according to the elements of a column. Thus, at one stroke, we have proved our theorem for all possible positions of the four points.

We can generalize this formula so that it will give the *area of any polygon*. Imagine that you had, say, the following problem in surveying: To determine the area of a rectilinear field after having measured the coordinates of the corners $1, 2, \cdots, n - 1, n$ (see Fig. 11). One who is not accustomed to operate with signs would then sketch the shape of the polygon, divide it up into triangles by drawing diagonals, perhaps, and then according to the particular shape of the field, paying especial regard to whether some of the angles are re-entrant, find the area as the sum or difference of the areas of the partial triangles. However, we can give at once a general formula which will give the correct result quite mechanically without any necessity of looking at the figure: If O is any point in the plane, say the origin, then the area of our polygon, the boundary being traversed in the sense $1, 2, \cdots, n$, will be

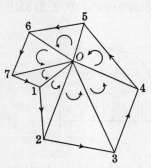

FIG. 11

$$(1, 2, 3, \cdots, n) = (0, 1, 2) + (0, 2, 3) + \cdots + (0, n - 1, n) + (0, n, 1),$$

whereby each triangle is to be taken with the sign determined by the sense in which the circuit about it is made. *The formula yields the area of the polygon positively or negatively according as the circuit of the polygon in the sense 1, 2, · · ·, n is counterclockwise or not.* It will suffice to write this formula. You yourselves can easily supply the proof.

Instead of pursuing this example further, I prefer to take up some especially interesting cases, which, to be sure, could not arise in surveying, namely, cases of *polygons which overlap themselves* as in the adjoining quadrilateral (see Fig. 12). If we wish here to talk at all about definite area, it can only be the value which our formula yields. Let us consider what this value means geometrically. At the outset we notice that this must be independent of the particular location of the point O. Let us place O, as conveniently as possible, at the

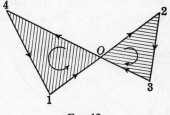

FIG. 12

point where the overlappings cross. Then the triangles $(0, 1, 2)$ and $(0, 3, 4)$ will be zero and there remains:

$$(1, 2, 3, 4) = (0, 2, 3) + (0, 4, 1).$$

The first triangle has negative area, the second positive area; hence the area of our overlapping quadrilateral, if we prescribe a circuit in the sense $(1, 2, 3, 4)$, is equal to the absolute value of the area of the part $(0, 4, 1)$ that was traversed in counterclockwise sense, *diminished* by that of the part $(0, 2, 3)$ that was traversed in clockwise sense.

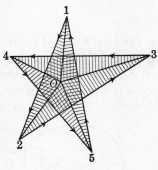

FIG. 13

As a second example, let us examine the adjoined *star pentagon* (see Fig. 13). If we take O in the middle part, all the partial triangles in the sum

$$(0, 1, 2) + (0, 2, 3) + \cdots + (0, 5, 1)$$

are traversed in the positive sense; their sum covers the five-cornered central part of the figure twice, and each of the five tips once. If we again consider a positive circuit around our polygon $(1, 2, 3, 4, 5, 1)$, we see that every part of the boundary is traversed counterclockwise and that, in particular, we have passed twice around the portion of the polygon which is doubly counted in the area, but only once around the remaining portions.

From these two examples we can infer the following *general rule: For any rectilinear polygon with arbitrary overlappings, our formula yields, as total area, the algebraic sum of the separate partial areas bounded by the polygonal line, whereby each of these partial areas is counted as often as we pass around its boundary when the circuit* $(1, 2, 3, \cdots, n, 1)$ *is made once, this counting to be made positively or negatively according as we pass around the partial area in counterclockwise or clockwise sense.* You will have no difficulty in establishing the truth of this general theorem.

Let us now pass from polygons to *areas with curvilinear boundaries.* We shall consider any closed curve whatever, which may cross itself any number of times. We assign a *definite sense of direction along this curve* and inquire

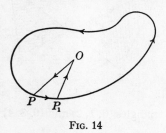

as to the area bounded by the curve. We find this area in a natural manner if we approximate the curve by polygons having an increasing number of shorter and shorter sides (see Fig. 14) and calculate the limit of the areas of these polygons, found in the way we have just described. If

FIG. 14

$$P(x, y) \qquad \text{and} \qquad P_1(x + dx, y + dy)$$

are two neighboring vertices of such an approximating polygon, then its area consists of a sum of elementary triangles (OPP_1), that is of summands:

$$\frac{1}{2} \begin{vmatrix} 0 & 0 & 1 \\ x & y & 1 \\ x + dx & y + dy & 1 \end{vmatrix} = \frac{1}{2}(x\,dy - y\,dx).$$

In the limit, this sum becomes the line integral

$$\frac{1}{2} \int (x\,dy - y\,dx)$$

taken along the curve, which, therefore, defines the area bounded by the curve. If we wish to interpret this definition geometrically, we can apply to the new case the result just given for polygons: *Each partial area enclosed by the curve is counted positively as many times as it is encircled in counterclockwise sense and negatively as many times as it is encircled in clockwise sense*

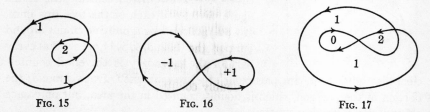

FIG. 15   FIG. 16   FIG. 17

while the given curve is traversed once in the prescribed sense. For a simple curve, such as that of Fig. 14, the integral yields, accordingly, the exact area bounded by the curve, taken positively. In Fig. 15, the outer part is counted once positively, the inner part twice; in Fig. 16, the left-hand part is negative, while the right-hand part is positive, so that, altogether, a negative area results; in Fig. 17, one part is not counted at all, since it is encircled once positively and once negatively. Of course, curves can arise which, in this sense, bound a zero area. We obtain such a curve if we take the curve in Fig. 16 symmetric with respect to the double point. Such a case presents nothing absurd when we recall that our determination of area rests upon a convenient assumption.

I shall now show you how appropriate these definitions are by considering *Amsler's Polar Planimeter.* This highly ingenious and very useful apparatus, constructed in 1854 by the mechanic Jacob Amsler of Schaffhausen, effects the determination of areas precisely in the sense of our discussion above. Let me consider, first, the *theoretical basis of the construction.*

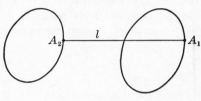

FIG. 18

We think of a rod A_1A_2 (see Fig. 18) of length l moved in the plane in such a way that A_1 and A_2 describe separate closed curves and the rod itself returns to its initial position. We wish to find the area which the rod sweeps out, counting the several parts of this area as positive or negative, according as they are swept out in one sense or in the other. To this end, we replace the continuous motion of the rod by a succession of arbitrarily small elementary motions from one position 1 2 to a neighboring one 1′ 2′, and we use the limit process as we do in every integration. The actual area swept out by the rod will be the limit of the sum of the "elementary quadrilaterals"

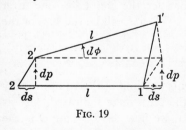

FIG. 19

(1, 1′, 2′, 2) formed by these elementary motions, and it is easy to see that the sense of the motion of the rod is taken into account properly if we give to each elementary quadrilateral the sign corresponding to a circuit in the sense 1, 1′, 2′, 2. Now we can resolve each elementary motion of the rod A_1A_2 into three steps (see Fig. 19):

(1) A translation in the direction of the rod by an amount ds.

(2) A translation *normal* to its direction by an amount dp.

(3) A rotation about the end A_2 through an angle $d\phi$.

In this way the areas $0 \cdot ds$, $l \cdot dp$, $(l^2/2)\, d\phi$, respectively, will be swept out. We can replace the area of the elementary quadrilateral by the sum of these three areas, since the error thus made would be an infinitesimal of higher order and would disappear in the limit process (which is, indeed, a simple process of integration). It is essential to note that this sum

$$l \cdot dp + \frac{l^2}{2} \cdot d\phi$$

agrees in sign with the area of the quadrilateral $(1, 1', 2', 2)$, if we measure $d\phi$ positively in counterclockwise sense and dp positively for translation toward the side of increasing ϕ.

Integration along the path of motion yields for the area swept out by $A_1 A_2$ the value

$$J = l \int dp + \frac{l^2}{2} \int d\phi.$$

The integral $\int d\phi$ represents the entire angle through which the rod turns with respect to its initial position. Since the rod returns to its initial position, $\int d\phi = 0$, unless the rod has made a complete revolution, so that the area is

(1) $$J = l \int dp.$$

If, however, the rod makes one or more complete turns before returning to its original position, which is possible with suitably chosen paths for A_1 and A_2, then $\int d\phi$ is a multiple of 2π, and we must add to the right-

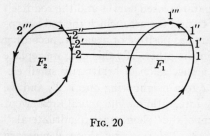

FIG. 20

hand side $+ \pi l^2$ for each complete turn in the positive sense and $- \pi l^2$ for each one in the negative sense. For the sake of simplicity we shall pass over this slight complication.

Now we can determine the area J in a somewhat different way (see Fig. 20). In the succession of elementary motions let the rod take, one after another, the positions $1\ 2$, $1'\ 2'$, $1''\ 2''$, $\cdots$. Then J will be the sum of the elementary quadrilaterals

$$J = (1, 1', 2', 2) + (1', 1'', 2'', 2') + (1'', 1''', 2''', 2'') + \cdots,$$

or, more exactly, the integral which represents the limit of this sum, whereby each quadrilateral is to be traversed in the sense here indicated, just as before. Using our earlier polygon formula, we now have, where O is the arbitrarily chosen origin of coordinates,

$$\begin{aligned}
J = {} & (0, 1,\ \ 1'\ ) + (0, 1',\ 2'\ ) + (0, 2',\ 2\ ) + (0, 2,\ \ 1\ ) \\
& + (0, 1',\ 1'') + (0, 1'',\ 2'') + (0, 2'',\ 2'\ ) + (0, 2',\ 1'\ ) \\
& + (0, 1'',\ 1''') + (0, 1''',\ 2''') + (0, 2''',\ 2'') + (0, 2'',\ 1'') \\
& + \ \cdot \quad \cdot \quad \cdot \quad \cdot \quad \cdot \quad \cdot \quad \cdot \quad \cdot \quad \cdot \quad \cdot \quad \cdot \quad \cdot \quad \cdot \quad \cdot
\end{aligned}$$

The second triangle here in each row is the same as the fourth triangle in the next following row, but traversed in the opposite sense,

$$[(0, 1', 2') = -(0, 2', 1'), \quad (0, 1'', 2'') = -(0, 2'', 1''), \quad \cdots],$$

so that these summands all cancel each other. Moreover, since the series of elementary quadrilaterals is closed, this summand $(0, 1, 2)$ will appear in the last row and will cancel $(0, 2, 1)$ of the first row. There will remain only the first and third triangles of each row. These first triangles, however, by what precedes, add up to the polygon $(1, 1', 1'', \cdots)$, and this, in the limit, is the *area F_1 of the curve described by the end A_1 of the rod*. Similarly, the third triangles, if we change the sign everywhere, add up to $(2, 2', 2'', \cdots)$, which, in the limit, is the *area F_2 of the curve described by A_2*. Thus we have, finally,

(2) $$J = F_1 - F_2.$$

Obviously both curves can cross each other arbitrarily, provided we define F_1 and F_2 with careful regard to our sign rule.

The *geometric theory* of the planimeter is contained in the two formulas (1) and (2). If, namely, we allow A_2 to move along a curve of known area F_2, and a tracing point at A_1 to glide along the boundary of F_1, we can at once determine the value of

(2') $$F_1 = F_2 + l \int dp$$

if we have a *device which allows us to measure $\int dp$*. Amsler created such a device—and that is the second part of his *mechanical invention*—by fixing a roller upon the rod A_1A_2 as axis, which rolls upon the paper with the motion of the rod. Let its distance from A_2 be λ and its radius ρ (see Fig. 21). The angle ψ, through which the roller turns with the motion of the rod, will be the sum of the angles $d\psi$ that arise in the elementary motions. Each $d\psi$ can be thought of as made up of the rotations $d\psi_1, d\psi_2, d\psi_3$ that come from the three simple movements of the rod into which we

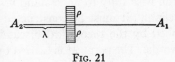

FIG. 21

resolved each of its elementary motions (p. 11). During the translation (1), the roller does not turn, so that $d\psi_1 = 0$; during the translation (2) of A_1A_2 normal to itself, in amount dp, the roller moves over the paper in amount $dp = \rho\, d\psi_2$, so that $d\psi_2 = dp/\rho$; during the rotation (3) about A_2, through the angle $d\phi$, the roller rim moves in amount $\lambda\, d\phi = \rho\, d\psi_3$, so that $d\psi_3 = (\lambda/\rho)\, d\phi$. We have then, finally,

$$d\psi = \frac{1}{\rho} dp + \frac{\lambda}{\rho} d\phi.$$

If we integrate over the entire path of motion, we have $\int d\phi = 0$ if A_1A_2 returns to its original position without making a complete turn, and the full turning angle of the Amsler roller will be

(3) $$\psi = \frac{1}{\rho}\int dp.$$

If the rod, however, makes one or more complete rotations, then there will appear appropriate multiples of $2\pi(\lambda/\rho)$ on the right; but of this, again, we we shall take no account.

Combining the formulas (2') and (3), we obtain finally the formula

$$F_1 - F_2 = l \cdot \rho \cdot \psi;$$

that is, the difference between the two areas encircled by the two ends of the rod is measured by the angle ψ through which the roller turns.

In the making of the instrument, it is desirable to *make F_2 zero.* Amsler brings this about in an admirable way by attaching A_2 to an arm which is made to rotate about a fixed point M. (See Fig. 22.) Then A_2 can move only back and forth on the arm of a circle and can therefore enclose no area, if we ignore the complicating possibility that A_2 makes one or more complete circuits about M. Because of this "*pole*" M, the whole instrument is often called a *polar planimeter*. The instrument is actually operated simply by causing the point A_1, provided with a *marking pencil*, to traverse the

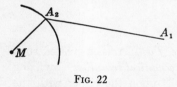

FIG. 22

boundary of the area one wishes to measure, and by then reading the angle ψ on the roller. We obtain thus the enclosed area $F_1 = l \cdot \rho \cdot \psi$. The constant of the instrument $l\rho$ can be determined by measuring a known area, say a unit square.

I can show you here a picture of the polar planimeter (see Fig. 23). Of course you must examine the instrument yourself, and manipulate it, if you wish fully to understand it. Naturally, if the instrument is to function reliably, it must be constructed in a manner more complicated than is implied by the theoretical discussion. In this connection, let me add a few words. The point M is carried by a heavy mass and is joined to A_2 by a rod.

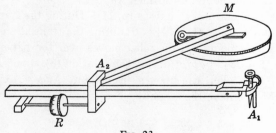

FIG. 23

The theoretically important rod A_1A_2, which we talked about, is not the second metal bar which you see on the instrument, but the ideal prolongation of the axis of the roller, which is parallel to that bar and which passes through the moving pencil point A_1. This sharp point is accompanied by a parallel blunt peg to keep the point A_1 from tearing the paper. The roller carries a vernier for finer readings and a marker for recording complete revolutions.

Instead of mentioning further details, I should like here to sound a general warning against neglecting the *actual practical demonstration* when such instruments are considered in illustration of a theory. The pure mathematician is often too prone to do so. Such neglect is just as unjustifiably one-sided as is the opposite extreme of the mechanician who, without taking an interest in the theory, loses himself in details of construction. Applied mathematics should supply here a bond of union. It should, in particular, take into account that the theoretical formulation of the principle is never exactly realized in the instrument: thus the joints of the apparatus will always be somewhat loose; the roller will always slide somewhat instead of only rolling; finally, the drawing paper is never a uniform plane, and one is never able to guide the pencil point exactly along the curve. To what extent such errors are important, to how many places, in consequence, the result read off of the roller can be relied upon, are of course questions of greatest importance in practice. To investigate such questions is the province of applied mathematics.

In connection with this diagram, I shall consider the place of these lectures with reference to two earlier courses of similar title, which appear likewise in mimeographed form: *Applications of Differential and Integral Calculus to Geometry, a Revision of Principles* [SS, 1901; prepared by C. H. Müller [1]], and *Introduction to Higher Geometry* [WS 1892–93 and SS 1893; prepared by Fr. Schilling [2]]. In the first one of these courses, there appears in the foreground the difference just mentioned between abstract and practical geometry. In fact we had, in that course, a seminar talk on the sources of error in Amsler's polar planimeter. In the other course, however, I developed somewhat thoroughly the theories of abstract geometry to meet the needs of the specialist who desires, in the spirit of research of today, to work independently in this field. In the present course, finally, I want to do a third thing: I should like to set forth, so to speak, the *elementary theory of geometry:* those things which, without question, every prospective teacher should know, and in particular, also, the things which are of elementary importance for applications in physics and mechanics. I shall be able to refer in this course only occasionally to things which belong to the first two fields mentioned above.

Returning now to our general considerations about areas and volumes,

---

[1] New printing, Leipzig, 1907. [Will appear shortly as vol. III of the present edition of *Elementary Mathematics*.]

[2] Two parts. New printing, Leipzig, 1907. [Out of print. Concerning the plan for a new edition, see the preface to vol. I, p. v.]

I shall give first a *historical note*. I wish to mention the man who first applied consistently the sign principle in geometry, the great geometrician A. F. Möbius, of Leipzig. The book in which he took this important step is a youthful work of the year 1827: *The Barycentric Calculus*.[1] It is one of the works which are decidedly fundamental for the newer geometry. The reading of his book is unusually pleasant, if only because of the beautiful presentation. The title refers to the fact that Möbius proceeds from the following considerations, which have to do with centers of gravity. At three fixed points O_1, O_2, O_3 of a plane are placed three masses m_1, m_2, m_3 which may be positive or negative, as in the case of electric charges. Then the center of gravity P is uniquely determined, and we can make it assume any position in the plane by varying m_1, m_2, and m_3. Now the three masses m_1, m_2, and m_3 are thought of as coordinates of P, so that P depends only upon the ratios of these magnitudes. This is the first instance of the introduction into geometry of what we now call *trilinear coordinates*. So much in explanation of the title of Möbius' book. As to its very interesting contents, we shall be concerned now mainly with §§ 17–20, where the principle of the sign is applied in determining the area of a triangle or the volume of a tetrahedron, and in which the definitions that I have mentioned are given.

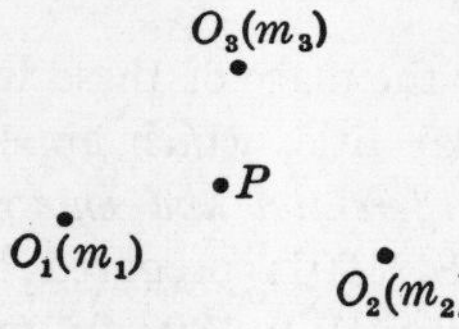

FIG. 24

I should remark also that Möbius, as an old man, extended these results in 1858 by a far-reaching discovery, which was first published, however, in 1865 in the paper entitled *On the determination of the volume of a polyhedron*.[2] In this he proved, namely, that *there are polyhedrons to which we cannot in any way assign a volume*, whereas we can, as we saw earlier, define area for any plane polygon no matter in how complicated a manner it overlaps itself. We shall now consider in detail these remarkable phenomena.

Let us start from the formula established above for the volume of the tetrahedron:

$$(1, 2, 3, 4) = \tfrac{1}{6} \begin{vmatrix} x_1 & y_1 & z_1 & 1 \\ x_2 & y_2 & z_2 & 1 \\ x_3 & y_3 & z_3 & 1 \\ x_4 & y_4 & z_4 & 1 \end{vmatrix}.$$

If we develop this determinant according to minors of the last column, this amounts—as we saw earlier (p. 7 et seq.), in the case of the triangle,—to resolving the tetrahedron into four others which have the faces of the given

[1] Leipzig, 1827 = *Collected Works*, vol. I (Leipzig, 1885), 633 pages.

[2] Berichte über die Verhandlungen der Königlich Sächsischen Gesellschaft der Wissenschaften (Mathemathisch-physikalische Klasse), vol. 17 (1865), p. 31 = *Collected Works*, vol. 2 (Leipzig, 1886), p. 473.

their bases and the origin as their common vertex. According

in the theory of determinants, we shall obtain, if we take the

2, 3, 4, the following formula:

$$= (0, 2, 3, 4) - (0, 3, 4, 1) + (0, 4, 1, 2) - (0, 1, 2, 3).$$

y minus signs appear, whereas, with the triangle, only plus

is that determinants of even order change sign under cyclic

while those of odd order do not. Of course we can get rid of

by suitable interchanges of rows, but we must then give up

er. We can write, for example,

$$= (0, 2, 3, 4) + (0, 4, 3, 1) + (0, 4, 1, 2) + (0, 2, 1, 3).$$

appreciate the law involved here, think of the tetrahedral

of paper and as folded down into the plane (2, 3, 4), whereby

kes three different positions (see Fig. 25). Then the vertices

three faces appear, in the last formula, in an order which

Fig. 25, to a counterclockwise circuit about all the triangles.

in the same result for this space figure, of course, without

vn of the faces. To each of the six edges there correspond two

s clear that, *when the circuit is made*

angles in the order indicated, each side

d once in one sense and once in the

law, which Möbius called the law of

s obviously set up a definite sense of

the face triangles, as soon as one is

ected for one face triangle. Our for-

ow: *A tetrahedron* (1, 2, 3, 4) *can be*

e sum of four tetrahedrons with the com-

x 0, provided that after choosing the cir-

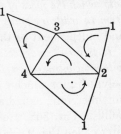

FIG. 25

3, 4) *for one triangle we select the circuit sense for the other faces*

öbius' law of edges.

defined the area of an arbitrary polygon earlier (p. 8), by re-

o triangles and generalizing the triangle formula, so now we

ass from the result just obtained to a *definition of the volume of*
an arbitrary polyhedron. In the present case, however, we must not only
allow the sides of a single polygonal face of our polyhedron to cross each
other, but must also allow the faces to intersect in an arbitrary way. We
now select an arbitrary auxiliary point O, and, as a first step, we define
the *volume of the pyramid* which projects from O one of the polygonal faces
of the polyhedron.

For this purpose we must first choose the sense for the boundary of the
base. [Suppose it to be the face (1, 2, 3, 4, 5, 6) (Fig. 26) of the polyhedron.]
This polygon has a definite area, according to what precedes, and we shall

set the volume of the pyramid equal to one-third of the product of its base by its height, as in elementary geometry, and merely add a positive or a negative sign according as the circuit (1, 2, 3, 4, 5, 6), viewed from O, is counterclockwise or the reverse. We see easily that this definition includes, as a special case, the earlier agreements as to the volume of the tetrahedron. Moreover, we can deduce this definition from that special case if we replace the polygon by its component triangles, so traversed that their sum will yield

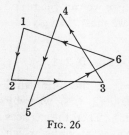

FIG. 26

its area, and then define the pyramid as the sum of the tetrahedra which these triangles project.

In order to represent the polyhedron, in the general case, as the sum of such partial pyramids, one must assign a definite sense of circuit for *each* of its faces, and the guide for this selection must be the law of edges, in view of what precedes: *We choose arbitrarily the sense of circuit for one face, then continue the circuits so that each edge of two contiguous faces is traversed in opposite senses.* If this process can be completed for the entire polyhedral surface without contradiction, then the *volume of the polyhedron is determined as the sum of the volumes of the partial pyramids into which the faces of the polyhedron, traversed in the sense indicated, project from an arbitrary point O.* It is easy to see that this determination is unique and independent of the position of O.

It is very remarkable, however, that this law of edges cannot be carried out without contradiction for every closed polyhedral surface; that is, there are polyhedra for which every attempt to fix a sign fails, and to which we cannot, therefore, assign a volume. This is the great discovery which Möbius published in 1865. He discusses there, among others, the surface which was later called the *Möbius band.* This surface is constructed by taking a long narrow rectangle of paper $A_1B_1A_2B_2$ (see Fig. 27) and, after a half turn, bringing the two ends together so that A_1 coincides with A_2 and B_1 with B_2. It is clear that the front and back faces of the sheet are thus brought into connection, so that a *surface* is formed *that has only one side.* We may de-

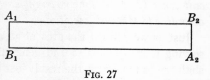

FIG. 27

scribe it as follows: A painter who wished to paint the strip would find that he needed twice as much paint as he had supposed from the length of the strip; for after painting down the length of the strip, he would find himself opposite the point of beginning and he would have to go around again to reach the starting place.

Instead of this curved sheet, we can set up a polyhedral surface (not closed) with plane parts of the same property, by dividing the original paper rectangle into triangles and creasing it along their edges. *To the strip of triangles thus obtained it is not possible to apply the law of edges.* At least five triangles are required, and they should be arranged as in Fig. 28, where the two half triangles, right and left, form one triangle (4, 5, 1) in the process of folding. If we choose here (1, 2, 3) as the positive sense of circuit and

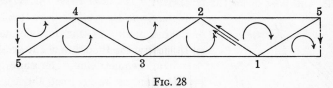

FIG. 28

continue to the left according to the law of edges, we obtain, in order, the senses (3, 2, 4), (3, 4, 5), (5, 4, 1), (5, 1, 2), so that finally 12 is traversed in the same sense as in (1, 2, 3), which contradicts the law of edges. Looked at from above, the folded strip appears as a five-cornered figure with the five sides 1 3, 3 5, 5 2, 2 4, 4 1 as diagonals, as sketched in the adjoining figure (Fig. 29). With this zone of triangles Möbius constructs a *closed polyhedron* by joining its free edges—these five diagonals—by means of triangles with an arbitrary point in space O, most suitably chosen above the middle of the pentagon. In other words, he sets up a five-sided pyramid with intersecting

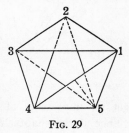

FIG. 29

faces. It is, of course, likewise impossible to apply the law of edges to this closed polyhedron with ten triangular faces, so that we cannot talk about its *volume*.[1]

Another one-sided polyhedron, which is closed and simple in construction, can be obtained easily in the following way from an octahedron *ABCDEF* (see Fig. 30). Select four faces of the octahedron that are not consecutive, that have, thus, a vertex but no edge in common (say *AED*, *EBC*, *CFD*, *ABF*), and the three diagonal planes *ABCD*, *EBFD*, *AECF*. The heptahedron [2] so formed has the same edges as the octahedron, for in every edge of the latter two contiguous faces of the heptahedron meet (namely, a face and a diagonal-plane of the octahedron). The diagonals of the octahedron are not to be considered as edges of this heptahedron since for it the diagonal planes are not consecutive. The diagonals *AC*, *BD*, *EF* are, rather, lines along which the heptahedron intersects itself. We can prove the one-sidedness of this heptahedron by using again the law of edges. If we pick

---

[1] Compare the application in graphostatics of this one-sided polyhedron in my paper *Ueber Selbstspannung ebener Diagramme*, Mathematische Annalen, vol. 67, p. 438 [= Klein, F., *Gesammelte Mathematische Abhandlungen*, vol. 2, p. 692, Berlin, 1922].

[2] [First mentioned in the literature by C. Reinhardt, *Zu Möbius' Polyedertheorie*, Verhandlungen der Königlich Sächsischen Gesellschaft der Wissenschaften (mathematisch-physikalische Klasse), vol. 37, 1885.]

out, namely, the successive faces AED, $EDFB$, ECB, $ABCD$, assign for the
first one a sense of circuit, and determine the sense for the others by the law
of edges, it turns out that the edge AD is traversed twice in the same sense.

With this I bring to a close the consideration of numbers as the measure
of contents, and pass on to the treatment of *additional elementary geometric*

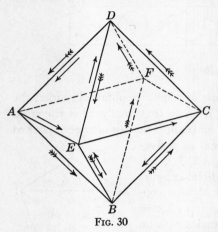

FIG. 30

magnitudes. Just as the name Möbius
has guided us thus far, we shall now
follow the thoughts of the great Stet-
tin geometrician, Hermann Grassmann, as he first set them down in
1844 in his *Lineale Ausdehnungslehre.*[1]
This book, like that of Möbius, is
rich in ideas, but, unlike Möbius'
book, it is written in a style that is
extraordinarily obscure, so that for
decades it was not considered nor
understood. Only when similar trains
of thought came from other sources
were they recognized belatedly in
Grassmann's book.   If you wish to
get an impression of this abstract manner of writing, you need only
glance at the chapter headings of this book.   They are: *Derivation of the
Notion of Pure Mathematics, Deduction of the Theory of Extension, Exposition of the Theory of Extension, Form of Presentation,*—then there follows
Survey of the General Theory of Forms.   Only after you have fought your way
through these expositions, will you come to the purely abstract presentation
of the material, which is still very hard to understand.   It was not until a
later revision of the *Ausdehnungslehre*[2] appeared in 1862 that Grassmann
used a somewhat more accessible presentation, with the use of coordinates.
Moreover, Grassmann coined the word *Ausdehnungslehre* (theory of extension) to imply that his developments were applicable to any number of
dimensions, while geometry was, for him, the application of this new entirely abstract discipline to ordinary space of three dimensions.   This new
word did not, however, take root.   One speaks today briefly of *n-dimensional
geometry.*

Let us make use of our familiarity with analytic coordinates in forming
an acquaintance with the Grassmann notions.   Confining ourselves, first,
to plane geometry, we shall use the Grassmann Principle as the title of the
next chapter.

---

[1] Leipzig, 1844. See *Gesammelte mathemathische und physikalische Werke,* vol. 1 (Leipzig,
1894), 2nd edition, Leipzig, 1898.

[2] Berlin, 1862. See *Werke,* vol. 1, Part 2, Leipzig, 1896.

II. THE GRASSMANN DETERMINANT PRINCIPLE FOR THE PLANE

Let us recall the fundamental explanations of the first chapter. There, using the coordinates of three points, we set up the determinant

$$\begin{vmatrix} x_1 & y_1 & 1 \\ x_2 & y_2 & 1 \\ x_3 & y_3 & 1 \end{vmatrix}$$

and interpreted it as twice the area of a triangle, i.e., as the area of a parallelogram. Now let us consider, in addition, the forms made with two points, and with one point, respectively:

$$\begin{vmatrix} x_1 & y_1 & 1 \\ x_2 & y_2 & 1 \end{vmatrix} \quad \text{or} \quad \begin{vmatrix} x_1 & y_1 & 1 \end{vmatrix}$$

which we call *matrices*. Every such matrix is to represent the *totality of determinants which can be made from it by omitting one column, or two columns, respectively*. Thus we obtain from the first matrix, by omitting the first and then the second column, the two-rowed determinants

$$Y = y_1 - y_2, \qquad X = x_1 - x_2$$

and by omitting the third column, the determinant $N = x_1 y_2 - x_2 y_1$. The notation is chosen so that it will be appropriate for geometry of space. We must inquire what geometric configuration is determined by these three determinants X, Y, and N. We shall look upon this configuration as a new elementary geometric magnitude that has the same justification as the area of the triangle. From the second one-rowed matrix, we get, as one-rowed determinants, beside the number 1, the coordinates (x_1, y_1) themselves. They determine the point which has these coordinates as the simplest elementary magnitude, and they require no further investigation.

It will now be comprehensible if I give a general enunciation of the Grassmann principle: *We consider, in the plane, as well as in space, all matrices (with fewer rows than columns) whose rows are formed from the coordinates of a point and 1, and we inquire what geometric configurations are determined by the determinants which result when we omit a sufficient number of columns.*

In this principle, which is here set up somewhat arbitrarily, and which only gradually will disclose itself as a useful guide through the mass of elementary geometric configurations, we shall recognize eventually a natural development of an extensive group of ideas which embrace the entire system of geometry.

But let us return to the concrete problem: What is given in the figure (see

Fig. 31) of two points 1 and 2, if we know the determinants X, Y, and N? Obviously there remains still one degree of freedom in the position of the

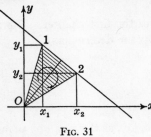

FIG. 31

points, since it takes four magnitudes to fix them. I assert: *We obtain the same triple of values X, Y, and N if, and only if, 1 is the endpoint and 2 the initial point of a segment, with definite length and direction, which is free to move on a definite straight line.* Here, as well as in what follows, we think of the arrow as placed so as to indicate direction from the initial point 2 toward the endpoint 1.

That the line joining 1 and 2 is determined by X, Y, and N follows at once from the fact that its equation

$$\begin{vmatrix} x & y & 1 \\ x_1 & y_1 & 1 \\ x_2 & y_2 & 1 \end{vmatrix} = 0$$

can be written in the form $Y \cdot x - X \cdot y + N = 0$. From this one sees also that this *line is determined if only the ratios $X : Y : N$ are known.* Furthermore, we see from our earlier consideration of length of segments and of area of triangles that X and Y represent the projections upon the x axis and the y axis of the segment $(1, 2)$ with the direction from 2 toward 1, and N represents twice the area of the triangle $(0, 1, 2)$ taken with the sense of circuit $(0, 1, 2)$. Obviously, then, the only changes in position of the points 1, 2 which leave X, Y, and N unchanged are translations of the segment $(1, 2)$ along its line, with maintenance of its length and its sense. This proves my assertion. Grassmann called such a segment of definite length and sense lying upon a definite line a *Linienteil (directed line-segment).* The word *vector* is more usual today, in German literature, or to be more exact, *Linienflüchtiger Vector (line-bound vector)*. We speak simply of a *vector*, or of a *free vector*, if the segment is allowed to move parallel to itself (under maintenance of length and sense) even outside of its line. *The line-bound vector, determined by the matrix*

$$\begin{vmatrix} x_1 & y_1 & 1 \\ x_2 & y_2 & 1 \end{vmatrix},$$

in other words, by the determinants X, Y, and N, is the first elementary geometric configuration that we consider according to the Grassmann principle.

I remark, at once, that the quantities X and Y by themselves, determine a *free vector*, since they are unaltered by the parallel translation of the segment outside of the line. Similarly, the ratios $X : Y : N$, equivalent to two quantities, determine only the *unlimited straight line*, not the length of a segment upon it. The free vector and the unlimited straight line are thus auxiliary configurations that we encounter here. The principle which will guide us in the introduction of auxiliary configurations will be developed later.

These notions play a very important role in mechanics in the study of *elementary statics*, where, traditionally, they have presented themselves naturally on their own account. As long as we operate in the plane, we shall be concerned here with the *statics of plane rigid systems*. For geometric treatment, one can consider the *Linienteil* (*directed line-segment*) as the full equivalent of the *force* which is applied to the system, the point of application of which may be moved at will in the direction of the force because of the rigidity of the body. Let us represent the force here in the spirit of the old mechanics: A rope is attached at the point 2 and a pull is given whose intensity is measured by the segment 12 (see Fig. 32). I recall, as an example of the vivid

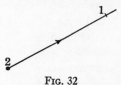

Fig. 32

way of thinking in the old mechanics, in contrast to the abstract modern way of presentation, that there always used to be the picture of a hand pulling on the rope.[1] Of the coordinates of the directed line-segment (X, Y, N), *the first two are called the components of the force, while N is the moment of turning about* O. For, from the equation of the line one gets the perpendicular upon it from O as $p = N/\sqrt{x^2 + y^2}$ so that N is actually the product of the distance p and the length $\sqrt{x^2 + y^2}$ of the segment, i.e., the magnitude of the force. We can consider these three magnitudes together as the coordinates of the force. The analytic definition gives for them in every case—this is especially important—well-determined signs, which we can interpret geometrically, just as before. To be sure, it should be noted here that, in deference to the symmetry of the formulas, we have departed from the customary method in mechanics of determining the sign of the turning moment. In fact, it is customary to use the determinant formed from the coordinates of the initial point 2 and the two coordinates (X, Y) of the free vector:

$$\begin{vmatrix} x_2 & y_2 \\ X & Y \end{vmatrix} = \begin{vmatrix} x_2 & y_2 \\ x_1 - x_2 & y_1 - y_2 \end{vmatrix},$$

which obviously is equal and opposite to our N. But this small discrepancy can hardly give rise to confusion, if it is once known.

The first problem of the mechanics of rigid bodies is to find the resultant of an arbitrary system of such forces (X_i, Y_i, N_i), $(i = 1, 2, \cdots, n)$. This amounts, analytically, to forming the line-bound vector with the coordinates

$$\sum_{i=1}^{n} X_i, \qquad \sum_{i=1}^{n} Y_i, \qquad \sum_{i=1}^{n} N_i.$$

[1] See, for example, the tables in Varignon, *Nouvelle Mécanique ou Statique*, Paris, 1775.

Very elegant methods for the geometric solution of this problem are developed in *graphical statics*. With two forces, we use simply the well known parallelogram law, while for $n > 2$, we have to do with the polygon of forces. In general, we find a unique line-bound vector as the resultant of any system of forces. There are, however, exceptions, for example, where the system consists of two parallel forces which are equal and are oppositely directed on two different lines, (X, Y, N_1), and $(-X, -Y, N_2)$, $(N_1 \neq -N_2)$. The resultant has the components $(0, 0, N_1 + N_2)$, numbers which obviously cannot be the coordinates of a vector. The elementary presentation can do nothing with this phenomenon and must always reckon with these irreducible, so-called *couples*, which always disturb the simplicity and generality of the theorems. We can easily fit these apparent exceptions into our system, however, if we consider that our earlier formulas, applied formally to the components $(0, 0, N_1 + N_2)$, yield $\sqrt{0^2 + 0^2} = 0$ as the intensity of the resultant and

$$ p = \frac{N_1 + N_2}{0} = \infty $$

as its distance from the origin. Thus, if, in the case of an ordinary force, one allows its distance p from the origin to become infinite and its intensity $\sqrt{X^2 + Y^2}$ to approach zero so that the product $p \cdot \sqrt{X^2 + Y^2}$, which is the turning moment, remains finite, the components assume precisely those exceptional values, so that one can look upon the *resultant* $(0, 0, N_1 + N_2)$ *of a couple as an infinitesimal but infinitely remote force with a finite turning moment*. This fiction is extremely convenient and useful for advancing science, and corresponds entirely to the customary introduction of infinitely remote elements into geometry. Above all, we are able, on the basis of this extension of the notion of force, to enunciate the *perfectly general* theorem that an *arbitrary number of forces acting in a plane have, in all cases, a single force as a resultant*, whereas in the elementary presentation one must always drag along the alternative concept of a couple.

Let me now complete our discussions by studying the *behavior of our elementary magnitudes under transformation of the rectangular coordinates*. That will supply a valuable principle of classification for the application, in its finer shades, of the Grassmann system.

The *formulas for the change of coordinates*, i.e., the expressions for (x', y'), the coordinates of the point for the new position of the axes, in terms of the original coordinates (x, y), for the four fundamental transformations of rectangular coordinate systems are as follows:

1. For *parallel translation:*

$$(A_1) \qquad \begin{cases} x' = x + a, \\ y' = y + b. \end{cases}$$

2. For *rotation through an angle* ϕ:

(A_2)
$$\begin{cases} x' = x \cos \phi + y \sin \phi, \\ y' = -x \sin \phi + y \cos \phi \cdot \end{cases}$$

3. For *reflection in the x axis:*

(A_3)
$$x' = x, \quad y' = -y.$$

4. For *a change in the unit of measure:*

(A_4)
$$x' = \lambda x, \quad y' = \lambda y.$$

If we combine with one another transformations of these four sorts for all values of the parameters a, b, ϕ, λ, we obtain the equations for the *most general transition possible from one rectangular coordinate system to another* with simultaneous change of unit. The combination of all possible translations and rotations corresponds to the totality of *ordinary movements* of the coordinate system within the plane. The totality of these transformations forms a *group*, i.e., the combination of any two of them gives again a transformation of the totality, and the inverse of any transformation is always represented. The special transformations (A) from which all the others can be derived are called *generators of the group.*

Before we inquire how these separate transformations change our determinants X, Y, and N, I shall enunciate *two general principles* which I have habitually emphasized and have put into the foreground in these fundamental geometric discussions. Although in this generality they sound at first somewhat obscure, they will, with concrete illustrations, soon become clear. One of them is *that the geometric properties of any figures must be expressible in formulas which are not changed when one changes the coordinate system*, i.e., when one subjects all the points of the figure simultaneously to one of our transformations; *and, conversely, any formula which, in this sense, is invariant under the group of these coordinate transformations must represent a geometric property.* As simplest examples, which all of you know, let me remind you of the expression for the distance or for the angle, in the figure of two points or of two lines. We shall have to do repeatedly with these and with many other similar formulas in the following pages. For the sake of clearness, I shall give a trivial example of non-invariant formulas: The equation $y = 0$, for the figure consisting of the point (x, y) of the plane, says that this point lies on the x axis, which is, after all, a thoroughly unessential fact, foreign to the nature of the figure, useful only in serving to describe it. Likewise, every non-invariant equation represents some relation of the figure to external, arbitrarily added, things, in particular to the coordinate system, but it does not represent any geometric property of the figure.

The *second principle* has to do with a system of analytic magnitudes which are formed from the coordinates of points $1, 2, \cdots$, such as our X, Y, and N, for example. If this system has the property of transforming into itself, in a definite way, under a transformation of coordinates, i.e., *if the system of magnitudes formed from the new coordinates* of the points 1, 2, $\cdots$, *expresses itself in terms exclusively of these magnitudes* formed in the same way from the old coordinates (the coordinates themselves not appearing explicitly), *then we say that the system defines a new geometric configuration, i.e., one which is independent of the coordinate system. In fact, we shall classify all analytic expressions according to their behavior under coordinate transformation, and we shall define as geometrically equivalent two series of expressions which transform in the same way.*

We shall now make all this clear, using the material supplied by the Grassmann elementary magnitudes. To that end, we subject our two points (x_1, y_1), (x_2, y_2) to the same coordinate transformation.

1. Let us begin with the *translation* (A_1):

$$x_1' = x_1 + a, \qquad x_2' = x_2 + a,$$
$$y_1' = y_1 + b, \qquad y_2' = y_2 + b.$$

Comparing the coordinates of the vector before and after the transformation, we have

$$X = x_1 - x_2, \qquad Y = y_1 - y_2, \qquad N = x_1 y_2 - x_2 y_1,$$
$$X' = x_1' - x_2', \qquad Y' = y_1' - y_2', \qquad N' = x_1' y_2' - x_2' y_1'.$$

It follows immediately that

(B_1)
$$\begin{cases} X' = X, \\ Y' = Y, \\ N' = N + bX - aY. \end{cases}$$

In precisely the same way, we obtain as transformation formulas:

2. Upon *rotation* (A_2):

(B_2)
$$\begin{cases} X' = X \cos \phi + Y \sin \phi, \\ Y' = -X \sin \phi + Y \cos \phi, \\ N' = N. \end{cases}$$

3. Upon *reflection* (A_3):

(B_3)
$$\begin{cases} X' = X, \\ Y' = -Y, \\ N' = -N. \end{cases}$$

4. Upon *change of unit of length* (A_4):

(B_4)
$$\begin{cases} X' = \lambda X, \\ Y' = \lambda Y, \\ N' = \lambda^2 N. \end{cases}$$

In the last formulas (B_4), there is a difference in the behavior of the magnitudes, in that the exponent of λ in the multiplying factor is not always the same. We express this difference in physics by introducing the notion of dimension: X and Y have the dimension 1, of a line; N the dimension 2, of an area.

When we examine these four groups of formulas, we notice that the vector (directed line-segment) defined by the three determinants X, Y, and N actually satisfies our definition of a geometric magnitude. The new coordinates X', Y', and N' express themselves exclusively in terms of X, Y, and N.

We see more if throughout we look at the first two equations only, into which N does not enter. The two coordinates (X', Y') of the vector in the new coordinate system depend solely upon the original values (X, Y) of these coordinates; in particular, they are unchanged under translation, and, in the other cases, the relation of (X, Y) to (X', Y') is just the same as that of (x, y) to (x', y'). In view of the second principle, enunciated above, we can say *that the two coordinates X and Y determine a geometric configuration independently of the coordinate system*, and we know already that this configuration is the *free vector*. We have thus found the formerly announced systematic principle that occasions the introduction of this configuration alongside of the vector (Linienteil).

The following considerations lie in the same field. Since X', Y', and N' occur, in all four groups of formulas, as *homogeneous* linear functions of X, Y, and N, we see, by division of the equations, that the ratios $X' : Y' : N'$ depend only on the ratios $X : Y : N$. Thus *these ratios $X : Y : N$ determine a geometric configuration independently of the coordinate system*, without regard to the actual values of the three magnitudes themselves, and we recognized this configuration earlier as the *unlimited straight line*.

Let us now apply our formulas (B), in particular, to a *couple*, for which

$$X = 0, \qquad Y = 0.$$

Then, of course,

$$X' = 0, \qquad Y' = 0,$$

while in the four separate cases:

$$
\begin{array}{lll}
(C_1) & N' = & N, \\
(C_2) & N' = & N, \\
(C_3) & N' = & -N, \\
(C_4) & N' = & \lambda^2 N.
\end{array}
$$

If we use the customary expression *invariant* for a magnitude which changes, under the operations of a group of transformations, at most by a factor, and if we call the invariant *absolute* or *relative* according as this factor is 1 or not, we can express formulas (*C*) in these words: The *moment of turning of a couple is a relative invariant with respect to all rectangular coordinate transformations in the plane.*

Let us compare with this the behavior under coordinate transformation of the elementary geometric magnitude which we studied at the beginning, the *area of the triangle:*

$$\Delta = \tfrac{1}{2} \begin{vmatrix} x_1 & y_1 & 1 \\ x_2 & y_2 & 1 \\ x_3 & y_3 & 1 \end{vmatrix}.$$

Parallel translation (*A*₁) does not change this determinant, since it only adds *a* to the elements of the first column and *b* to those of the second, i.e., the *a*-tuple and *b*-tuple, respectively, of the elements of the third column. Consequently we have

$$(D_1) \qquad \Delta' = \Delta.$$

Similarly, the three other transformations yield

$$(D_2) \qquad \Delta' = \Delta,$$
$$(D_3) \qquad \Delta' = -\Delta,$$
$$(D_4) \qquad \Delta' = \lambda^2\Delta,$$

all of which we might easily infer at once from the geometric significance of the area of the triangle. However, these formulas agree precisely with (*C*): *The area of a triangle and hence every area* (which can always, indeed, be expressed as the sum of triangles) *behaves under arbitrary transformation of coordinates precisely as does the turning moment of a couple.* According to our second general principle, we may look upon both things, therefore, as equivalent geometrically, and we can interpret this statement in the following way: If we have in the plane any couple with turning moment *N*, and if we define, in any way, a triangle with area $\Delta = N$, this equality is preserved under all coordinate transformations, i.e., *we can illustrate the turning moment of a couple, regardless of the system of coordinates, by the area of a triangle, or by the area of a parallelogram, or by the area of any other plane figure.* Just how this geometric correspondence is to be brought about, will appear later when we come to the analogous, but somewhat more complicated, and therefore more instructive, relations in space.

With this I shall leave the geometry of the plane, in which these abstractions are almost trivially simple. To every analytic formula one can assign a good geometric meaning, whereby full analytic generality finds its way automatically into geometry. In this connection, an essential assumption, which must again be emphasized, is that the proper conventions should be made concerning the signs of the geometric configurations.

III. THE GRASSMANN PRINCIPLE FOR SPACE

We shall carry out the corresponding investigations for space in complete analogy with the foregoing considerations for the plane. We start therefore from the matrices which can be formed with the coordinates of 1, 2, 3, or 4 points:

$$\begin{vmatrix} x_1 & y_1 & z_1 & 1 \end{vmatrix}, \quad \begin{vmatrix} x_1 & y_1 & z_1 & 1 \\ x_2 & y_2 & z_2 & 1 \end{vmatrix}, \quad \begin{vmatrix} x_1 & y_1 & z_1 & 1 \\ x_2 & y_2 & z_2 & 1 \\ x_3 & y_3 & z_3 & 1 \end{vmatrix}, \quad \begin{vmatrix} x_1 & y_1 & z_1 & 1 \\ x_2 & y_2 & z_2 & 1 \\ x_3 & y_3 & z_3 & 1 \\ x_4 & y_4 & z_4 & 1 \end{vmatrix}.$$

The determinants of the first matrix represent the point coordinates themselves and require no further consideration. The fourth matrix is already a four-rowed determinant, and gives, as we know, the six-fold volume of the tetrahedron (1, 2, 3, 4), which we can call a *space-segment* (*Raumteil*) in agreement with the terminology to be introduced later. We can, moreover, think of it simply as the volume of a parallelopiped with the edges 4 1, 4 2, 4 3 (see Fig. 33), which Grassmann called a *Spat* (the word *Spat* is taken from the miners' word *Kalkspat*).

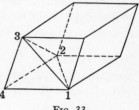

FIG. 33

New configurations are supplied by the second matrix and by the third matrix. The two-rowed matrix represents the aggregate of the following *six determinants of second order*, which arise by the deletion of two columns:

$$(1) \quad \begin{cases} X = x_1 - x_2, & Y = y_1 - y_2, & Z = z_1 - z_2, \\ L = y_1 z_2 - y_2 z_1, & M = z_1 x_2 - z_2 x_1, & N = x_1 y_2 - x_2 y_1; \end{cases}$$

similarly, the third matrix represents the following *four determinants of third order*:

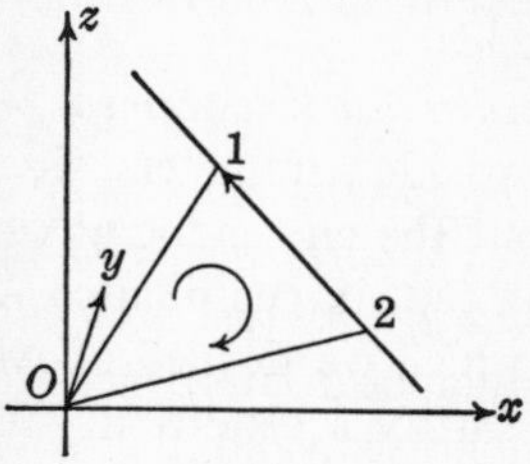

$$(2) \quad \begin{cases} \mathfrak{L} = \begin{vmatrix} y_1 & z_1 & 1 \\ y_2 & z_2 & 1 \\ y_3 & z_3 & 1 \end{vmatrix}, & \mathfrak{M} = \begin{vmatrix} z_1 & x_1 & 1 \\ z_2 & x_2 & 1 \\ z_3 & x_3 & 1 \end{vmatrix}, \\ \mathfrak{N} = \begin{vmatrix} x_1 & y_1 & 1 \\ x_2 & y_2 & 1 \\ x_3 & y_3 & 1 \end{vmatrix}, & \mathfrak{P} = - \begin{vmatrix} x_1 & y_1 & z_1 \\ x_2 & y_2 & z_2 \\ x_3 & y_3 & z_3 \end{vmatrix}. \end{cases}$$

FIG. 34

First, as to the six determinants (1), we can infer, from the corresponding discussion for the plane, that X, Y, and Z are the projections upon the coordinate axes of the segment joining 2 to 1, while L, M, and N are double the areas of the projections upon the coordinate planes of the triangle (0, 1, 2), taken in the sense 0, 1, 2 (see Fig. 34). All these magnitudes remain obviously unchanged when we move the segment (1, 2) along its line, preserving its length and its sense. They represent what we shall call a *directed line-segment* (*Linienteil*) or *line-bound vector* (*linienflüchtiger Vector*) *of space*. The quantities X, Y, and Z themselves remain unchanged if one moves the vector out of its line parallel to itself; they therefore determine a *free vector*. Similarly the five ratios $X : Y : Z : L : M : N$ are not changed by arbitrarily changing the length or sense of the directed line-segment on its line. Thus they determine the *unlimited straight line*.

The four determinants (2) determine, first of all, the plane of the three points 1, 2, 3; for we can write the equation

$$\begin{vmatrix} x & y & z & 1 \\ x_1 & y_1 & z_1 & 1 \\ x_2 & y_2 & z_2 & 1 \\ x_3 & y_3 & z_3 & 1 \end{vmatrix} = 0$$

obviously in the form

$$\mathfrak{L}x + \mathfrak{M}y + \mathfrak{N}z + \mathfrak{P} = 0.$$

Hence the ratios $\mathfrak{L} : \mathfrak{M} : \mathfrak{N} : \mathfrak{P}$ determine the *unlimited plane*. We see, further, that $\mathfrak{L}$, $\mathfrak{M}$, $\mathfrak{N}$ are double the areas of the projections upon the coordinate planes of the triangle (1, 2, 3), always taken in the boundary sense 1, 2, 3, and that $\mathfrak{P}$ is six times the volume of the tetrahedron (0, 1, 2, 3), again with that sign which corresponds to this succession of vertices. Now these four magnitudes obviously are unchanged when, and only when, the triangle (1, 2, 3) is so moved and deformed in its plane that its area and its boundary sense are unchanged, and they determine thus a triangle or a plane area with this freedom of motion, which Grassmann calls a *plane-segment* (*Ebenenteil*) or a *plane-magnitude* (*Plangrösse*). The first three coordinates $\mathfrak{L}$, $\mathfrak{M}$, and $\mathfrak{N}$ of the plane-segment also remain unchanged when we move the plane of the triangle parallel to itself. They determine then, as to area and boundary sense, a triangle which is free to move in space parallel to itself, a so-called *free plane-magnitude*.

If we turn now to a closer examination of the *directed line-segment* we notice first that it is determined in space by five variable parameters, since its two endpoints have together six coordinates, but the one endpoint can be moved arbitrarily along a straight line. Thus the six coordinates X, Y, Z, L, M, and N of the *directed line-segment*, which we defined above, cannot be independent of one another, but must satisfy a condition. We can deduce this condition most simply from the laws of determinants, which are, indeed, always the key to our theories. We consider the determinant

$$\begin{vmatrix} x_1 & y_1 & z_1 & 1 \\ x_2 & y_2 & z_2 & 1 \\ x_1 & y_1 & z_1 & 1 \\ x_2 & y_2 & z_2 & 1 \end{vmatrix} = 0,$$

which vanishes identically because two rows coincide, element for element. We develop it as the sum of products of corresponding minors of the first and last pairs of rows. The first summand, which contains the two enclosed minors, is simply $N \cdot Z$, and for the whole determinant we get

$$(3) \qquad 2(N \cdot Z + M \cdot Y + L \cdot X).$$

Hence we have the identity $X \cdot L + Y \cdot M + Z \cdot N = 0$ as the necessary condition for the six coordinates of any directed line-segment. It is easy to show that the equation (3), between the six magnitudes, suffices in order for them to represent, by means of formulas (1), the coordinates of a directed line-segment. I hardly need to go into this very elementary discussion.

I shall now go over again to the *application of these notions to mechanics.* Just as in the plane (p. 23), we now have the directed line-segment representing a *force applied to a rigid body in space,* including the point of application, the magnitude, and the direction. Of the six coordinates of the directed line-segment, we call X, Y, and Z *the components of the force parallel to the coordinate axes* and L, M, and N *the turning moments about these axes.*[1] The three components X, Y, and Z determine the magnitude and direction of the force, whose direction-cosines are in the ratios $X : Y : Z$. We obtain the force as the diagonal of the parallelopiped whose edges are the segments X, Y, and Z on the coordinate axes. With the same construction, using L, M, and N, we get a definite direction called the *direction of the axes of the resultant turning moment.* The equation of condition (3) shows, according to a well-known formula of space geometry, *that the direction of the force and that of the axis of the resultant turning moment are at right angles to each other.* Just as in the plane, so here we shall include, as *couple,* the limiting case where $X = Y = Z = 0$, while L, M, and N do not all vanish, in the notion of directed line-segment. A simple passage to the limit shows that one should mean here an *infinitely remote infinitesimal force whose turning moment remains finite.* The elementary theory avoids this form of expression and looks upon a couple only as the combination of two equal, oppositely directed, forces acting upon different parallel lines: (X, Y, Z, L_1, M_1, N_1) and $(-X, -Y, -Z, L_2, M_2, N_2)$, whose sum gives, in fact, just such coordinates $(0, 0, 0, L_1 + L_2, M_1 + M_2, N_1 + N_2)$, as we have just assumed.

We have to consider now the *composition of a system of arbitrary forces acting upon a rigid body:* X_i, Y_i, Z_i, L_i, M_i, N_i, $(i = 1, 2, \cdots, n)$. Much time is spent on this problem in elementary books and lectures, whereas we can dispose of it rapidly here because our analytic formulas make superfluous that consideration of separate cases which a neglect of the rule of signs imposes upon the tedious elementary discussion. The fundamental principle of composition is that we set up the sums:

---

[1] Again we have chosen the sign opposite to that which is usually taken in mechanics.

$$\Xi = \sum_{i=1}^{n} X_i, \qquad H = \sum_{i=1}^{n} Y_i, \qquad Z = \sum_{i=1}^{n} Z_i,$$

$$\Lambda = \sum_{i=1}^{n} L_i, \qquad M = \sum_{i=1}^{n} M_i, \qquad N = \sum_{i=1}^{n} N_i$$

and consider them as the *coordinates of the system of forces* or, according to an appropriate term introduced by *Plücker*, as *coordinates of the Dyname.* Here, again, we distinguish the three *components along the axes* and the three *turning moments about them.* Now this system of forces will not, in general, be a *single force,* since the six sums will not necessarily satisfy the condition for the coordinates of a single directed line-segment

$$\Xi \cdot \Lambda + H \cdot M + Z \cdot N = 0.$$

This is the new thing that comes up in space as opposed to the plane, namely, that a *system of forces acting upon a rigid body does not necessarily reduce to a single force.*

In order to gain a concrete picture of the nature of a system of forces, we shall try to represent it in the simplest possible way as the resultant of the fewest possible forces. We shall prove *that we can consider every system as the resultant of a single force and of a couple whose axis is parallel to the line of action of that force, the so-called central axis of the system; and this resolution is unique.* This theory of the composition of forces acting upon rigid bodies had its classical presentation in Poinsot's *Eléments de statique,* which appeared first in 1804, and which, since then, has gone through new editions.[1] We speak, indeed, of *Poinsot's central axis.* The treatment by Poinsot was an elementary geometric one, and was very involved, just as it still is in elementary instruction.

To *prove,* now, the above theorem, we note that any single force which could arise by the withdrawal of a couple from the system must have Ξ, H, and Z as components parallel to the axes. Thus the turning moments of the couple must be proportional to Ξ, H, and Z if its axis is to be parallel to the central axis. We assume its six coordinates to be 0, 0, 0, $k\Xi$, kH, kZ, where k is a parameter still to be determined. To get from this couple our system (Ξ, H, Z, Λ, M, N), we must add to it the system

$$\Xi, H, Z, \Lambda - k\Xi, M - kH, N - kZ.$$

The theorem would be proved if one could determine k so that this system would be a single force. A necessary and sufficient condition for this is that the coordinates satisfy (3), i.e., that

$$\Xi(\Lambda - k\Xi) + H(M - kH) + Z(N - kZ) = 0.$$

[1] Twelfth edition by J. Bertrand, Paris, 1877.

From this we get uniquely

$$k = \frac{\Xi\Lambda + HM + ZN}{\Xi^2 + H^2 + Z^2},$$

for we may assume that the denominator is different from zero, otherwise we should be dealing with a couple instead of with a proper system. If one assigns to k this value, which Plücker calls the *parameter of the Dyname*, one actually resolves the system into a couple and a single force, and the method of proof shows that the resolution is unique.

Now the question arises as to what *geometric representation* one can associate with this resolution. These investigations go back again to Möbius, to his *Lehrbuch der Statik* [1] of 1837. Here he inquires about an *axis around which the turning moment of the system would be zero*, the so-called *null-axis*. The system of all these null-axes he calls a *null-system*. It is in this connection that this word, no doubt familiar to you, has its origin.

We must now define the *general notion of turning-moment*, or *moment*, which finds application here. Let two directed line-segments $(1, 2)$ and $(1', 2')$ be given in space (see Fig. 35). Construct with them the tetrahedron $(1, 2, 1', 2')$, whose volume is

$$\frac{1}{6} \cdot \begin{vmatrix} x_1 & y_1 & z_1 & 1 \\ x_2 & y_2 & z_2 & 1 \\ x_1' & y_1' & z_1' & 1 \\ x_2' & y_2' & z_2' & 1 \end{vmatrix}.$$

Developing this determinant as the sum of products of minors of the first and last pairs of rows, as we did with the identically vanishing determinant (p. 30), we get $\frac{1}{6}(XL' + YM' + ZN' + LX' + MY' + NZ')$, where X', $\cdots$, N' are the coordinates of the directed line-segment $(1', 2')$. The bilinear combination of the coordinates of both directed line-segments which appear here,

$$XL' + YM' + ZN' + LX' + MY' + NZ',$$

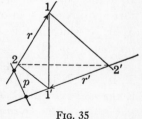

FIG. 35

will be called the *moment of one directed line-segment with respect to the other*. It is equal to *six times the volume of the tetrahedron whose vertices are the endpoints of the directed line-segments*, and it is consequently an independent geometric magnitude. If r and r' are the lengths of the directed line-segments, ϕ the angle between them, and p the common perpendicular to their two lines, it follows from elementary geometry that the moment is $r \cdot r' \cdot p \cdot \sin \phi$, if the sign of ϕ is properly chosen.

If, instead of the directed line-segment $(1, 2)$ we choose the *unlimited*

[1] Leipzig, 1837. See *Werke*, vol. 3, Leipzig, 1896.

straight line, then the moment of the directed line-segment $(1', 2')$ with reference to the line will be defined as its moment, in the preceding sense, taken with reference to a directed line-segment of length $r = 1$ on that line, i.e., $r'p \sin \phi$. This is the result of dividing the preceding expression by $r = (\sqrt{X^2 + Y^2 + Z^2})$ so that finally, the *moment of a directed line-segment* (X', Y', Z', L', M', N') *with respect to an unlimited line which contains the directed line-segment* (X, Y, Z, L, M, N) is

$$\frac{XL' + YM' + ZN' + LX' + MY' + NZ'}{|\sqrt{X_2 + Y_2 + Z_2}|}.$$

This value depends, in fact, only upon the ratios of the six magnitudes $X, \cdots, N$, along with a sign common to them, so that it is fully determined when the *unlimited line and a direction on it* are known. This moment is precisely what is known in statics as the *turning-moment of a force, represented by a directed line-segment, about the line as axis,* although a different sign is commonly chosen (see p. 31).

We shall now consider the *moment, or turning-moment, of a system of forces, of a Dyname,*

$$\Xi = \sum_{i=1}^{n} X'_i, \cdots, N = \sum_{i=1}^{n} N'_i.$$

By this we shall naturally mean the sum of the moments of the several forces, i.e., the expression

$$\left|\begin{array}{l} \sum_{i=1}^{n} \dfrac{XL'_i + YM'_i + ZN'_i + LX'_i + MY'_i + NZ'_i}{|\sqrt{X^2 + Y^2 + Z^2}|} \\ \\ = \dfrac{X\Lambda + YM + ZN + L\Xi + MH + NZ}{|\sqrt{X^2 + Y^2 + Z^2}|}. \end{array}\right.$$

If, in this expression, we identify the unlimited line of $X, \cdots, N$ with the three positive axes, in order, the expression takes on, in order, the values Λ, M, N, which justifies the designations for these quantities which we used previously (p. 32).

Now we can take up the question raised by Möbius. A given system $\Xi, H, \cdots, N$ has the moment 0 with respect to a line $(X:Y:\cdots:N)$ (this is the *null-axis*) if $\Lambda X + MY + NZ + \Xi L + HM + ZN = 0$. Thus the *null-system of the Dyname is the totality of the straight lines* $(X:Y:\cdots:N)$ *given by this equation.* But that is the most general linear homogeneous equation for the six quantities $X, \cdots, N$, since the coefficients $\Lambda, \cdots, Z$, as coordinates of a Dyname, can be six arbitrary quantities. Now Plücker, along with Möbius, the pioneer in analytic geometry of the nineteenth century, investigated just such totalities of straight lines which are defined by an arbitrary linear homogeneous equation, in a connection which we shall discuss more fully later, and called them *linear complexes. Thus the null-system of Möbius is exactly the same as the line complex of Plücker.*

We shall now try to give as *clear a picture as possible* of this null-system, although, of course, we cannot speak of a geometric figure in the proper meaning of that word, since the null-system fills space infinitely often. Nevertheless, its grouping can be understood quite simply. To this end, according to the plan always to be followed in these lectures, we shall select the coordinate axes as conveniently as possible, which we accomplish here by choosing the *central axis of the Dyname as the z axis.* Since, as we know, the Dyname is the resultant of a single force acting along the central axis, and a couple with its axis parallel to that central axis, the four coordinates Ξ, H, Λ, M must all vanish, by our choice of the z axis, so that Z represents the magnitude of the single force and N the turning moment of the couple about its axis. The parameter of the Dyname is, therefore,

$$k = \frac{\Xi\Lambda + HM + ZN}{\Xi^2 + H^2 + Z^2} = \frac{N}{Z}.$$

The equation of the linear complex in the new coordinate system has then the simple form $NZ + ZN = 0$, or, after division by Z,

(1) $$k \cdot Z + N = 0.$$

We use this form as the basis of the rest of our discussion. If $P_1(x_1, y_1, z_1)$ and $P_2(x_2, y_2, z_2)$ are two points on a line $(X : Y : Z : L : M : N)$ of the null-system, then since $Z = z_1 - z_2$ and $N = x_1 y_2 - x_2 y_1$, the equation (1) gives, for the coordinates of any two points of a null-line, the condition

(2) $$k(z_1 - z_2) + (x_1 y_2 - x_2 y_1) = 0.$$

If now we keep P_2 fixed, then (2) is the equation for the coordinates (x_1, y_1, z_1) of all points P_1 which lie with P_2 on a line of the null-system. If, for the sake of clearness, we write, as running coordinates, (x, y, z) in place of (x_1, y_1, z_1), we see that all the points P_1 fill a plane whose equation is

(2') $$y_2 x - x_2 y + k \cdot z = kz_2.$$

This plane contains the point P_2, since the equation is satisfied by $x = x_2$, $y = y_2$, $z = z_2$. We have thus proved *that through any point P_2 in space there pass infinitely many null-lines which form a plane pencil of rays that fill the plane* (2'). Our problem will be solved if we can get a clear picture of the position of this plane (null-plane) which corresponds to every point P_2.

The two expressions $N = x_1 y_2 - x_2 y_1$, $Z = z_1 - z_2$, which occur in (2), have the property of remaining unchanged under translations of space parallel to the z axis, as well as rotations about it; for translations leave x and y, hence also N, and likewise the difference $z_1 - z_2$, all unchanged, whereas **rotations** have no effect upon the z coordinate, i.e., upon Z, and leave N, as area in the xy plane, unchanged. Consequently, equation (2), and therefore the *null-system* which it determines, *goes into itself under screw motions of space about the central axis*—for that is the meaning of the z axis—*and translations along it.*

This theorem makes our problem much easier. *If we only know which plane in the null-system belongs to any point of the positive half of the x axis, then we know automatically also the null-plane which belongs to each point of space;* for, by translating that half-axis along, and turning it about the z axis, we can bring one of its points into coincidence with any point in space, whereby, according to our theorem, the corresponding null-planes go into

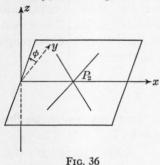

themselves. In other words: *The null-planes of the points of a half ray which is perpendicular to this central axis have a position with reference to the ray and the central axis which is independent of the choice of the ray.*

If we now confine ourselves to the x axis, setting $y_2 = z_2 = 0$, we get from (2′) as the equation of the plane belonging to the point P_2 with abscissa $x_2 : kz - x_2 y = 0$. It passes through the x axis itself, since $y = z = 0$ satisfies the equation identically (see Fig. 36).

FIG. 36

If we write the equation in the form $z/y = x_2/k$, we infer that the angle of inclination ϕ of the plane to the horizontal (xy plane) has the trigonometric tangent

$$\tan \phi = \frac{x_2}{k}$$

and the position of our plane is fully determined. In Fig. 37, its trace in the vertical yz plane is sketched.

From what has been said above, we can state the result independently of the special choice of coordinate system. *To every point at a distance r from the central axis, thought of as vertical, there belongs a plane of the null-system which contains the perpendicular from the point upon the axis, and whose angle of inclination to the horizontal plane has the trigonometric tangent r/k.* If we move the point on a half ray perpendicular to the axis, then the corresponding plane of the null-system will be horizontal for $r = 0$, and will turn, with increasing r, up or down (according as $k \gtrless 0$) and will

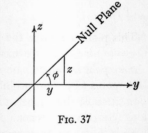

FIG. 37

approach the vertical asymptotically when r becomes infinite. I can make these relations clearer to you by means of a *Schilling model* (see Fig. 38) in which there is a movable arm which slides along and turns about the central axis, and which carries a plane sheet that rises in the proper way as it recedes from the axis.

Let us now consider, in particular, the *direction of the normal* which belongs to the plane through the point P_2. Its direction cosines have the same ratios as the coefficients in the equation of the plane $(2')$, i.e., $y_2 : (-x_2) : k$.

We can think of this same direction as the direction of motion of the point P_2 under an *infinitesimal screw movement* of space. Indeed, if we turn space as a rigid body around the z axis through the finite angle ω and move it, at the same time, parallel to the z axis by the amount c, every point (x, y, z) will go into the new position given by the equations

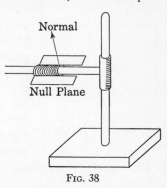

Normal

Null Plane

$$x' = x \cos \omega - y \sin \omega,$$
$$y' = x \sin \omega + y \cos \omega,$$
$$z' = z + c.$$

We pass from this finite screw motion to an infinitesimal one by replacing ω by $-d\omega$ and setting $c = k\,d\omega$. The minus sign means that

Fig. 38

for $k > 0$ the turning in the xy plane is negative, if the translation is in the positive z direction, i.e., that the screw motion is negative (left-handed). Neglecting quantities of second and higher orders in $d\omega$, that is, putting $\cos d\omega = 1$, $\sin d\omega = d\omega$, we obtain

$$x' = x + y\,d\omega, \qquad y_1 = -x\,d\omega + y, \qquad z' = z + k\,d\omega.$$

The increments of the coordinates of a definite point P_2 under this infinitesimal screw motion are $dx_2 = y_2\,d\omega$, $dy_2 = -x_2\,d\omega$, $dz_2 = k\,d\omega$, that is, P_2 will be moved in the direction

$$dx_2 : dy_2 : dz_2 = y_2 : (-x_2) : k.$$

This is, in fact, precisely the direction along the normal (3). *Thus, if we give to space an infinitesimal screw motion about the central axis such that the motion along this axis is k times the angle of rotation (taken negatively), then the plane of the null-system of parameter k which belongs to any point of space will be normal to the arc traversed by the point.*

Since the representation of a screw motion is very easy, we can get in this way a vivid picture of the arrangement of the planes in a null-system. For example, the greater the distance r of a point from the central axis, the longer is the horizontal projection $r\,d\omega$ of the elementary path which it traverses in the screw motion, the flatter is the path itself, since the rise, $k\,d\omega$, is constant, hence the steeper is the plane of the null-system, since it is normal to that path. If we combine infinitely many of these infinitesimal screw motions into a continuous screw motion of space, every point at a distance r from the central axis will describe a *helix* whose inclination to the horizontal has $-k/r$ for its trigonometric tangent, and whose *pitch* is therefore $2\pi k$, independent of r. *The planes normal to this helix are the planes of the null-system.*

In conclusion, having talked only about the planes of the null-system, let us now try to get a *clear picture of the null-axes.* We take any null-axis g (see Fig. 39) and draw the common perpendicular between g and the central

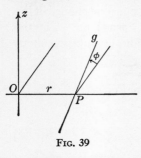

FIG. 39

axis, meeting the latter in O, and g in P. Then PO, as a perpendicular from P to the central axis, belongs to the null-system, and OPg must be the plane of the null-system belonging to P. Since g is perpendicular to OP, it makes with the horizontal the same angle ϕ as the null-plane, i.e., $\tan \phi = r/k$, where $r = OP$. *Thus we obtain all the null-axes, if, through every point P of every half ray perpendicular to the central axis we draw that normal to this ray which makes with the horizontal*

an angle whose trigonometric tangent is $\tan \phi = r/k$, *where r is the distance of P from the central axis.*

We can make this construction a little clearer. *We take a circular cylinder of radius r whose axis is the central axis and draw on it all helices whose inclination ϕ to the horizontal plane is given by* $\tan \phi = r/k$. *The totality of tangents to these helices is obviously identical with the totality of null-axes at the distance r from the central axis. By varying r, we get all the null-axes.* As we move outward, these helices get steeper. They have at each point the corresponding null-plane as osculating plane and they are therefore at right angles to the previously mentioned helices, which are at every point normal to the null-plane.

After this discussion, which has exhibited a double connection between helices and the null-system, we can understand why this whole theory has been associated with that of helices. Sir Robert Ball used this designation in

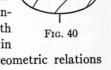

FIG. 40

his *Theory of Screws*,[1] in which he discussed all the geometric relations connected with a system of forces acting upon a rigid body.

Let us now return to our systematic development. We had obtained, by using Grassmann's principle, the four elementary geometric configurations, the *point*, the *line-segment (Linienteil)*, the *plane-segment (Ebenenteil)*, and the *space-segment (Raumteil)*. As in the plane, we shall now examine the behavior of these configurations, under transformation of the rectangular coordinate system, and classify them according to the general principle announced above.

---

[1] Dublin, 1876.

IV. CLASSIFICATION OF THE ELEMENTARY CONFIGURATIONS OF SPACE ACCORDING TO THEIR BEHAVIOR UNDER TRANSFORMATION OF RECTANGULAR COORDINATES

Above all, of course, we should obtain a view of all possible transformations of a rectangular coordinate system in space. These transformations are really fundamental for all geometry of space, so that, for this very reason, we could not overlook them in these lectures. The most general change in the coordinate system that comes up for consideration is made up, as in the plane, of the following component parts: (1) translation; (2) rotation about the origin; (3) reflection; (4) change in the unit of length.

The equations of *translation* are, of course,

$$(A_1) \qquad \begin{cases} x' = x + a, \\ y' = y + b, \\ z' = z + c. \end{cases}$$

The equations of *rotation*, in any case, have the form

$$(A_2) \qquad \begin{cases} x' = a_1 x + b_1 y + c_1 z, \\ y' = a_2 x + b_2 y + c_2 z, \\ z' = a_3 x + b_3 y + c_3 z. \end{cases}$$

We shall consider at once the determination of the coefficients, which is more complicated here than in the plane. The combination of all possible transformations of these two sorts yields all the *proper movements* of the coordinate system in space.

Just as, in the plane, we reflected in an axis, so here we can consider *reflection in a coordinate plane*, say the xy plane, and we obtain

$$x' = x, \qquad y' = y, \qquad z' = -z.$$

But we can write these formulas more symmetrically by using three minus signs, in the form

$$(A_3) \qquad x' = -x, \qquad y' = -y, \qquad z' = -z.$$

This is a *reflection in the origin*, sometimes called *inversion*.[1] In the plane,

$$x' = -x, \qquad y' = -y$$

is not a reflection, but a turning through $180°$; and, generally, inversion in the origin is a reflection only in spaces of an odd number of dimensions. If the number is even, it is a rotation.

---

[1] Sometimes the designation "inversion" is used for the totally different transformation by means of reciprocal radii.

A *change in the unit of length*, finally, is given by the equations

(A_4) $x' = \lambda x, \quad y' = \lambda y, \quad z' = \lambda z \quad \text{where} \quad \lambda > 0.$

If $\lambda < 0$, this transformation involves a reflection, in addition to a change in unit length.

It remains for us to consider in greater detail the *formulas for rotation*. The most general rotation about the origin depends, as you know, upon three parameters, because, first, the direction cosines of the axis of rotation represent two independent quantities and, in addition, the angle of rotation is arbitrary. A symmetrical treatment of all rotations in terms of three independent parameters is furnished by the *theory of quaternions*, which you will find discussed in my lectures [1] of last winter. Moreover, Euler had set up the formulas in question before quaternions were invented. I shall give here the treatment that one usually finds in textbooks on mechanics and which makes use of the nine direction cosines of the new axis with reference to the old. We start from the form of the equations of transformation given above:

(1) $\begin{cases} x' = a_1x + b_1y + c_1z, \\ y' = a_2x + b_2y + c_2z, \\ z' = a_3x + b_3y + c_3z. \end{cases}$

Let us consider one point $x, y = 0, z = 0$ of the old x axis. It has, with reference to the new system, the coordinates $x' = a_1x, y' = a_2x, z' = a_3x$, that is, a_1, a_2, a_3 *are the cosines of the angles which the new axes make with the old x axis*. Similarly, b_1, b_2, b_3 and c_1, c_2, c_3 are the cosines of the angles which the new axes make with the old y axis and the old z axis, respectively.

These nine coefficients of the equations of transformation are not at all independent of one another. We can deduce the relations between them from the interpretation just given, or we can make use of the known relations that obtain in every *orthogonal substitution*, i.e., in every rotation or reflection with fixed origin:

(2) $x'^2 + y'^2 + z'^2 = x^2 + y^2 + z^2,$

which states that the *distance* from O is *invariant*. We shall choose the second method:

α) We substitute (1) in (2) and obtain, by comparing coefficients, the following six relations among the nine quantities $a_1, \cdots, c_3$:

(3) $\begin{cases} a_1^2 + a_2^2 + a_3^2 = 1, & b_1^2 + b_2^2 + b_3^2 = 1, & c_1^2 + c_2^2 + c_3^2 = 1, \\ b_1c_1 + b_2c_2 + b_3c_3 = 0, & c_1a_1 + c_2a_2 + c_3a_3 = 0, & a_1b_1 + a_2b_2 + a_3b_3 = 0. \end{cases}$

[1] See Part I, p. 58 et seq.

β) We multiply the three equations (1) by the three quantities a, b, c respectively, and add. Solving them by means of (3), we obtain

(4)
$$\begin{cases} x = a_1 x' + a_2 y' + a_3 z', \\ y = b_1 x' + b_2 y' + b_3 z', \\ z = c_1 x' + c_2 y' + c_3 z'. \end{cases}$$

This is obviously the so-called *transposed linear substitution* which arises from (1) by interchanging rows and columns in the array of coefficients.

γ) On the other hand, solving equations (1) by the rules of determinants, we find

$$x = \frac{1}{\Delta} \begin{vmatrix} x' & b_1 & c_1 \\ y' & b_2 & c_2 \\ z' & b_3 & c_3 \end{vmatrix}, \quad \cdots, \text{ where } \Delta = \begin{vmatrix} a_1 & b_1 & c_1 \\ a_2 & b_2 & c_2 \\ a_3 & b_3 & c_3 \end{vmatrix}.$$

The coefficient of x' here must be the same as in the first equation (4), that is,

(5)
$$\frac{1}{\Delta} \begin{vmatrix} b_2 & c_2 \\ b_3 & c_3 \end{vmatrix} = a_1,$$

and similarly, *each coefficient of the orthogonal substitution must be equal to the corresponding minor of the array of coefficients, divided by the determinant Δ.*

δ) We shall now calculate the determinant Δ. To that end, we set up its square by the law of multiplication of determinants:

$$\begin{vmatrix} a_1 & b_1 & c_1 \\ a_2 & b_2 & c_2 \\ a_3 & b_3 & c_3 \end{vmatrix} \cdot \begin{vmatrix} a_1 & b_1 & c_1 \\ a_2 & b_2 & c_2 \\ a_3 & b_3 & c_3 \end{vmatrix} = \begin{vmatrix} a_1^2 + a_2^2 + a_3^2 & b_1 a_1 + b_2 a_2 + b_3 a_3 & c_1 a_1 + c_2 a_2 + c_3 a_3 \\ a_1 b_1 + a_2 b_2 + a_3 b_3 & b_1^2 + b_2^2 + b_3^2 & c_1 b_1 + c_2 b_2 + c_3 b_3 \\ a_1 c_1 + a_2 c_2 + a_3 c_3 & b_1 c_1 + b_2 c_2 + b_3 c_3 & c_1^2 + c_2^2 + c_3^2 \end{vmatrix},$$

where the columns of the first determinant are multiplied by those of the second. According to the formulas (3) this product determinant is

$$\Delta^2 = \begin{vmatrix} 1 & 0 & 0 \\ 0 & 1 & 0 \\ 0 & 0 & 1 \end{vmatrix} = 1,$$

so that finally $\Delta = \pm 1$. In order to decide which sign to choose, we note that we have thus far used only the relation (2), which is satisfied equally in rotation and in reflection. Now, among all orthogonal transformations, *rotations* have the property that they *can be generated from the identical transformation $x' = x, y' = y, z' = z$, by continuous variation of the coefficients,* corresponding to a continuous movement of the coordinate system from the original to the new position. On the other hand, the substitution which we call, in general, reflection, arises by continuous modification of the inversion $x' = -x, y' = -y, z' = -z$, whereas this inversion itself cannot be generated continuously from the identical transformation. However, the determinant of the substitution is a continuous function of the coefficients, and it must change continuously when we change the identical transformation continuously into an arbitrary rotation. Its value at the start is

$$\begin{vmatrix} 1 & 0 & 0 \\ 0 & 1 & 0 \\ 0 & 0 & 1 \end{vmatrix} = +1.$$

Since its value, as we have seen, is always either $+1$ or -1, it must of necessity remain always $+1$ for rotations, for an abrupt change to -1 would mean a discontinuity. Hence *for every rotation the determinant Δ has the value*

(6) $$\Delta = \begin{vmatrix} a_1 & b_1 & c_1 \\ a_2 & b_2 & c_2 \\ a_3 & b_3 & c_3 \end{vmatrix} = +1,$$

and, similarly, for *every reflection*, we must have $\Delta = -1$.

The formula (5) now takes the simple form:

(7) $$a_1 = \begin{vmatrix} b_2 & c_2 \\ b_3 & c_3 \end{vmatrix}.$$

Thus *each coefficient in the array of substitutions of rotation for the rectangular coordinate system is equal to the corresponding minor.*

We come now to our real problem, to find out how the coordinates of the elementary space configurations, the line-segment X, Y, Z, L, M, N, the plane-segment $\mathfrak{L}$, $\mathfrak{M}$, $\mathfrak{N}$, $\mathfrak{P}$, and finally the space-segment T, behave under the four kinds of change of the rectangular system of coordinates.

To write down all the formulas of transformation would take too much space, and it would also eventually become tedious. Therefore I shall mention only a few points that deserve special notice. First, I make the remark, which you can easily verify, that in all formulas of transformation of the coordinates of a line-segment, the first three coordinates X', Y', Z' in the new system are expressed in terms of X, Y, Z alone, and, in fact, as linear homogeneous functions of them. The quantities L, M, N do not enter. Thus, *according to the general principle already announced (p. 25 et seq.) the totality of the three quantities X, Y, Z must, in itself, determine a geometric configuration independent of the system of coordinates.* This is the free vector which we have mentioned (p. 30). In the same way, the three coordinates $\mathfrak{L}$, $\mathfrak{M}$, $\mathfrak{N}$ of the plane-segment are transformed without regard to the fourth, $\mathfrak{P}$, *so that they also have geometric significance independent of the coordinate system.* They represent the *free plane-magnitude* already mentioned (p. 30).

We shall now find out, by special calculation, how the *coordinates of the free vector X, Y, Z, behave under our transformations (A_1), $\cdots$, (A_4) (p. 39).* For that purpose, we replace only in $X' = x_1' - x_2'$, $\cdots$ the x_1', $\cdots$ by x, y, z, by means of the formulas (A_2), and we obtain at once the following formulas.

1. For *translation:*

(B_1) $$X' = X, \qquad Y' = Y, \qquad Z' = Z.$$

2. For *rotation:*

(B_2) $$\begin{cases} X' = a_1X + b_1Y + c_1Z, \\ Y' = a_2X + b_2Y + c_2Z, \\ Z' = a_3X + b_3Y + c_3Z. \end{cases}$$

3. For *inversion:*

(B_3) $$X' = -X, \qquad Y' = -Y, \qquad Z' = -Z.$$

4. For *change of unit length:*

(B_4) $$X' = \lambda X, \qquad Y' = \lambda Y, \qquad Z' = \lambda Z.$$

Thus, *under translation of the system of coordinates, the coordinates of the free vector remain unchanged; otherwise, however, they behave like the point coordinates themselves.*

Let us compare with this the formulas of transformation for a *couple,* which we obtain from the formulas of transformation of the coordinates of a line-segment by putting $X = Y = Z = 0$. Then, of course,

$$X' = Y' = Z' = 0,$$

and, for the moments of turning with respect to the new axes, we get the following formulas.

1. For *translation:*

(C_1) $$L' = L, \qquad M' = M, \qquad N' = N.$$

2. For *rotation:*

(C_2) $$\begin{cases} L' = a_1L + b_1M + c_1N, \\ M' = a_2L + b_2M + c_2N, \\ N' = a_3L + b_3M + c_3N. \end{cases}$$

3. For *inversion:*

(C_3) $$L' = L, \qquad M' = M, \qquad N' = N.$$

4. For *change of unit length:*

(C_4) $$L' = \lambda^2 L, \qquad M' = \lambda^2 M, \qquad N' = \lambda^2 N.$$

The coordinates of a couple are unchanged by translation of the system of co-ordinates, and by inversion; they behave, under rotation, like point coordinates; and they are multiplied by the factor λ^2 under change of the unit of length, i.e., they have the dimension 2 (of an area), whereas the free vector, like point coordinates, has the dimension 1.

The formulas (C_1), (C_3), (C_4) are derived without any difficulty; perhaps (C_2) needs some explanation. Indeed, with the aid of formulas (A_2), we get

$$L' = \begin{vmatrix} y_1' & z_1' \\ y_2' & z_2' \end{vmatrix} = \begin{vmatrix} a_2x_1 + b_2y_1 + c_2z_1 & a_3x_1 + b_3y_1 + c_3z_1 \\ a_2x_2 + b_2y_2 + c_2z_2 & a_3x_2 + b_3y_2 + c_3z_2 \end{vmatrix}.$$

If we multiply out the last determinant, we get $3 \cdot 3 + 3 \cdot 3 = 18$ terms, of which three sets of two terms (e.g., $a_2x_1 \cdot a_3x_2 - a_3x_1 \cdot a_2x_2, \cdots$) cancel. The remaining twelve terms can be collected into the following sum of products of determinants:

$$L' = \begin{vmatrix} b_2 & c_2 \\ b_3 & c_3 \end{vmatrix} \cdot \begin{vmatrix} y_1 & z_1 \\ y_2 & z_2 \end{vmatrix} + \begin{vmatrix} c_2 & a_2 \\ c_3 & a_3 \end{vmatrix} \cdot \begin{vmatrix} z_1 & x_1 \\ z_2 & x_2 \end{vmatrix} + \begin{vmatrix} a_2 & b_2 \\ a_3 & b_3 \end{vmatrix} \cdot \begin{vmatrix} x_1 & y_1 \\ x_2 & y_2 \end{vmatrix}.$$

According to formula (7), the first factors are equal to a_1, b_1, c_1, while the second factors are L, M, N. Thus the formula given above for L' has been obtained. The two other formulas for M' and N' follow similarly.

As a third configuration, let us now consider the *free plane-magnitude*. Very simple calculations like those above, which I shall leave for you to carry out, lead to the result *that the components* $\mathfrak{L}$, $\mathfrak{M}$, $\mathfrak{N}$ *of a free plane-magnitude transform, in all cases, just as do the coordinates* L, M, N *of a couple.*

For the sake of clearness, let us combine these results into a *little table*. It gives the transformed first coordinate, from which the others come by cyclic interchange.

	Translation	Rotation	Inversion	Change of Unit Length
Free Vector	X	$a_1X + b_1Y + c_1Z$	$-X$	λX
Couple	L	$a_1L + b_1M + c_1N$	L	$\lambda^2 L$
Free Plane-Magnitude	$\mathfrak{L}$	$a_1\mathfrak{L} + b_1\mathfrak{M} + c_1\mathfrak{N}$	$\mathfrak{L}$	$\lambda^2\mathfrak{L}$

We have now obtained the precise foundation for a series of geometric statements which appear in the textbooks frequently not at all, or only incidentally, and in a form in which their simple geometric content is not readily apparent. Often the geometric configurations which we consider here are not at all separated in the clear cut manner which we consider necessary, and, as a result, a whole series of interesting relations is completely obscured. For example, even with Poinsot, the concepts of couple and free plane-magnitude, from the start, are always tied together. Obviously this makes the discussion more difficult to understand. For us, a comparison of the last two lines of the above table shows, according to a general principle stated earlier, *that a couple and a free plane-magnitude are to be thought of as fundamental geometric configurations of the same sort*, because they behave in the same way under all changes of the rectangular coordinate system.

Let us make the content of this statement still clearer. If a couple L, M, N is given and we set up a relation between it and a plane magnitude $\mathfrak{L}$, $\mathfrak{M}$, $\mathfrak{N}$, by means of the equations $\mathfrak{L} = L$, $\mathfrak{M} = M$, $\mathfrak{N} = N$ (or if we set it up in reverse order, starting from $\mathfrak{L}$, $\mathfrak{M}$, $\mathfrak{N}$), then this coincidence remains unaffected by any transformation of coordinates. It must therefore be susceptible of pure geometric description without making use of a coordinate system. For this purpose, we start with the plane magnitude $\mathfrak{L}$, $\mathfrak{M}$, $\mathfrak{N}$, and specialize the coordinate system most conveniently by setting $\mathfrak{L} = \mathfrak{M} = 0$. Then the free plane-magnitude represents a triangle $(1, 2, 3)$ lying in the xy plane or parallel to it, such that $\mathfrak{N}$ is twice its area, i.e., equal to the area of the parallelogram $(1, 1', 2, 3)$, where the sign is to be determined by the circuit sense $11'\, 2$ (see Fig. 41). I assert, now, that the corresponding couple, with the moments $L = 0$, $M = 0$, $N = \mathfrak{N}$ can be formed with the opposite

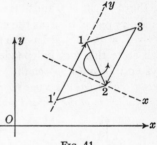

FIG. 41

parallelogram sides $(1, 1')$ and $(2, 3)$, with the arrow heads at 1 and 2. To prove this, I choose the system of coordinates in the xy plane still more conveniently, namely, with the y axis in the line 1 1' and the x axis through the point 2. (Drawn dotted in Fig. 41.) Then the two line-segments $(1, 1')$ and $(2, 3)$, and likewise the couple formed by them, have the turning-moments $L = 0$ and $M = 0$. Moreover, the third turning-moment for the line-segment $(1, 1')$ is also zero, so that finally N is equal to the turning-moment of $(2, 3)$:

$$N = \begin{vmatrix} x_2 & y_2 \\ x_3 & y_3 \end{vmatrix} = x_2 \cdot y_3,$$

(for $x_2 = x_3$ and $y_2 = 0$, according to our assumption). On the other hand, for this position of the coordinate system, the third coordinate of the plane-segment is

$$\mathfrak{N} = \begin{vmatrix} 0 & y_1 & 1 \\ x_2 & 0 & 1 \\ x_2 & y_3 & 1 \end{vmatrix} = x_2 \cdot y_3,$$

that is, the product of the base y_3 of the parallelogram by the height x_2. Thus $N = \mathfrak{N}$ in sign as well as magnitude, which proves my statement.

We can state this as a general result, without reference to a special coordinate system. *A free plane-segment, represented by a parallelogram of definite contour sense, and the couple given by two opposite sides of the parallelogram, with arrows directed opposite to that sense, are geometrically equivalent configurations, i.e., they have equal components with reference to every coordinate system.* Thus this theorem permits, at any time, the replacement of a couple by a parallelogram, or of the latter by a couple.

We need pay no further attention to the second row of the table (p. 44), and we shall compare the first and the third rows, i.e., the *free vector and the free plane-magnitude*. We notice, first, that both behave in the same manner, under translation and rotation, but that a difference appears when we add reflection or even a change of the unit of length. In order to follow this in detail, we think of a plane magnitude $\mathfrak{L}, \mathfrak{M}, \mathfrak{N}$ given in the familiar (right-handed) coordinate system, and we associate with it a free vector by means of the equations $X = \mathfrak{L}, Y = \mathfrak{M}, Z = \mathfrak{N}$. These equations will remain unaffected if we restrict ourselves to movements of the system of coordinates, but they will be modified by reflection or by change of the unit of length. If we wish to give geometric expression to them, we cannot get along without taking account of the sense of the coordinate system and of the unit of length. In fact, if we again place the system of coordinates as before, so that $\mathfrak{L} = \mathfrak{M} = 0$ and $\mathfrak{N}$ is equal to the area of the parallelogram $(1, 1', 2, 3)$ in the xy plane, then, as the figure shows (see Fig. 42), $\mathfrak{N} > 0$, and the vector $X = Y = 0, Z = \mathfrak{N}$ has the positive direction of the z axis. Obviously, we can state this fact independently of the special position of the coordinate system: *In order to obtain, in a right-handed system of coordinates, the free vector which has the same coordinates as a given plane-magnitude, we erect a normal to the plane, toward that side from which the contour of the parallelogram*

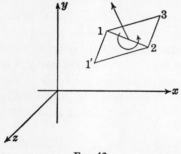

FIG. 42

representing the plane-magnitude appears counterclockwise, and we lay off on it a segment equal to the area of the parallelogram. The equality between the coordinates of the vector and of the plane-magnitude persists, no matter how one translates or rotates the coordinate system. It ceases, however, if we perform an inversion, or if we change the unit of length. For example, if we measure in decimeters, instead of in centimeters, the measure of the area is divided by 100, that of the vector-segment only by 10; likewise, under inversion, the vector changes sign, but not the plane-magnitude.

We can identify a free plane-magnitude completely with a free vector only if we choose once for all a definite sense for the system of coordinates and a definite unit of length. Each person is free, of course, to impose such a restriction according to his whim, but he must recognize the arbitrary nature of his choice, if he would come to an understanding with others. All these things are, as you see, very clear and simple, but they must always be borne in mind because the historical development has left a certain confusion in present day physics. A word, therefore, concerning the *history of these matters*.

Grassmann's theory of extension, of 1844, because it was so hard to read, as I have emphasized, made little impression upon our physics and mechanics. The development by W. R. Hamilton in Dublin, at about the same time, had much more influence in England. Hamilton was the inventor of *quaternions*, which I considered at length [1] during the winter semester. I need add here only that he also introduced the word *vector* for what we have called *free vector*, whereas he did not expressly use the notion of *line-bound vector*. Furthermore, he did *not distinguish between free plane-magnitude and free vector*, because, at the outset, he assumed a definite determination of the coordinates as to sense and as to unit of length. This usage went over into physics, where, for a long time, no distinction was made between real vectors and plane-magnitudes. To be sure, there arose gradually, in finer investigations, the need for a separation of two forms, according to their behavior under inversion, both of which had been called indiscriminately *vector*, and for this purpose, the adjectives "*polar*" and "*axial*" were introduced. *A polar vector changes its sign under inversion, and is thus identical with our free vector; an axial vector does not change under inversion, and agrees, therefore, with our free plane-magnitude* (whereby we take no account of dimension). Eventually, physics had to recognize here a difference which is surprising in some ways, and which occurs still in the usual presentations, but which, in our general treatment, appears from the start as quite natural.

Let us now give an example which will clarify this discussion. The statement that electric excitation is a polar vector means that it is measured by three quantities X, Y, Z, which transform according to the first row of our table (p. 44). The corresponding statement that magnetic field strength is an axial vector means that its three components change according to the last row in the table. To be sure, I leave here undetermined the question as to the dimension of these components, as that would take us too far into physical details.

Along with the word *vector*, Hamilton introduced the word *scalar*, which also plays an important role in physics today. *A scalar is simply a quantity that is an invariant under all of our transformations of coordinates*, i.e., a quantity which, under changes of the coordinate system, itself changes either not at all, or only by a factor. If we go into detail, we can *distinguish different shades in the notion of scalar*. Let us consider, first, as example, the *space-segment, or the volume of the tetrahedron:*

$$T = \tfrac{1}{6} \begin{vmatrix} x_1 & y_1 & z_1 & 1 \\ x_2 & y_2 & z_2 & 1 \\ x_3 & y_3 & z_3 & 1 \\ x_4 & y_4 & z_4 & 1 \end{vmatrix}$$

---

[1] See Part I, p. 58 et seq.

This transforms, as is easily verified by calculation, as follows:

Under	Translation	Rotation	Inversion	Change of Unit Length
over into	T	T	$-T$	$\lambda^3 T$

Such a quantity, which is unchanged by translation or rotation, but is changed in sign by reflection, is called a *scalar of the second kind*, while a *scalar of the first kind* is unchanged also by inversion. The dimension, which is given by the fourth column, is not considered in this statement.

We can also easily set up *scalars of the first kind*. The simplest examples are $X^2 + Y^2 + Z^2$, where X, Y, Z are the coordinates of a free vector, and $\mathfrak{L}^2 + \mathfrak{M}^2 + \mathfrak{N}^2$, where $\mathfrak{L}$, $\mathfrak{M}$, $\mathfrak{N}$ are the coordinates of a free plane-magnitude. That these quantities remain, in fact, unchanged by all movements and reflections (not by changes in the unit of length) can be inferred from the table on page 44, if we also take into account equations (3), page 40, for the coefficients of rotation. They must, therefore, have a pure geometric meaning. Indeed we know that they represent the square of the length of the vector, or, as the case may be, of the area of the plane-segment.

We shall now inquire *how we can obtain, from combinations of given fundamental configurations (vectors and scalars of both kinds), additional configurations of the same species.* We shall consider first a very simple example. Let T be a scalar of the second kind, say the volume of a tetrahedron, and let X, Y, Z be the coordinates of a polar vector. We consider the three quantities $T \cdot X$, $T \cdot Y$, $T \cdot Z$. They transform, under movements, just as do the vector components X, Y, Z themselves. Under inversion, however, they remain unchanged, because both factors change sign. Thus these three magnitudes represent an axial vector. Similarly, starting with an axial vector $\mathfrak{L}$, $\mathfrak{M}$, $\mathfrak{N}$, we can obtain a polar vector $T \cdot \mathfrak{L}$, $T \cdot \mathfrak{M}$, $T \cdot \mathfrak{N}$.

Now we shall take *two polar vectors X_1, Y_1, Z_1 and X_2, Y_2, Z_2* and we shall form from them all sorts of characteristic combinations, starting with a purely analytic procedure. We shall examine the behavior of the newly formed magnitudes under transformation of coordinates and we shall decide from this what sort of geometric quantities they represent.

1. We start with the three sums $X_1 + X_2$, $Y_1 + Y_2$, $Z_1 + Z_2$. They transform in just the same way, obviously, as do the vector components themselves; hence they represent a new *polar vector* which has with the two given vectors a purely geometric relation which is independent of the system of coordinates.

2. The bilinear combination of both vector components

$$X_1 X_2 + Y_1 Y_2 + Z_1 Z_2$$

remains unchanged by all movements and reflections, as is easily verified by calculation; hence it represents a *scalar of the first sort*, which, as such, must admit a purely geometric definition.

3. The three minors of the matrix formed from the components

$$\begin{vmatrix} X_1 & Y_1 & Z_1 \\ X_2 & Y_2 & Z_2 \end{vmatrix}$$

behave, as is easily shown, just as do the coordinates of a *free plane-magnitude or of an axial vector*, which must then be connected with the given vectors independently of the coordinate system.

4. We consider finally *three polar vectors*, and form out of their nine components the determinant

$$\begin{vmatrix} X_1 & Y_1 & Z_1 \\ X_2 & Y_2 & Z_2 \\ X_3 & Y_3 & Z_3 \end{vmatrix}.$$

This remains unchanged under all movements, but it changes sign under reflection, so that it defines a *scalar of the second kind*.

I shall indicate the geometric interpretation of these configurations. After the result is once stated, you can easily complete the proofs, if you will only start from a properly specialized position of the coordinate system.

Interpretation of 1. The interpretation of the so-called *sum of the two vectors*, defined here, is well known. If the two vectors are drawn from the same point, then *the diagonal*, drawn from that point, of the *parallelogram*

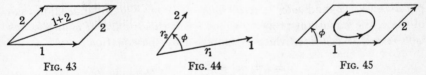

FIG. 43   FIG. 44   FIG. 45

formed from them represents this sum. [*Rule of the "parallelogram of forces."* (See Fig. 43.)]

Interpretation of 2. If the vectors have the *lengths* r_1 *and* r_2, and if the *angle between their directions is* ϕ (see Fig. 44), then the *bilinear combination is* $r_1 r_2 \cos \phi$.

Interpretation of 3. We consider, again, a *parallelogram, whose sides are parallel to the vectors* 1 *and* 2, *and we think of it as traversed in the sense given by the succession of the directions of* 1 *and* 2 (see Fig. 45); then we have a completely determined free plane-magnitude, precisely the one defined above by its three coordinates. Moreover, *the absolute value* of its area is given by $r_1 \cdot r_2 \mid \sin \phi \mid$.

Interpretation of 4. If the three vectors all start from one point, they form the *three edges of a parallelopiped* (see Fig. 46) whose volume, with properly determined sign, will be equal to the scalar of the second kind defined by the determinant.

Let me speak now of the way in which these processes appear elsewhere in the literature, where it is not customary to give primary importance, as we

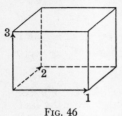

FIG. 46

do here, to an investigation of the behavior of certain analytic expressions under transformation of the coordinates, i.e., to a rational and simple theory of invariants. In the usual treatments, a certain nomenclature in mechanics and physics has been evolved, following Grassmann and Hamilton. It is customary to speak about the so-called vector algebra, and about vector analysis, which compares the rules of formation of new vectors and scalars from given vectors with the elementary rules of operation upon ordinary numbers.

We first note that the operation appearing in No. 1 is called, as already indicated, simply the *addition of the two vectors* 1 *and* 2. Justification for this designation is found in the validity of certain formal laws which characterize the addition of ordinary numbers, in particular, the *commutative and the associative laws*. The first of these laws states that the definition of the "sum" is independent of the order in which the two vectors 1 and 2 are used. The second of the two laws states that the addition of the sum of 1 and 2 to a vector 3 gives the same result as the addition of 1 to the sum of 2 and 3. In a much freer manner, the operations defined in No. 2 and in No. 3 have been called *multiplication*, and we distinguish between *inner or scalar multiplication* (No. 2) and *outer or vector multiplication* (No. 3). Indeed, in each of these, the important property called *the distributive law of multiplication with respect to addition*, which is expressed by the equation

$$a_1(a_2 + a_3) = a_1a_2 + a_1a_3,$$

is valid. In fact, for inner multiplication, we have

$$X_1(X_2 + X_3) + Y_1(Y_2 + Y_3) + Z_1(Z_2 + Z_3)$$
$$= (X_1X_2 + Y_1Y_2 + Z_1Z_2) + (X_1X_3 + Y_1Y_3 + Z_1Z_3).$$

The analogous property for outer multiplication can be derived with equal simplicity. As to the other formal laws of multiplication, which I discussed fully in my lectures [1] last winter, I may say that the commutative law $(a \cdot b = b \cdot a)$ holds for inner multiplication, but not for outer multiplication, since the small determinants of the matrix which defines the outer product change sign when the vectors 1 and 2 are interchanged.

---

[1] See Part I, p. 9.

I may add that the outer product of two polar vectors is often defined simply as a vector, without sufficiently emphasizing its axial character. Of course, on the basis of the general relation given above (p. 46), we can replace the free plane-magnitude by a vector, and we obtain the following rule. *The outer product of two vectors 1 and 2 is a vector 3 of length $r_1 r_2 \mid \sin \phi \mid$, perpendicular to the plane of 1 and 2, and so directed that the vectors 1, 2, 3 are oriented to each other as are the positive x, y, z axes, respectively, to one another* (see Fig. 47). It must not be forgotten, however, that this definition depends essentially upon the kind of coordinate system and upon the unit of length.

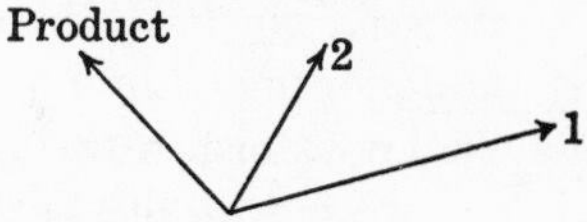

FIG. 47

Why this *language of vector analysis* has been so firmly adopted I am unable fully to understand. It may well have some connection with the fact that many people derive much pleasure from such formal analogies with the common time-honored operations of reckoning. In any event, these names for the vector operations have been accepted with tolerable generality. However, the choice of a definite symbolism for these operations, in particular for the different kinds of multiplication, has resulted in a great divergence of opinion. In my preceding course of lectures,[1] I explained that there remains great disagreement, in spite of all efforts. Meanwhile, an international commission was set up at the recent mathematical Congress in Rome, and was asked to propose a unified notation. Whether any sort of agreement will be reached even among the members of this Commission, and whether the great body of mathematicians will accept its proposals, only time will tell. It is extraordinarily difficult to induce a large number of individuals, bent upon going comfortably in their own ways, to reconcile their divergent views, except under the compelling force of legislative enactment or of material interest. I prefer not to talk here about the notation of vector analysis; otherwise I might unwittingly create a new one.

I do not wish to end this discussion without pointing out, with emphasis, that, for our general standpoint, the *questions of ordinary vector analysis constitute only a chapter* out of a profusion of more general problems. For example, *line-bound vectors, restricted plane-magnitudes, screws, and systems of forces* are, strictly speaking, not considered in vector analysis. For a real understanding of the operations of vector algebra themselves, however, it is actually necessary to take a broader view of them. Only then does the principle which inheres in them, namely, that of defining geometric magnitudes according to their behavior under the various kinds of transformation of rectangular coordinates, find full expression. As to the literature concerning all these questions, I mention first the work in which I explained our general principle of classification and applied it, in particular, to the above men-

---

[1] Part I, p. 65.

tioned theory of screws: *Zur Schraubentheorie von Sir Robert Ball*.[1] I should mention also the Encyclopedia articles by E. Timerding (*Geometrische Grundlegung der Mechanik eines starren Körpers*, Enz. IV, 2) and M. Abraham (*Geometrische Grundbegriffe der Mechanik deformierbarer Körper*, Enz. IV, 14).

[The Committee which was set up in Rome for the unification of vector notation did not have the slightest success, as was to have been expected. At the following Congress in Cambridge (1912), they had to explain that they had not finished their task, and to request that their time be extended to the meeting of the next Congress, which was to have taken place in Stockholm in 1916, but which was omitted because of the war. The committee on units and symbols met a similar fate. It published in 1921 a proposed notation for vector quantities, which aroused at once and from many sides the most violent opposition. This plan is printed in volume I (1921) of the Zeitschrift für angewandte Mathematik und Mechanik, page 421 et seq. The comments of the opponents are published in the second volume (1922) of the same journal. The terminology which is usual today in vector calculation comes historically, in the main, from two sources, from Hamilton's quaternion calculus and from Grassmann's theory of extension. The developments of Grassmann were hard to read and remained unknown to German physicists; for a long time they formed a sort of esoteric doctrine for small mathematical groups. The ideas of Hamilton, on the other hand, made their way into English physics, mainly through Maxwell. In his *Treatise on Electricity and Magnetism* (2 vols., Oxford, 1873), however, Maxwell used, in his vector equations, the representation by components almost exclusively. He made little use of a particular notation, through fear of not being understood, although in his opinion it was desirable, for many purposes in physical deliberations, to avoid the introduction of coordinates and to draw attention instantly to a point in space instead of to its three coordinates, and to the direction and magnitude of a force rather than to its three components. That which today is called the vector calculus of the physicist is derived from the work of the telegraph engineer Heaviside and the American scholar J. W. Gibbs. The latter published in 1881 his *Elements of Vector Analysis*. Although Heaviside, as well as Gibbs, were Hamiltonians at the start, they both took over Grassmann's ideas into their calculus. Indirectly, through the works of these two authors, the vector calculus, and with it Grassmann's theory of extension, as well as Hamilton's quaternion calculus, made its way into German physics. The first book that introduced the vector calculus into the circle of German physicists, and that after the manner of Heaviside, was A. Föppl's *Einführung in die Maxwell'sche*

---

[1] *Zeitschrift für Mathematik und Physik*, vol. 47, p. 237 et seq., and *Mathematische Annalen*, vol. 67, p. 419 = F. Klein, *Gesammelte Mathematische Abhandlungen*, vol. 1, p. 503 et seq.

Theorie, which appeared in 1894. Both Grassmann and Hamilton had this in common, that the object of each was to operate with directed magnitudes themselves, and only later to go over to their components. It is remarkable that both generalized the meaning of the word "product." This may be due to the fact that, from the outset, they associate their developments with the theory of complex numbers of more than two terms. (See my presentation of quaternions in Vol. I, p. 58 et seq.) Otherwise, however, the technical terms of the two are entirely different, as has been shown already. The terms line-segment, plane-segment, plane-magnitude, inner and outer product, come from Grassmann, while the words scalar, vector, scalar product, and vector product, come from Hamilton. The disciples of Grassmann, in other ways so orthodox, replaced in part the appropriate expressions of the master by others. The existing terminologies were merged or modified, and the symbols which indicate the separate operations have been used with the greatest arbitrariness. On these accounts, even for the expert, a great lack of clearness has crept into this field, which is mathematically so simple.

The principle announced on page 25 is a guiding star through this confusion. According to it, we can characterize the theories of Grassmann and Hamilton as follows. While Grassmann in his *Lineale Ausdehnungslehre* studies the theory of those invariants which belong to the group of affine [1] transformations which leave the origin of coordinates unchanged, he builds on the group of rotations in his later *Vollständige Ausdehnungslehre,* as does Hamilton also in his *Quaternions.* Hamilton's procedure in this is thoroughly naive. It did not occur to him that there is anything arbitrary in the choice of the orthogonal group. Other differences can arise, as already explained, if inversion, that is, reflection of all the coordinate axes in the origin, is admitted on the one hand or is excluded as superfluous on the other. The whole situation can best be made clear with the notions *outer product* (free plane-magnitude), *vector product,* and *vector.* If we select the group of orthogonal transformations but exclude inversion, we make no distinction between these three types of quantity. For this reason, Grassmann, in his *Vollständige Ausdehnungslehre,* represents the free plane-magnitude (a parallelogram with a sense of rotation) by means of a vector, which he calls the complement of the plane-magnitude, and which corresponds completely to the vector which the physicist designates as a vector product. But if inversion is admitted, then "plane-magnitude" and "vector product" are to be considered equivalent geometric configurations, but different from that of "vector." This corresponds to the customary distinction in physics between polar and axial vectors. If we now go over to the group of affine transformations, we can no longer consider Grassmann's free plane-magnitude and the vector product as geometric quantities of the same kind.]

---

[1] These transformations are discussed later in this book (see p. 70 et seq.).

V. DERIVATIVE MANIFOLDS

This completes what I wished to say here about elementary configurations of geometry, and I shall now turn to *the higher configurations which arise by combination of these.* I shall do this in *historical form*, so that you can get a picture of the development of geometry in the different centuries.

A. *Up to the end of the eighteenth century only points were commonly used as elementary configurations.* Other elementary configurations appeared at times, but never systematically. As configurations derived from points, there were considered *curves and surfaces* as well as more general *configurations* made up of parts of different curves and surfaces. Let us consider, briefly, how varied such configurations may be.

1. In *elementary instruction,* and sometimes even in the introductory course in analytic geometry, it would appear as though the whole of geometry were confined to the *straight line,* the *plane,* the *conic sections,* and *surfaces of the second order.* Of course that is a very narrow view. Even the knowledge of the ancient Greeks went beyond this, in part, for they included certain higher curves which they considered as "geometric loci." To be sure, these things had not reached down into ordinary instruction.

2. Let us compare with this the state of knowledge *around 1650,* when analytic geometry began with *Fermat* and *Descartes.* In those days, scholars distinguished between *geometric and mechanical curves.* The first type included particularly the conic sections, but included also certain higher curves such as those which are now called *algebraic curves;* the second type included such curves as those defined by some *mechanism,* e.g., the *cycloids,* which arise when a wheel rolls. Such curves belong for the most part to the curves now called *transcendental* curves.

3. Both these types of curves are included under *analytic curves,* which were defined later. These are curves whose *coordinates x, y* can be represented as *analytic functions of a parameter t,* i.e., briefly, as power series in *t.*

4. In recent times, consideration has often been given to *non-analytic curves,* whose coordinates $x = \phi(t)$, $y = \psi(t)$ cannot be developed into power series. Such are, for example, the curves defined by continuous functions without derivatives. This implies *a more general notion of curve, which includes the analytic curve as a special case.*

5. Finally, through the development, in recent times, of the theory of aggregates, which I have discussed before,[1] a concept has appeared which was heretofore unknown, namely, the *infinite point set.* This is a *totality of*

---

[1] See Part I, p. 250 et seq.

infinitely many points, a point cluster, which may not exactly form a curve, but which is still defined by a certain law. If we wish to find, in our concrete perception, something that corresponds fairly well to a point set, we might look at the milky way, in which more careful search discloses ever more and more stars. The actual infinity of the abstract point set theory is replaced here by the infinity of the mathematics of approximation.

Within the scope of this course of lectures there will not be room, unfortunately, for more than this brief account of these disciplines, in particular for *infinitesimal geometry* and *point set theory,* although these are, of course, likewise important parts [1] of geometry. They are, however, treated thoroughly in many special lectures and books. Hence we shall give only this indication of their place in the whole field of geometry, in order that we may treat more fully things that are not so often treated elsewhere.

However, I should like to add to this account an explanation of the *difference between analytic and synthetic geometry,* which always plays a part in such discussions. According to their original meaning, synthesis and analysis are different methods of presentation. Synthesis begins with details, and builds up from them more general, and finally the most general, notions. Analysis, on the contrary, starts with the most general, and separates out more and more the details. It is precisely this difference in meaning which finds its expression in the designations synthetic and analytic chemistry. Likewise, in school geometry, we speak of the *analysis of geometric constructions:* we assume there that the desired triangle has been found, and we then dissect the given problem into separate partial problems.

In higher mathematics, however, these words have, curiously, taken on an entirely different meaning. *Synthetic geometry is that which studies figures as such, without recourse to formulas, whereas analytic geometry consistently makes use of such formulas as can be written down after the adoption of an appropriate system of coordinates.* Rightly understood, there exists only a *difference of gradation* between these two kinds of geometry, according as one gives *more prominence to the figures or to the formulas.* Analytic geometry which dispenses entirely with geometric representation can hardly be called geometry; synthetic geometry does not get very far unless it makes use of a suitable language of formulas to give precise expression to its results. Our procedure, in this course, has been to recognize this, for we used formulas from the start and we then inquired into their geometric meaning.

In mathematics, however, as everywhere else, men are inclined to form parties, so that there arose *schools of pure synthesists* and *schools of pure analysts,* who placed chief emphasis upon absolute "purity of method," and who were thus more one-sided than the nature of the subject demanded. Thus the analytic geometricians often lost themselves in blind calculations,

---

[1] Part III will contain something about these things.

devoid of any geometric representation. The synthesists, on the other hand, saw salvation in an artificial avoidance of all formulas, and thus they accomplished nothing more, finally, than to develop their own peculiar language formulas, different from ordinary formulas. Such exaggeration of the essential fundamental principles into scientific schools leads to a *certain petrifaction;* when this occurs, stimulation to renewed progress in the science comes principally from "outsiders." Thus, in the case of geometry, it was investigators in function theory who first made clear the difference between analytic and non-analytic curves, a difference which had never received sufficient attention either from the scientific representatives, or in the textbooks, of either of the two schools. Similarly, it was the physicists, as we have seen, who gave currency to vector analysis, although the fundamental notions are found in Grassmann. Even in texts on geometry today, vectors are often scarcely mentioned as independent concepts.

From time to time, it has been proposed that geometry, as an independent subject of instruction, be separated from mathematics, and that, generally speaking, mathematics, for purposes of instruction, be resolved into its separate disciplines. In fact, there have been created, especially in foreign universities, special professorships for geometry, algebra, differential calculus, etc. From the preceding discussion, I should like to draw the inference that the creation of such narrow limits is not advisable. On the contrary, the greatest possible living interaction of the different branches of the science which have a common interest should be permitted. Each single branch should feel itself, in principle, as representing mathematics as a whole. Following the same idea, I favor the most active relations between mathematicians and the representatives of all the different sciences.

With this, I bring our digression to an end and I shall resume consideration of the historical development.

B. Let us consider now *the powerful impulse that geometric investigation received, from 1800 on,* when the so-called *newer geometry* stepped into the foreground. Today we call it, rather, *projective geometry,* because the operation of projection, which I shall discuss at length later, plays a chief role. The name newer is still used a good deal, but really inappropriately, because many still newer tendencies have appeared since then. As the first pathfinding investigator, I would name J. V. Poncelet, whose *Traité des proprietiés projectives des Figures* [1] appeared in 1822.

The difference between the synthetic and the analytic direction also played a role, from the first, in the further development of this projective geometry. As representing the first type, I mention the Germans J. Steiner and Ch. von Staudt; among the second group, in addition to A. F. Möbius, comes, above

---

[1] Second edition, Paris, 1865–66.

all, J. Plücker. The fundamental works of these men, which have even today an active influence, are: Steiner's *Systematische Entwickelung der Abhängigkeit geometrischer Gestalten von einander,*[1] von Staudt's *Geometrie der Lage,*[2] Möbius' *Baryzentrische Kalkül,*[3] and, finally, Plücker's *Analytisch-geometrische Entwickelungen.*[4]

If I were to set forth the most important guiding principles of these "newer" geometries, I should put first the following ideas.

1. As the chief accomplishment of *Poncelet*, I should select his giving prominence for the first time to the thought that there are *other configurations that have equal justification with the point. In particular,* we may, in the plane, set the *unlimited line* over against the point, and in space we can compare the *unlimited plane* and the point. In a large number of the theorems in geometry, we can replace the word "point" by the word "line" or by the word "plane," as the case may be. This is the *principle of duality.*

Poncelet, in his developments, started from the *theory of reciprocal polars,* the *polar theory of the conic sections.* As is well known, to every point p there belongs, with reference to a definite conic, a straight line π, the polar of the point, which may be defined, perhaps, as the line joining the points of contact of tangents drawn from p to the conic (see Fig. 48). Conversely, there belongs to every line π a pole p, and the reciprocal relation obtains that if a point p' lies on π, then π', the polar of p', goes through p. From

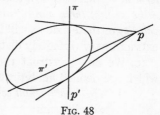

FIG. 48

this special one-to-one relation between points and lines in the plane, which the conic establishes, together with the analogous correspondence between points and planes in space, which is set up by a surface of the second order, Poncelet concluded *that one could "dualize" in this way all theorems of geometry which have to do with properties of position, the mutual incidence of point and line, or of point and plane.* A famous example is the *theorem of Pascal,* concerning the hexagon inscribed in a conic, which dualizes into *Brianchon's theorem* concerning the hexagon of tangents circumscribed about the conic.

2. As time went on, *a deeper study of the principle of duality* led to its being detached from the theory of polars, and to its recognition as a *consequence of the peculiar constitution of projective geometry.* This beautiful systematization appears first in the work of Gergonne and of Steiner. You need only read the preface of Steiner's *Systematische Entwickelungen,*[5] where he pictures in enthusiastic words how projective geometry first brought order into

---

[1] Berlin, 1832 = Gesammelte Werke, 13d, I (Berlin, 1881), p. 229 et seq. Reprinted in nos. 82, 83 of Ostwald's *Klassiker der exakten Wissenschaften.*

[2] Nürnberg, 1847.

[3] See p. 17.

[4] Two vols., Essen, 1828, 1831,

[5] Cited above, p. 233.

the chaos of geometric theorems, and how everything arranges itself so naturally in it.

As I shall often have occasion to speak of this discipline in the course of these lectures, I should like to give a *brief survey* of it now. The principle of duality may be stated as follows. In the *fundamental notions and the fundamental theorems (axioms) of geometry, the point and the plane, in space, or the point and the line, if we restrict ourselves to the plane, always enter symmetrically*, i.e., these axioms, and hence the theorems logically derived from them, are dual by pairs. The so-called mass relations of elementary geometry, such as distance, angle, etc., do not, in the first instance, appear at all in this discipline. We shall see, later, how they can be fitted in supplementarily. In detail, the composition of the structure is as follows.

(a) *Three kinds of configurations* are used as the simplest ones for a foundation: *the point, the (unlimited) straight line, the (unlimited) plane.*

(b) The following relations (called *theorems of connection or axioms of connection*) exist between these fundamental configurations: *Two points determine a line, three non-collinear points determine a plane; two planes determine a line; three non-collinear planes determine a point.* The *unrestricted validity* of these axioms will be brought about by the skillful introduction of extraordinary (infinitely distant) elements in a way to be explained later.

(c) We now construct the *linear fundamental configurations* (i.e., those which are defined analytically by linear equations).

I. The *fundamental configurations of the first kind*, each consisting of ∞^1 elements:

(α) The totality of points on a line: a *rectilinear point range.*

(β) The totality of planes through a line: *an axial pencil of planes.*

(γ) The lines through a point in a plane: a *(plane) pencil of lines.*

II. *Fundamental configurations of the second kind*, each consisting of ∞^2 elements:

(α) The plane as locus of its points: a *field of points.*

(α') The plane as locus of its lines: a *field of lines.*

(β) The planes through a fixed point: a *pencil of planes.*

(β') The lines through a fixed point: a *pencil of lines.*

III. *Fundamental configurations of the third kind*, each consisting of ∞^3 elements:

(α) Space as the locus of its points: a *space of points.*

(β) Space as the locus of its planes: a *space of planes.*

In this entire structure, complete duality appears everywhere. We can exhibit the whole body of projective geometry in two mutually dual ways if, using the given fundamental elements, we start on the one hand from points, and on the other either from lines, if we are concerned with geometry of the plane, or from planes if we are thinking of geometry of space.

3. This structure can be represented in another manner, and more conveniently, if we follow the *analytic way* and inquire, for that purpose, in the first place, in what form the *principle of duality appears with Plücker*. We can write the *equation of the straight line* in the plane, if the constant term is not zero, as follows:

$$ux + vy + 1 = 0.$$

The line is determined if we know the values of the coefficients u and v, which, moreover, appear in this form symmetrically with the running coordinates x and y. Now it is Plücker's thought to look upon u and v as the *"coordinates of the line" and as having equal justification with the point coordinates x and y, and as being considered, at times, as variable instead of them*. With this new point of view, x and y have fixed values, and the equation expresses the condition that a variable line passes through a fixed point: it is the equation of this point in line coordinates. Finally, it is not necessary, in the form of expression used, to show a preference for either of these configurations. We can leave entirely undetermined which pair of quantities we will consider constant and which variable. Then the equation expresses the *condition for the "united position" of point and line. Now the principle of duality lies in this, that every equation in x and y, on one hand, and in u and v on the other hand, is completely symmetrical. Everything that we said above concerning the duality that is inherent in the axioms of connection rests in this property.*

In space, of course, the equation of the line will be replaced by the *equation of the plane*

$$ux + vy + wz + 1 = 0.$$

As a result of these considerations, geometry can be developed analytically by looking upon either x, y, z or u, v, w as the fundamental variables and, accordingly, by simply interchanging the words point and plane. In this way, then, arises the familiar *two-way development of geometry*, which you find emphasized in many texts, where dual theorems appear side by side on the same page, separated by a vertical line. Let us cast a rapid glance at the *higher configurations* which arise in this way, always in *dual pairs*, whereby we shall, in a sense, obtain a continuation of the above dual scheme of linear configurations.

To start with, we look upon x, y, z as *definite, non-constant functions* ϕ, χ, ψ *of a parameter t*. These three functions will then represent a *space curve*, which, in particular (when ϕ, χ, ψ satisfy identically a linear equation with constant coefficients), can be a *plane curve*, or, finally (when they satisfy two such linear equations), can degenerate into a *straight line*. In the same way, considering u, v, w as functions of t, we obtain a *singly infinite succession of planes*, which we can consider most conveniently as the tangent planes of a *developable surface*. As special cases we get, as the first case, that all the planes pass through a point, i.e., that they envelop a cone, and, as the second case, that they all go through a *fixed line*.

Secondly, if we consider x, y, z as *functions of two parameters t and t'*, we get a *surface*, which, in particular, can degenerate into a *plane*. The dual of this is the *double infinity of planes enveloping a surface*, which can degenerate into a *pencil of planes* through a point.

Let us collect these results into a table:

$\begin{aligned} x &= \phi\,(t) \\ y &= \chi\,(t) \\ z &= \psi\,(t) \end{aligned}$	Curve (*Plane curve*) (*Straight line*)	$\begin{aligned} u &= \phi\,(t) \\ v &= \chi\,(t) \\ w &= \psi\,(t) \end{aligned}$	Developable surface (*Cone*) (*Straight line*)
$\begin{aligned} x &= \phi\,(t, t') \\ y &= \chi\,(t, t') \\ z &= \psi\,(t, t') \end{aligned}$	Surface· (*Plane*)	$\begin{aligned} u &= \phi\,(t, t') \\ v &= \chi\,(t, t') \\ w &= \psi\,(t, t') \end{aligned}$	Surface (*Point*)

This will suffice as an example of a dual scheme which men have found pleasure in developing, these many years.

4. One finds even in Plücker an *essential extension of this entire subject*. Just as he looked upon the three coefficients in the equation of the plane as variable plane coordinates, so he conceived the notion of considering, *quite generally, the constants upon which any geometric configuration depends*—e.g., the nine coefficients in the equation of a surface of order two—*as variable coordinates of this configuration, and he investigated what an equation between them might signify*. Of course, one can no longer talk of "duality," in any real sense, since this depended upon the special property that the equation of the plane, as well as that of the straight line (see p. 59 et seq.), was symmetrical in coefficients and coordinates.

Plücker himself carried out this idea especially for *straight lines in space*. A straight line in space is given, in point coordinates, by two equations, which Plücker writes in the form

$$x = rz + \rho, \qquad y = sz + \sigma.$$

The *four constants r, s, ρ, σ* in these equations are to be called the *coordinates of the line in space*. It is easy to show how they are related to the six ratios $X : Y : \cdots : N$, derived by Grassmann's principle from two points of the line, which we have used before (p. 30 et seq.). Plücker now considers an *equation $f(r, s, \rho, \sigma) = 0$* between the four coordinates. It separates out from the four-fold infinity of straight lines in space a three-fold infinity of lines which Plücker calls a *line complex*. We have already mentioned (p. 35) the simplest case of this manifold, the *linear complex*. *Two equations*

$$f(r, s, \rho, \sigma) = 0, \qquad g(r, s, \rho, \sigma) = 0$$

determine a *line-congruence*, which is also called a *system of rays*. The first of these names implies that we are concerned with those straight lines in which the two complexes $f = 0$, $g = 0$ coincide. Finally, *three equations* of the same sort, $f = g = h = 0$ determine a simply infinite family of straight lines which cover a certain surface called a *ruled surface*.

Plücker gave this presentation in 1868–69 in his book entitled *Neue Geometrie des Raumes gegründet auf die Betrachtung der geraden Linie als Raumdement*.[1] He died as the printing of the first part was nearly finished, and I, as his assistant, was able to win my spurs by editing the second part.

Plücker's general principle of considering any configuration as a space element and its constants as coordinates has led to other interesting developments. Thus the eminent Norwegian mathematician Sophus Lie, who worked many years in Leipzig, had great success with his *geometry of the sphere*. Here the space element is the sphere, which, like the straight line, depends upon four parameters. I mention, further, Study's *Geometrie der Dynamen*,[2] of a later date, where a whole series of interesting investigations of this nature are connected with the notion of the "dyname," which we have discussed above.

C. The "new geometry" which we have been discussing is based primarily on the prominence given to the unlimited line and the unlimited plane as space elements. Grassmann's developments, beginning in 1844, went beyond this, however. Here he placed the *limited line-segment, plane-segment, space-segment* in the foreground and assigned components to them according to his *determinant principle*, all of which we have discussed thoroughly. The beautiful thing about this is that it corresponds to the needs of mechanics and physics far more effectively than do, for example, line geometry and the principle of duality.

Of course, these different directions are by no means so sharply separated from one another as I have made it appear in my attempt to give you a clearer view of each of them. The fact of the matter is that Plücker gives *more* weight to the unlimited line, Grassmann *more* to the line-segment, while, with each of them, the other configuration sometimes appears. In particular, Study might just as well be placed in the present rubric as in the preceding one.

I must emphasize, however, that Grassmann by no means confined himself to things that were immediately applicable, but that, with unfettered creative instinct, he went far beyond that. His most important contribution is that he introduced the general notion of *n point coordinates* $x_1, x_2, \cdots, x_n$, instead of the three x, y, z, and so he became the real *creator of geometry of space, R_n, of n dimensions*. Following his general principle, he considered, in

[1] Parts 1, 2, Leipzig, 1868 and 1869.
[2] Leipzig, 1903.

such a higher space, the matrices of the coordinates of $2, 3, \cdots, n+1$ points, whose minors then gave him a whole series of fundamental configurations of R_n, corresponding to the line-segment and the plane-segment. I have mentioned already that Grassmann called the abstract discipline thus created the theory of extension.

This notion of R_n has been extended in recent times to include the consideration of *infinitely many coordinates* $x_1, x_2, \cdots ad$ *infinitum*, and one speaks of *space* R_∞ *of infinitely many dimensions*. That such a notion can make sense can be seen if we think of operating with power series: a power series is determined by the totality of its infinitely many coefficients, and it can, to that extent, be represented by a point in R_∞.

The remarkable thing here, as has been recognized in general by mathematicians, is that this way of speaking geometrically of n and, indeed, of infinitely many variables, has proved to be of real use. By means of it, discussions become more vivid than when they are confined to abstract analytic expression. The student acquires soon such facility in the use of the new geometric representation as to make it appear that he is really at home in R_n or R_∞. What measure of truth lies behind this phenomenon, and whether, perhaps, a natural gift of the human mind comes to light, which is ordinarily limited in its development by experience in space of only two or three dimensions—that is a question to be decided by psychologists and philosophers.

If I am to give you a survey of the role of mathematics in general culture, I must devote a word to the turn which was given to geometry of higher dimensions in 1873 by the astronomer Zöllner of Leipzig. We have here one of the rare cases where a mathematical expression has gone over into everyday use. Nowadays everybody uses expressions involving the "fourth dimension." This *popularizing of the fourth dimension* arose from experiments made before Zöllner by the spiritualist Slate. Slate announced himself as a medium who had direct intercourse with the spirits, and his exhibitions consisted, among others, in causing objects to disappear and to reappear. Zöllner believed in these experiments and set up for their explanation a physico-metaphysical theory which was widely accepted. He postulated that for the real physical phenomenon, there is really a space of four or more dimensions, of which we, because of our limited endowment, can appreciate only a three-dimensional section $x_4 = 0$. He argued that an especially gifted medium who, perhaps, is in touch with beings living outside this world of ours, can remove objects from it, which would then become invisible to us, or he can bring them back again. He attempts to make these relations clear by picturing beings who are restricted to a two-dimensional surface, and whose perceptions have this limitation. We may think of the mode of life of certain animals, e.g., mites. If an object is removed from the surface in which these creatures live, it would appear to them to disappear entirely (that is how it is conceived), and it was in analogous fashion that Zöllner explained Slate's experiments. Various attempts have been made to picture the existence of these two-dimensional beings. Especially amusing is the one in an anonymous English booklet *Flatland*.[1] Here the author paints exactly the appearance of a two-dimensional world: the individual beings differ through their geometric form, being more complicated the more highly organized they are. Regular polygons are the highest beings. Women, of whom the author seems to have a poor opinion, have simply the form of a dash; and so it goes.

I hardly need to add here that the mathematical conception of geometry of higher dimensions has nothing to do with Zöllner's metaphysical notions. Mathematics shows itself here as a *pure normative science*, to use a modern expression, which considers the possible connections of things, and which exists quite independently of the facts of natural science or of metaphysics.

After this digression, I should like to consider, in somewhat more detail, the higher manifolds which, as *combinations of Grassmann's elementary manifolds*, in particular of vectors, can be placed alongside of the combinations of points, planes, etc., which we have already discussed. We come here to the further *development of the real vector-analysis*, which, thanks especially to Hamilton, has become one of the most valuable tools of mechanics and physics. I place before you Hamilton's *Elements of Quaternions*, as well as the *Vector Analysis*,[2] already mentioned (p. 52) by the likewise distinguished American J. W. Gibbs.

The new notion which is added here to our already familiar concepts of vector and scalar, is the *connecting of these quantities with the points of space:* To every point in space we assign a definite scalar $S = f(x, y, z)$ and we speak then of a *scalar field*. On the other hand, we attach to every point in space a definite vector

$$X = \phi(x, y, z), \qquad Y = \psi(x, y, z), \qquad Z = \chi(x, y, z)$$

and we call the totality of these vectors a *vector field*.

In this way we designate two of the most important geometric notions, which are used everywhere in modern physics. It will suffice if I recall a few examples of their wide application. The density of a *mass distribution*, the *temperature*, the *potential energy* of a continuous extended system, always thought of as a function of position, are examples of scalar fields. The *field of force*, in which a definite force is applied at each point, is the typical example of a vector field. I will cite the following additional examples. In the theory of elasticity, the *field of displacements* of a deformable body, when we assign to each point a line-segment that indicates the amount and direc-

---

[1] *A Romance of Many Dimensions*. By a Square. London, 1884. The purpose of the author here is really to make comprehensible the possibility of a geometry of higher dimensions.

[2] Edited by E. B. Wilson, New York, 1901.

tion of its displacement, is a vector field. Similarly, in hydrodynamics, the *field of velocities*, and finally, in electrodynamics, the *electric and magnetic field*, in which to each point is assigned a definite electric and a magnetic vector, are examples of vector fields. Since at every point we can combine the vector of the magnetic field strength, which is of axial nature, with the polar vector of the electric field strength, to form a screw, the electromagnetic field can be interpreted also as an example of a *screw-field*.

Hamilton showed how these fields could be made available in the simplest way, for the methods of differential and integral calculus. To this end, it is fundamental to remark that the differentials dx, dy, dz, whose ratios determine the direction of displacement at a point of space, represent a *free vector*, i.e., *that they behave, under transformation of coordinates, as do free vector components*. This follows easily from the fact that they arise by a limit process from the coordinates of a small linear segment passing through the point x, y, z.

More important, but more difficult to grasp, is a second remark that *the symbols of partial differentiation*

$$\frac{\partial}{\partial x}, \quad \frac{\partial}{\partial y}, \quad \frac{\partial}{\partial z}$$

also have the character of free vector components, i.e., if we go over to a new rectangular coordinate system x', y', z', the new symbols $\partial/\partial x'$, $\partial/\partial y'$, $\partial/\partial z'$ behave toward the old as do the transformed coordinates of a vector (and, specifically, a *polar vector*).

This will be clear, at once, if we carry it out for a rotation of the system of coordinates

$$(1) \qquad \begin{cases} x' = a_1 x + b_1 y + c_1 z, \\ y' = a_2 x + b_2 y + c_2 z, \\ z' = a_3 x + b_3 y + c_3 z. \end{cases}$$

As we showed earlier (p. 41), these formulas of rotation have the characteristic that their solution is obtained simply by the interchange of rows with columns in the system of coefficients:

$$(2) \qquad \begin{cases} x = a_1 x' + a_2 y' + a_3 z', \\ y = b_1 x' + b_2 y' + b_3 z', \\ z = c_1 x' + c_2 y' + c_3 z'. \end{cases}$$

If we have, now, any function of x, y, z, we can, by means of (2), express it as a function of x', y', z', and we shall have, according to the known rules for partial differentiation,

$$\frac{\partial}{\partial x'} = \frac{\partial}{\partial x}\frac{\partial x}{\partial x'} + \frac{\partial}{\partial y}\frac{\partial y}{\partial x'} + \frac{\partial}{\partial z}\frac{\partial z}{\partial x'},$$

$$\frac{\partial}{\partial y'} = \frac{\partial}{\partial x}\frac{\partial x}{\partial y'} + \frac{\partial}{\partial y}\frac{\partial y}{\partial y'} + \frac{\partial}{\partial z}\frac{\partial z}{\partial y'},$$

$$\frac{\partial}{\partial z'} = \frac{\partial}{\partial x}\frac{\partial x}{\partial z'} + \frac{\partial}{\partial y}\frac{\partial y}{\partial z'} + \frac{\partial}{\partial z}\frac{\partial z}{\partial z'}.$$

The derivatives of x, y, z with respect to x', y', z' are immediately available from (2), and we get

$$\frac{\partial}{\partial x'} = a_1\frac{\partial}{\partial x} + b_1\frac{\partial}{\partial y} + c_1\frac{\partial}{\partial z},$$

$$\frac{\partial}{\partial y'} = a_2\frac{\partial}{\partial x} + b_2\frac{\partial}{\partial y} + c_2\frac{\partial}{\partial z},$$

$$\frac{\partial}{\partial z'} = a_3\frac{\partial}{\partial x} + b_3\frac{\partial}{\partial y} + c_3\frac{\partial}{\partial z}.$$

A comparison with (1) shows, in fact, agreement with the transformation formulas for point coordinates, and thus for vector components.

An essentially simpler calculation would show also that, under *translation* of the system of coordinates, the three symbols $\partial/\partial x$, $\partial/\partial y$, $\partial/\partial z$ are unchanged, but that, under *inversion*, the sign changes, so that the statement is proved. To be sure, we have taken no account of changes in the unit of length, i.e., of dimension. If we do this, we find that our symbols have the dimension -1, because of the differentials of coordinates that appear in the denominators.

We shall now perform, with this Hamilton vector symbol ($\partial/\partial x$, $\partial/\partial y$, $\partial/\partial z$), the same operations that we performed earlier with vectors. Let me remark, in advance, that we may call the result of the operation $\partial/\partial x$ upon a function $f(x, y, z)$, that is, $\partial f/\partial x$, symbolically, *the product of $\partial/\partial x$ and f*, since the formal laws of multiplication, insofar as we are here concerned with them, in particular the distributive law

$$\frac{\partial(f + g)}{\partial x} = \frac{\partial f}{\partial x} + \frac{\partial g}{\partial x},$$

hold for these combinations.

Now let a *scalar field $S = f(x, y, z)$* be given, and let us multiply this scalar by the components of the Hamilton vector symbol, in the sense just outlined, i.e., let us form the vector

$$\frac{\partial f}{\partial x}, \qquad \frac{\partial f}{\partial y}, \qquad \frac{\partial f}{\partial z}.$$

We have already seen (p. 48) that the product of a scalar by a vector is again a vector. Since, in the proof of this theorem, only such properties of multiplication are used as persist also in our symbolic multiplication, it follows that *these three partial derivatives of the scalar field define a vector which depends on x, y, z and is thus a vector field. The connection between this vector field and the scalar field is independent of the particular system of coordinates chosen.* This vector field, with the sign changed, is called the *gradient of the scalar field*, a term taken from meteorology. Thus, in the familiar weather charts of the newspapers, the air pressure at each point is indicated as a scalar field S, while the curves $S = $ const. are drawn and the corresponding values of S are indicated. The gradient gives, then, the direction of the most rapid drop in air pressure and is always normal to these contour curves.

One can always form a scalar $X^2 + Y^2 + Z^2$ from the vector components X, Y, Z. Hence we can obtain, from the gradient of a scalar, *a new scalar field:*

$$\left(\frac{\partial f}{\partial x}\right)^2 + \left(\frac{\partial f}{\partial y}\right)^2 + \left(\frac{\partial f}{\partial z}\right)^2,$$

which must be connected with it, and therefore with the original scalar field, in a manner independent of the system of coordinates. This scalar is equal to the *square of the length of the gradient*, or, as it is called, to the *square of the slope of the scalar field f.*

Applying this same principle, we can form, from the vector symbol $\partial/\partial x$, $\partial/\partial y$, $\partial/\partial z$, a symbolic scalar, by multiplying symbolically each component by itself, i.e., by applying the operation which it implies twice. This yields the *operation*

$$\frac{\partial^2}{\partial x^2} + \frac{\partial^2}{\partial y^2} + \frac{\partial^2}{\partial z^2},$$

which has, thus, scalar character, i.e., it is invariant under transformation of coordinates. If we "multiply" this scalar symbol by a scalar field f, we get, necessarily, again a *scalar field*

$$\frac{\partial^2 f}{\partial x^2} + \frac{\partial^2 f}{\partial y^2} + \frac{\partial^2 f}{\partial z^2},$$

whose relation to the first one is independent of the çoordinate system. If we think of a liquid flowing in a field, whose initial density is 1, and whose velocity at each point is given by the gradient of f, then the density at each point increases, in the first instant of time dt, by an amount equal to this scalar multiplied by dt. Hence we call

$$-\left(\frac{\partial^2 f}{\partial x^2} + \frac{\partial^2 f}{\partial y^2} + \frac{\partial^2 f}{\partial z^2}\right)$$

the *divergence of the gradient of f.*

Formerly, following Lamé, it was customary to call a scalar field $S = f(x, y, z)$ also a *point function (fonction du point)*, and to call the first scalar field connected with it, $(\partial f/\partial x)^2 + (\partial f/\partial y)^2 + (\partial f/\partial z)^2$, the *first dif-*

ferential parameter and the second, $\partial^2 f/\partial x^2 + \partial^2 f/\partial y^2 + \partial^2 f/\partial z^2$, the second differential parameter.

In similar manner, we shall now combine our vector symbol with a given (*polar*) *vector field:*

$$X = \phi(x, y, z), \qquad Y = \chi(x, y, z), \qquad Z = \psi(x, y, z).$$

Indeed, we shall do this with the aid of both kinds of multiplication of two vectors with which we have become acquainted:

(a) By *inner multiplication* there results a scalar, which, in the already familiar notation of symbolic multiplication, may be written in the form:

$$\frac{\partial X}{\partial x} + \frac{\partial Y}{\partial y} + \frac{\partial Z}{\partial z}.$$

Since this result also is independent, of course, of x, y, z, it also represents a *scalar field* whose relation to the given vector field is independent of the system of coordinates. It is called, in the sense defined above, the *divergence* of that field.

(b) *Outer multiplication* yields the matrix:

$$\begin{vmatrix} \dfrac{\partial}{\partial x} & \dfrac{\partial}{\partial y} & \dfrac{\partial}{\partial z} \\ X & Y & Z \end{vmatrix},$$

whose three determinants are to be read as:

$$\frac{\partial Z}{\partial y} - \frac{\partial Y}{\partial z}, \qquad \frac{\partial X}{\partial z} - \frac{\partial Z}{\partial x}, \qquad \frac{\partial Y}{\partial x} - \frac{\partial X}{\partial y}.$$

These define, according to what precedes, a *plane-magnitude*, or, as the case may be, an *axial vector* or an *axial vector field*. The connection between the two vector fields is again independent of the choice of the coordinate system. According to Maxwell, this vector field is called the *curl* of the given one. In Germany, the German word *quirl*, of like germanic origin, is used. Occasionally, this is called also *rotor*, or *rotation*.

We have thus obtained, through *systematic geometric investigation*, all those quantities which the physicist must always have at hand in his study of the various vector fields. It is *pure geometry*, however, that we are studying. I must emphasize this all the more, since these things are often regarded as belonging to physics, and are therefore discussed in books and lectures on physics, instead of in geometry. In the nature of the case, such an attitude is thoroughly unjustified, and it is comprehensible only as a residue of the historical development. When the time came, physics had to create the weapons which it needed, and which it did not find ready at hand in mathematics.

There exists here the same *misunderstanding* which I mentioned often last semester in the field of analysis. In the course of time, physics developed all sorts of mathematical needs. Hence it often created valuable stimulation to mathematical science. But mathematical instruction, especially as it is given in the schools, even today, pays no attention to these changes. It goes along in the same old rut which it has followed for centuries, and leaves it to physics laboriously to provide its own aids, although these would supply much more appropriate material for mathematical instruction than do the traditional topics. You observe that in the life of the intellect there is also a law of inertia. Everything continues to move along its old rectilinear path, and every change, every transition to new and modern ways, meets strong resistance.

With this I leave the first main part, which has taught us the various kinds of geometric manifolds, the *objects of geometry*. Now we shall concern ourselves with a particular *method*, which is of greatest importance for the more exact study of these manifolds.

PART TWO

GEOMETRIC TRANSFORMATIONS

That which we now undertake is one of the most important chapters of scientific geometry. In its fundamental ideas and in its simpler portions it offers, however,—and I wish especially to point this out in these lectures— very stimulating material for school instruction. Geometric transformations are, after all, nothing more than a *generalization of the simple notion of function*, which our modern reform tendencies are striving to make the central point of mathematical instruction.

I begin with a discussion of *point transformations*, which constitute the simplest class of geometric transformations. They let the point persist as space element, i.e., they bring every point into correspondence with another point—in contrast with other transformations which carry the point over into other space elements, such as the straight line, the plane, the sphere, etc. Here again I place the *analytic treatment* in the foreground, since it often enables us to give the most accurate expression of the facts.

The analytic expression of a point transformation is what analysis calls the *introduction of new variables* x', y', z':

$$\begin{cases} x' = \phi(x, y, z), \\ y' = \chi(x, y, z), \\ z' = \psi(x, y, z). \end{cases}$$

We can interpret such a system of equations geometrically in two ways, I might say *actively* and *passively*. *Passively, it represents a change in the system of coordinates*, i.e., the new coordinates x', y', z' are assigned to the point with the given coordinates x, y, z. This is the meaning we have always had in mind previously in our study of the changes of the rectangular system of coordinates. For general functions ϕ, χ, ψ, these formulas include, of course, over and above that, the transition to other kinds of coordinate systems, e.g., trilinear coordinates, polar coordinates, elliptic coordinates, etc.

In contrast with this, the *active* interpretation holds the coordinate system fast and changes space. To every point x, y, z, the point x', y', z' is made to correspond, so that there is, in fact, a transformation of the points in space. It is with this conception that we shall be concerned in what follows.

We shall obtain the *first examples* of point transformations, in the sense of these remarks, if we consider again the formulas which, before (see p. 39

et seq.), *passively* interpreted, represented a translation, a rotation, a reflection, or a change in the unit of length, and we shall now interpret them

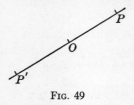

FIG. 49

actively. It is easy to see that the first two of these groups of formulas represent a *translation of space*—thought of as rigid—and a *rotation about O*, respectively, with respect to the immovable system of coordinates. The third group gives an *inversion of the points of space* in the origin O. [Every point x, y, z goes into $-x$, $-y$, $-z$, symmetric to it with respect to O (see Fig. 49).] The last one represents a so-called *similarity transformation of space*, with O as center.

We now start our real investigations with a particularly simple group of point transformations, which includes all the foregoing as subcases, namely, the *affine transformations*.

I. AFFINE TRANSFORMATIONS

An affine transformation is defined analytically when x', y', z' *are linear integral functions of* x, y, z:

(1)
$$\begin{cases} x' = a_1x + b_1y + c_1z + d_1, \\ y' = a_2x + b_2y + c_2z + d_2, \\ z' = a_3x + b_3y + c_3z + d_3. \end{cases}$$

The name, which goes back to *Möbius* and *Euler*, implies that, in such a transformation, infinitely distant points correspond again to infinitely distant points, so that, in a sense, the "ends" of space are preserved. In fact, the formulas show at once that x', y', z' become infinite with x, y, z. This is in contrast to the general projective transformations, which we shall study later, in which x', y', z' are fractional linear functions, and by which, therefore, certain finite points will be moved to infinity. These affine transformations play an important role in physics under the name of *homogeneous deformations*. The word "homogeneous" implies (in contrast to heterogeneous) that the coefficients are independent of the position in space under consideration; the word "deformation" reminds us that, in general, the form of any body will be changed by the transformation.

The transformation (1) can be made up of displacements, in amounts d_1, d_2, d_3, parallel to the three coordinate axes, together with the homogeneous linear transformation

(2)
$$\begin{cases} x' = a_1x + b_1y + c_1z, \\ y' = a_2x + b_2y + c_2z, \\ z' = a_3x + b_3y + c_3z, \end{cases}$$

which leaves the position of the origin unchanged (centro-affine transformation), and which is somewhat more convenient to use. We start the consideration of this type (2).

1. We inquire about the possibility of solving the system of equations (2). As the theory of determinants shows, this depends essentially upon whether the *determinant* of the system of coefficients of the transformation

$$(3) \qquad \Delta = \begin{vmatrix} a_1 & b_1 & c_1 \\ a_2 & b_2 & c_2 \\ a_3 & b_3 & c_3 \end{vmatrix}$$

vanishes or not. We shall consider the first case later; *for the present we shall assume that* $\Delta \neq 0$. Then (2) *has an unique solution of the form*

$$(4) \qquad \begin{cases} x = a_1'x' + b_1'y' + c_1'z', \\ y = a_2'x' + b_2'y' + c_2'z', \\ z = a_3'x' + b_3'y' + c_3'z', \end{cases}$$

where $a_1', \cdots, c_3'$ are the minors of Δ, divided by Δ itself. Thus to each point x, y, z we may say not only that there corresponds a point x', y', z', but also that there is *only one*, and the transition from x', y', z' to x, y, z is again an affine transformation.

2. We now ask *how the manifolds in space change under these affine transformations*. To begin with, let us take a plane

$$Ax + By + Cz + D = 0,$$

substituting the expressions (4) for $x, y, z,$ as equation for the corresponding manifold, we obtain

$$A'x' + B'y' + C'z' + D' = 0,$$

where the $A', \cdots, D'$ are certain combinations of $A, \cdots, D$ and of the coefficients of the transformation. In view of (1), we see that *every* point of the second plane arises from an appropriate point of the first. *Thus to every plane there corresponds another plane.* Since a straight line is the intersection of two planes, it *follows necessarily that to every line there corresponds another line.* Möbius calls transformations that have this property *collineations*, since they express the "collinearity" of three points, i.e., the property of lying upon a line. Hence *an affine transformation is a collineation.*

If we investigate in the same way a *surface of the second degree*

$$Ax^2 + 2Bxy + Cy^2 + \cdots = 0,$$

using equations (4) to replace x, y, z by x', y', z', we obtain a quadratic equation. Hence *an affine transformation transforms every surface of second degree into another of the same sort, and, similarly, every surface of degree n into another of that same degree.*

We shall be especially interested, later, in those surfaces which correspond to a *sphere*. In the first place, they will be surfaces of the second degree, since a sphere is a special surface of this sort. However, since all points of the sphere are finite, so that none of them can be carried to infinity, the transformed surface must be one of the second degree which lies wholly in a finite region, i.e., it must be an *ellipsoid*.

3. Let us now see what happens to a *free vector* with the components $X = x_1 - x_2$, $Y = y_1 - y_2$, $Z = z_1 - z_2$. Using formulas (2) for the coordinates of the points 1 and 2, we get, for the components $X' = x_1' - x_2'$, $Y' = y_1' - y_2'$, $Z' = z_1' - z_2'$ of the corresponding segments $1'\,2'$,

$$(5) \qquad \begin{cases} X' = a_1 X + b_1 Y + c_1 Z, \\ Y' = a_2 X + b_2 Y + c_2 Z, \\ Z' = a_3 X + b_3 Y + c_3 Z. \end{cases}$$

It follows that these new components depend only upon X, Y, Z and not upon the separate values of the coordinates $x_1, y_1, z_1;\ x_2, y_2, z_2$, that is, all segments 1 2 with the same components X, Y, Z correspond to segments $1'\,2'$ with the same components X', Y', Z'. In other words, *under an affine transformation, a free vector always corresponds to another free vector.* There is essentially more in this statement than in the statement that a line always corresponds to a line. Indeed, let us take equal segments on two parallel lines, both in the same sense. Since these represent the same free vector, the corresponding segments must represent one and the same vector, i.e., they must be parallel, equal, and have the same sense (see Fig. 50). *To every*

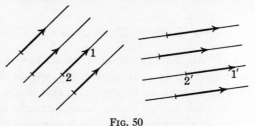

Fig. 50

system of parallel lines there correspond again parallel lines, and to equal segments on them there correspond equal segments. These properties are rather remarkable, since—as it is easy to show—the absolute length of a segment and the absolute value of the angle between two lines are changed, in general, by an affine transformation.

4. Let us now consider *two vectors of unequal length on the same line*. One of these will be transformed into the other by multiplication by a scalar.

Since X', Y', Z', in (5) are homogeneous linear functions of X, Y, Z, the corresponding vectors will differ by the same scalar factor, which means that their lengths are to each other as the lengths of the first vectors. We can state this as follows: *Two straight lines which correspond in an affine transformation are "similar," i.e., corresponding segments on the two lines have the same ratio.*

5. Finally, let us compare two tetrahedron volumes $T = (1, 2, 3, 4)$ and $T' = (1', 2', 3', 4')$. We have

$$6T' = \begin{vmatrix} x_1' & y_1' & z_1' & 1 \\ x_2' & y_2' & z_2' & 1 \\ x_3' & y_3' & z_3' & 1 \\ x_4' & y_4' & z_4' & 1 \end{vmatrix}$$

$$= \begin{vmatrix} a_1x_1 + b_1y_1 + c_1z_1, & a_2x_1 + b_2y_1 + c_2z_1, & a_3x_1 + b_3y_1 + c_3z_1, & 1 \\ a_1x_2 + b_1y_2 + c_1z_2, & a_2x_2 + b_2y_2 + c_2z_2, & a_3x_2 + b_3y_2 + c_3z_2, & 1 \\ a_1x_3 + b_1y_3 + c_1z_3, & a_2x_3 + b_2y_3 + c_2z_3, & a_3x_3 + b_3y_3 + c_3z_3, & 1 \\ a_1x_4 + b_1y_4 + c_1z_4, & a_2x_4 + b_2y_4 + c_2z_4, & a_3x_4 + b_3y_4 + c_3z_4, & 1 \end{vmatrix},$$

or, applying the known theorem for multiplying determinants,

$$6T' = \begin{vmatrix} a_1 & b_1 & c_1 & 0 \\ a_2 & b_2 & c_2 & 0 \\ a_3 & b_3 & c_3 & 0 \\ 0 & 0 & 0 & 1 \end{vmatrix} \cdot \begin{vmatrix} x_1 & y_1 & z_1 & 1 \\ x_2 & y_2 & z_2 & 1 \\ x_3 & y_3 & z_3 & 1 \\ x_4 & y_4 & z_4 & 1 \end{vmatrix}.$$

The first factor is Δ, the second $6T$, so that we have $T' = \Delta \cdot T$. *Under affine transformations all tetrahedron volumes and hence all space volumes (as sums of tetrahedron volumes, or as limits of such sums) are multiplied by a constant factor, namely by Δ, the determinant of the substitution.*

These few theorems which we have deduced from the analytic definition of affine transformation suffice to give us a *clear geometric picture* of this transformation. Their proofs have been simpler than those ordinarily given, because we had at hand, in the vector concept, the proper means for presenting them.

We get the clearest picture of the affine transformation if we start with a *sphere* in the space R of the coordinates x, y, z. To this sphere, as we know, there will correspond an *ellipsoid* in the space R' of the coordinates x', y', z'. If we now consider a *system of parallel chords of the sphere*, we know, by No. 3 above, that to these chords will correspond also parallel chords of the ellipsoid (see Fig. 51). Further, since corresponding point rows are similar (No. 4), the *middle points of the chords of the sphere* must also be in correspondence with the *middle points of the chords of the ellipsoid*. Since the midpoints of the chords of the sphere lie in a plane, the mid-points of the chords

of the ellipsoid, by virtue of the fundamental property No. 2, must also lie
in a plane, which is called a *diametral plane of the ellipsoid.* Now all diametral
planes of the sphere contain its *center M,* which bisects every chord of the
sphere which passes through it (*diameter of the sphere*); hence the correspond-

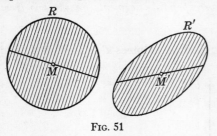

FIG. 51

ing point M' (*center of the ellipsoid*)
lies in every diametral plane and
bisects every chord through it (*diameter of the ellipsoid*).

It is also important to see what
corresponds to a system of *three mutually perpendicular diametral planes
of a sphere.* This system has obviously the characteristic property
that each of the three planes bisects chords parallel to the intersection of
the other two planes. This property persists under affine transformation.
Hence *to each of the infinitely many triples of mutually perpendicular diametral
planes of a sphere there corresponds a triple of diametral planes of the ellipsoid which have the property that chords parallel to the intersection of two
of the planes are bisected by the third.* Such groups of planes are called *triples
of conjugate diametral planes;* their intersections are called *triples of conjugate
diameters.*

I may assume that you know that an ellipsoid contains three so-called
principal axes, i.e., *a triple of mutually perpendicular conjugate diameters.*
By what precedes, to these there must correspond under our affine transformation three mutually perpendicular diameters of the sphere in R. Let
us assume, for simplicity, that the center of the ellipsoid and the center of
the sphere are the origins in R' and R, respectively, and, by appropriate rotation, let us make these two perpendicular triples the x', y', z' and x, y, z
axes in R' and R, respectively. It is a matter of arbitrary choice whether
we think here of the space, or of the coordinate axes, as being turned. In
either case, the operation is effected by a linear homogeneous substitution
of coordinates of the special sort that we have considered. Since a succession
of linear homogeneous substitutions always yields another substitution of
the same sort, the equations of the transformation which carries R into R'
will be of the form (2) in the new coordinates:

$$x' = a_1x + b_1y + c_1z,$$
$$y' = a_2x + b_2y + c_2z,$$
$$z' = a_3x + b_3y + c_3z.$$

With the new coordinate system thus chosen, the x' axis corresponds to the
x axis, i.e., when $y = z = 0$ so is $y' = z' = 0$. It follows that $a_2 = a_3 = 0$,
and, similarly, that $b_1 = b_3 = c_1 = c_2 = 0$. *If we ignore incidental rotations,
every affine transformation is a so-called "pure affine transformation":*

$$(6) \qquad \begin{cases} x' = \lambda x, \\ y' = \mu y, \qquad \text{where} \qquad \Delta \gtrless 0, \\ z' = \nu z, \end{cases}$$

or, as the physicists say, *a pure strain*. We may interpret these equations geometrically in the following simple way: *space is stretched by a factor* λ (*compressed if* $|\lambda| < 1$) *parallel to the* x *axis, and also reflected if* $\lambda < 0$; *and similarly, with respect to the other two coordinate directions, by the factors* μ *and* ν *respectively.* In brief, we can look upon a pure affine transformation as a *uniform stretching of space in three mutually perpendicular directions*, which affords as clear a geometric picture as one could desire.

If we admit *oblique parallel coordinates*, the relations are still simpler. We take, in the space R, an arbitrary system of axes x, y, z, rectangular or oblique, without changing the position of the origin, and we use the lines corresponding to these as axes x', y', z' in R'. The new axes will be, in general, oblique. Now the formulas for transition from rectangular to oblique coordinates, with fixed origin, are linear homogeneous equations of the form (2). Since the combination of two such substitutions always leads to another of the same sort, the equations of the affine transformation must have the form (2), even after applying the above oblique coordinates. However, with our selection of axes, they must carry the three axes of R into those of R'; hence we can conclude, after a repetition of the above argument, that the equations reduce actually to the form (6). *Thus, if we make use of* (*oblique*) *parallel coordinates in connection with two corresponding axis triples, the equations* of an affine transformation *assume the simple special form* (6).

In connection with our discussion, there is a beautiful solution of the problem of finding a mechanism with which we can perform affine transformations. This problem arose in a course of lectures on mechanics which I gave during the winter semester, 1908–09. The best solution, both with regard to the underlying thought and with regard to the appropriate form

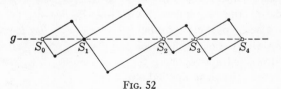

FIG. 52

of the mechanism, was furnished by R. Remak. He used, as kinematic unit, the so-called "Nürnberg shears," i.e., a chain of jointed rods which forms a series of similar parallelograms. The corners common to two successive parallelograms S_0, S_1, S_2, $\cdots$, under all deformations of the jointed system, form *similar point rows* on the line g which joins them, the common diagonal of the parallelograms. (See Fig. 52.) If we fashion a triangle from three such shears by jointing them together at any of the corners S, then the point system consisting of all the corners S, undergoes an affine transformation with every change of the total jointed system. This will become

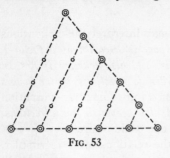

FIG. 53

clear (see Fig. 53) if we make an oblique coordinate system out of two of the diagonal lines of the shears. We can get additional points belonging to the same affine transformation if we insert additional shears of the same sort between any two points S of the triangle and consider their corners S. (In the figure, these shears are represented by their diagonal lines.) On this principle, we can set up [1] plane and space models of variable affine systems of the greatest variety.

I shall not go farther into the discussion of properties of affine transformations. Instead, I shall show how these transformations can be used.

In the first place, an example of how they *supply an excellent device for the discovery of new geometric theorems*. The affine transformation of the sphere into the ellipsoid, explained above, enables us to get *new theorems on the ellipsoid* from known properties of the sphere. For example, if we construct three mutually perpendicular diameters of the sphere, together with the six tangent planes at their ends, we have a circumscribed cube of volume $J = 8r^3$, where r is the radius of the sphere. Our affine transformation obviously carries each tangent plane of the sphere into a tangent plane of the ellipsoid. It follows, with the aid of the theorems above, that to the cube in space R there corresponds in space R' *a parallelopiped circumscribed about the ellipsoid*, whose faces, tangent at the ends of three conjugate diameters, are parallel to the corresponding diametral planes, and whose edges are parallel to those diameters. (Analo-

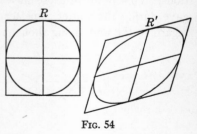

FIG. 54

gous relations hold in the plane for the circle and the ellipse; see Fig. 54.) The converse of this argument obviously holds also: To every parallelopiped circumscribed about an ellipsoid, in the way described above, there corresponds a cube circumscribed about the sphere, since to three conjugate diameters of the ellipsoid there correspond three mutually perpendicular diameters of the sphere. Now we know (p. 73) that, under an affine transformation, every volume is multiplied by the determinant Δ of the substitution, so that the volume of a parallelopiped of the above sort cir-

[1] A series of such models has appeared in the publishing house of Martin Schilling in Leipzig. See F. Klein and Fr. Schilling, *Modelle zur Darstellung affiner Transformationen in der Ebene und im Raume*, Zeitschrift für Mathematik und Physik, vol. 58, p. 311, 1910.

cumscribed about an ellipsoid is given by the formula $J' = J \cdot \Delta = 8r^3 \cdot \Delta$. This formula is clearly independent of how the parallelopiped lies, so that the parallelopiped has the same constant volume, no matter to what triple of conjugate diameters it belongs. If we select, in particular, as our triple, the principal axes, which are mutually perpendicular, we get a rectangular parallelopiped whose volume is $8abc$, where $2a$, $2b$, $2c$ are the lengths of the principal axes. In this way we determine the constant volume, and our theorem takes the following form. *All parallelopipeds which circumscribe an ellipsoid and whose faces are parallel to three conjugate diametral planes, have the same volume $J' = 8abc$, where a, b, c are the lengths of the semi-principal axes.* In order to show that this theorem is valid for all ellipsoids, it is necessary only to see that *every* ellipsoid can be generated from a sphere by affine transformation. This follows at once from the form (6) of the equations of the affine transformation. These equations show that the axes of that ellipsoid are to each other as $\lambda : \mu : \nu$, where λ, μ, ν are three arbitrary numbers.

Although I shall confine myself to this simple example of the applications of affine transformations to theoretical geometry, I wish to emphasize even more strongly that affine transformations have the greatest significance in *practice*.

Coming first to the needs of the physicist, it is to be noted that the affine transformations play a fundamental role in the theory of *elasticity*, in *hydrodynamics*, and, in fact, in every branch of the *mechanics of continua*. I hardly need to amplify this, for anyone who has busied himself at all with these disciplines knows well enough that as soon as consideration is confined to sufficiently small space elements, the problem has to do with homogeneous linear deformations.

I prefer to discuss here, at greater length, the *application to correct drawing*, which is used both by the physicist and by the mathematician. *Insofar as one has to do with parallel projection, one is concerned fundamentally solely with affine transformations of space.* Unfortunately, many sins are committed in this field of correct drawing. You can find unbelievable errors in books on mathematics in the depiction of space configurations, as well as in books on

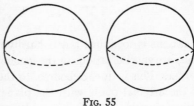

Fig. 55

physics in the representation of apparatus. To mention but one example, the sphere is very often pictured with the equator drawn as two intersecting circular arcs. (See Fig. 55.) Of course that is absurd; in fact, the correct representation is always an ellipse, as we shall see.

The principle of correct geometric drawing lies in the fact that the figure drawn is projected from a point upon the plane of the drawing. The relations are simplified if we think of that central point as lying at infinity, i.e., if we obtain the picture by means of a *pencil of parallel rays*. This is the case which interests us here. Incidentally, with these remarks we *enter the field of descriptive geometry*. I shall not give a systematic account, but I shall exhibit simply its orderly arrangement in the general edifice of geometry.

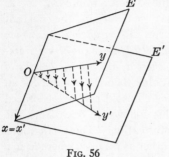

FIG. 56

Hence I shall not always give the details of proofs.

Let us begin by investigating the representation of a plane figure, i.e., the *projection of a plane E upon another E′ by means of a pencil of parallel rays*. For this purpose, we choose the origin O in the intersection of E and $E′$ (see Fig. 56), and the x axis along this line. Choose the y axis anywhere in E, e.g., perpendicular to the x axis, through O, and the $y′$ axis as the projection of the y axis upon $E′$ by the parallel pencil, so that we have in $E′$, in general, a system of oblique parallel coordinates. Then the coordinates of two corresponding points of E and $E′$ satisfy the relations

$$x′ = x, \qquad y′ = \mu \cdot y,$$

where μ is a constant depending upon the given position of the planes and the pencil. *Thus we have actually an affine transformation.* The proof of these

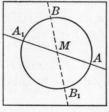
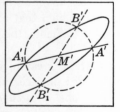

FIG. 57

equations is so simple that I hardly need to state it. Moreover, these equations are specializations of the general form (6) in that here $\lambda = 1$ and hence $x′ = x$. This is due, of course, to the fact that the x axis is the intersection of the original plane with the plane of the drawing, so that along it each point coincides with its image. We get at once all of the essential properties of the figure if we specialize for the plane the theorems deduced earlier for space, e.g., to every circle in E there corresponds an ellipse in $E′$, etc.

It is natural, now, to raise the *converse question: If two planes E and E′ have a given affine relation to each other, can they be so placed that one is the parallel projection of the other?* In order to decide this, let us start from an arbitrary circle in E and the corresponding ellipse in $E′$. (Instead of this, we might use any two corresponding ellipses.) To the center M of the circle there will correspond the center M' of the ellipse (see Fig. 57). *If we now place the circle of E in the plane E' so that its center falls at M', it will cut the ellipse in four points or not at all.* The limiting case of tangency will be disregarded, for the sake of simplicity.

In the *first case*, the one shown in the figure, we consider the two diameters $A'A_1'$, $B'B_1'$, of the ellipse, which go through the four points of intersection lying in E'. Corresponding to these—and equal to them by construction— are two diameters AA_1, BB_1, of the circle in E. Hence, by reason of a general property of affine transformations (No. 4, p. 72), corresponding segments on AA_1 and $A'A_1'$, as well as on BB_1 and $B'B_1'$, are equal. Now, if we lay the plane E upon E' so that M falls upon M' and so that one of these pairs of lines, say AA_1 and $A'A_1'$, coincides, and if we then turn E about this line as axis up into space, we have an affine transformation of the two planes, under which each point of their line of intersection corresponds to itself. Then it is easy to show, though I shall not carry out the proof, that, no matter what the angle between the planes may be, the joins of corresponding points are all parallel to each other, i.e., that the affine transformation between the two planes can, in fact, be effected by parallel projection.

If, however, our circle does not cut the ellipse, i.e., if its radius is smaller than the small semi-axis of the ellipse or larger than the large one, then, in the language of analysis, the two common diameters are imaginary and are not available for use in drawing; hence the construction is impossible. If it is still desired to bring about parallel projection, it becomes necessary to employ a *similarity transformation*, and to expand or shrink the circle by that transformation until the first case appears. We use such similarity transformations constantly in the making of pictures, in order to "change the scale." Thus we reach finally the *main theorem, that any affine relation between two planes can be effected in infinitely many different ways through combination of a similarity transformation with a parallel projection.*

We go over now to the *problem of representing all of space upon a plane by means of parallel projection,* which is much more important and interesting than this mapping of one plane upon another. To avoid tedious details, we shall agree always to admit a stretching or a shrinking of the picture by means of a similarity transformation. There arises, thus, the process which is called *axonometry* in descriptive geometry. This process plays an extraordinarily important role in practice. Every photograph is very nearly an axonometric mapping, if the object is only far enough away from the camera. (Strictly speaking, it is a central projection.) Exact axonometry is used especially, however, in most of the cases in which we wish to map geometric figures in space, physical apparatus, architectural parts, and so on. Very interesting examples of all sorts of axonometric mappings, which are also directly useful in instruction, can be found in the book entitled

Leitfaden der Projectionslehre by C. H. Müller and O Pressler.[1] It is shown there, for example, how to draw accurately a tangent compass, a buoy, crystals of the most varied kinds, and, to cite examples from the entirely different field of biology, cellular tissue, a beehive, and many other things.

Let me now state the theorem which connects axonometry with our discussion of affine transformations: *The mapping of space upon a plane by means of parallel projection and similarity transformation (axonometry) is effected analytically by an affine transformation with a vanishing determinant:*

(1)
$$\begin{cases} x' = a_1x + b_1y + c_1z \\ y' = a_2x + b_2y + c_2z, \\ z' = a_3x + b_3y + c_3z \end{cases} \quad \text{where} \quad \Delta = \begin{vmatrix} a_1 & b_1 & c_1 \\ a_2 & b_2 & c_2 \\ a_3 & b_3 & c_3 \end{vmatrix} = 0.$$

This is precisely the exceptional case which we postponed. Thus you see the importance of these "degenerate" transformations, which unfortunately are often unduly neglected. The converse is also true, namely, that *every such substitution, with $\Delta = 0$, gives an axonometric mapping.* This presupposes, to be sure, that neither all the coefficients of the substitution nor all the minors of second order vanish, for these possibilities would imply still further degenerations, which I shall pass over, since they can be investigated readily according to the following plan.

In order to prove our assertion, let us convince ourselves *that all points x', y', z' given by* (1) *(for arbitrary x, y, z) actually lie in one plane*, i.e., that there are three members k_1, k_2, k_3, such that we have

(2)
$$k_1x' + k_2y' + k_3z' = 0$$

identically in x, y, z. By (1), this identity is equivalent to the three homogeneous linear equations

(2′)
$$\begin{cases} k_1a_1 + k_2a_2 + k_3a_3 = 0, \\ k_1b_1 + k_2b_2 + k_3b_3 = 0, \\ k_1c_1 + k_2c_2 + k_3c_3 = 0, \end{cases}$$

and these determine precisely the ratios $k_1 : k_2 : k_3$ uniquely, provided that the determinant Δ vanishes but that the nine minors are not all zero. Hence all the image points x', y', z' actually lie in the plane (2) determined by equations (2′).

We shall now introduce, in the space R', a new rectangular system of coordinates such that the plane (2) becomes the $x'y'$ plane ($z' = 0$). Then there must correspond to every point of R a point in $z' = 0$, and the equations of our affine transformation, in the new coordinates, will have necessarily the form

(3)
$$\begin{cases} x' = A_1x + B_1y + C_1z, \\ y' = A_2x + B_2y + C_2z, \\ z' = 0. \end{cases}$$

---

[1] An exercise book for constructions in solid geometry, Leipzig, 1903.

The *six constants* $A_1, \cdots, C_2$ *are completely arbitrary*, since the determinant of the substitution vanishes in any case, by reason of the special form of the last row. The three minors may not all vanish however; that is

$$A_1 : B_1 : C_1 \neq A_2 : B_2 : C_2;$$

otherwise we should have the degeneration that we excluded above.

I shall now give the proof that the mappings of the space R upon the $x'y'$ plane E', defined analytically as above, are identical with the axonometric projections defined above. I shall present the proof in separate steps, by developing the chief properties of the transformation (3), much as we discussed earlier (p. 70 et seq.) the affine transformations with non-vanishing determinant.

1. In the first place, it is clear that to every point x, y, z of R there corresponds a unique point (x', y') in E'. Conversely, given a point (x', y') in E', the equations (3) show that the corresponding point (x, y, z) in R lies in two definite planes whose coefficients, by our assumption, are not proportional, and which have, therefore, a line of intersection. All the points of this line must correspond, in our transformation, to the same point (x', y'). If we now allow the point (x', y') to vary; each of the two planes will be moved parallel to itself, since the coefficients A_1, B_1, C_1 and A_2, B_2, C_2 remain unchanged. Thus their line of intersection remains parallel to itself, and we have the result *that to each point of E' there correspond all the points of one line of a double infinity of parallel lines in R*. This indicates immediately the connection between our mapping and the parallel projection of space.

2. Just as in No. 3 (p. 72) under the general affine transformation, we find now for the components X', Y' of the segment in E' which corresponds to the free vector X, Y, Z of R, the formulas

(4)
$$\begin{cases} X' = A_1 X + B_1 Y + C_1 Z, \\ Y' = A_2 X + B_2 Y + C_2 Z, \\ Z' = 0. \end{cases}$$

These show again that *to every free vector in R there corresponds a free vector X', Y' of the picture plane E'*, or, more precisely, if one displaces a segment in space R parallel to itself, preserving its length and sense, the corresponding segment in the plane E' also moves parallel to itself and maintains its length and sense.

3. We consider in particular the *unit vector* $X = 1$, $Y = Z = 0$, on the x axis, which goes from $(0, 0, 0)$ to $(1, 0, 0)$. To it there corresponds in E', by (4), the vector $X' = A_1$, $Y' = A_2$, which goes from the origin O' to the point whose coordinates are (A_1, A_2). In precisely the same way, there cor-

respond to the unit vectors on the y and the z axes the two vectors from O'
to the points (B_1, B_2) and (C_1, C_2), respectively. These three vectors in E',
which we shall call for brevity, (A), (B), (C) (see Fig. 58), can be chosen arbitrarily, since the coordinates of their endpoints determine the six arbitrary

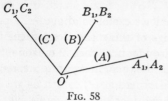

parameters of the affine transformation (3),
so that they completely determine the mapping. Now these three vectors *must not all
lie in the same line,* and we shall assume, for
simplicity, that no two of them lie in one
line. *The result is as follows: The three unit
vectors on the coordinate axes of R are mapped*

FIG. 58

*upon three arbitrary vectors through the origin O' in E', which, when they are
known, completely determine the affine transformation.*

4. In order to obtain *geometrically* the map of (A), (B), (C), we start from
any point $p(x, y, z = 0)$ of the xy plane. We get the vector from O to p by
multiplying the unit vector of the x axis by the scalar number x, and that of
the y axis by the number y, and by then adding the product vectors (see Fig.
59). However, we can transfer this construction at once to E', since the rela-

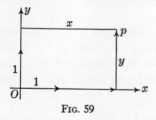

FIG. 59

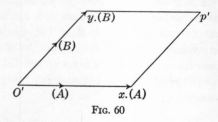

FIG. 60

tion between the xy plane and E' is obviously an ordinary two-dimensional
affine transformation (with non-vanishing determinant). We obtain, then,
the picture p' of p by means of the scalar multiplication of the vectors (A)
and (B) by x and y, respectively, and the
addition of the products by the parallelogram law (Fig. 60). In this way, we can construct in E', the map of any point, and hence,
point by point, any figure of the xy plane.

5. If we carry over these considerations to
an arbitrary point of the space R, we can
prove easily (see Fig. 61) the following result: *We obtain the picture p' of a point p*

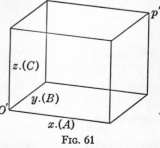

FIG. 61

*whose coordinates are (x, y, z), if we apply the parallelogram law for ad-
dition to the products of the vectors (A), (B), (C) by x, y, and z, respectively.* Since addition is commutative, we can perform this construction in

$1 \cdot 2 \cdot 3 = 6$ different ways, and we get p' as the terminal point of six different additive combinations of parallel and equal segments. The figure thus constructed (see Fig. 61) is obviously the representation of that rectangular parallelopiped in the space R which is bounded by the three coordinate planes and the planes through p parallel to them. We are accustomed, from our youth on, to look upon such plane figures as pictures of solid figures, especially when the appearance is heightened by drawing the front edges in heavier lines. This habit is so strong that this mapping of the parallelopiped seems almost trivial, whereas it represents really a very noteworthy theorem.

6. With the aid of this last construction, we can make in E' the picture of any figure in space, i.e., of all of its points. I shall consider only one example: If we have a *sphere*, with radius 1 and center at the origin O, then we shall consider primarily the circles in which it cuts the coordinate planes. The circle of intersection in the xy plane has the unit vectors on the x and the y axes as conjugate, i.e., as mutually perpendicular semi-diameters. Since we have an affine relation, there will correspond to it an ellipse (see Fig. 62) which has O' as center and the vectors (A) and (B) as conjugate semi-diameters, and which is

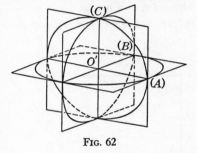

Fig. 62

thus inscribed in the parallelogram formed by the vectors $2(A)$ and $2(B)$. In the same way, the ellipses corresponding to the other two circles of intersection will have O' as center and (B), (C) and (A), (C) as conjugate semi-diameters.

7. Now that we have made a complete picture, showing the nature of the affine transformations (3) with vanishing determinant, we must take the last, decisive, step in our considerations, and show, namely, that these affine transformations actually arise through axonometric projection, as we have asserted. This requires, chiefly, the so-called *fundamental theorem of Pohlke*, which K. Pohlke, professor of descriptive geometry at the School of Architecture in Berlin, discovered in 1853 and published in his *Lehrbuch der darstellenden Geometrie* [1] in 1860. H. A. Schwartz published in 1863 [2] the first elementary proof of this theorem and gave, at the same time, a sketch of the interesting history of its discovery, which you should read.

Pohlke himself did not define axonometry analytically, but geometrically, as a representation of space by means of parallel rays (together, where necessary, with a similarity transformation). His theorem stated *that the*

---

[1] Two parts, 4th edition, Berlin, 1876. This theorem is in Part I, p. 109.
[2] Journal für die reine und angewandte Mathematik, vol. 63, p. 309 = *Gesammelte Mathematische Abhandlungen*, vol. 2, p. 1, Berlin, 1890.

three unit vectors on the coordinate axes of space could go over, under such a trans-formation, into three arbitrary vectors of E' through O'. That our analytically defined mapping actually led to three such vectors was apparent in No. 3; hence for us the underlying significance of Pohlke's theorem is *that our ana-lytically defined transformation (3) (p. 80) is effected by parallel projection and change of scale*, whereby the parallel lines mentioned in No. 1 become project-ing rays.

8. I should like to indicate an approximate plan for a direct analytical proof of the theorem thus formulated. If we fix our attention upon the two pencils of parallel planes in R:

$$A_1x + B_1y + C_1z = \xi, \qquad A_2x + B_2y + C_2z = \eta,$$

where ξ and η are variable parameters, then each pair of values of ξ and η determines one of the parallel lines in question. Now, if it were possible to

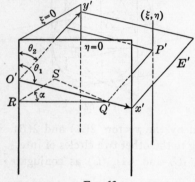

FIG. 63

place in the space R a picture plane E' containing a rectangular coordinate system x', y' with an appropriate unit of length, so that each ray ξ, η would pierce the plane E' in the point $x' = \xi$, $y' = \eta$, then the mapping (3) would ac-tually be brought about geometrically, as desired.

To this end, the planes $\xi = 0$, $\eta = 0$ must cut the plane E' in the coordi-nate axes $O'y'$ and $O'x'$ respectively, i.e., in mutually perpendicular lines. If θ_1, θ_2 (determining the position of E') are the angles between these axes and the line $\xi = \eta = 0$ (see Fig. 63), and if we denote by α the (known) angle between the planes $\xi = 0$ and $\eta = 0$, then, applying the cosine theorem of spherical trigonometry to the trihe-dral angle formed by $\xi = 0$, $\eta = 0$, and E', we find the cosine of the angle of $O'x'$, $O'y'$ to be

$$\cos \theta_1 \cos \theta_2 + \sin \theta_1 \sin \theta_2 \cos \alpha,$$

and this angle is a right angle if

(a) $$\operatorname{ctn} \theta_1 \cdot \operatorname{ctn} \theta_2 = -\cos \alpha.$$

Now every plane $A_1x + B_1y + C_1z = \xi$ cuts E' in a line $x' = $ constant. If Q' is its intersection with the x' axis, then the corresponding x' value, to within the undetermined scale factor λ of the coordinate system in E', is equal to $O'Q'$. If we drop perpendiculars $Q'S$ and $Q'R$ upon the plane $\xi = 0$ and the line $\xi = \eta = 0$, respectively, we shall have

$$O'Q' = \frac{Q'R}{\sin \theta_1}, \qquad Q'R = \frac{Q'S}{\sin \alpha},$$

and since $Q'S$, as the common perpendicular between the planes

$$A_1x + B_1y + C_1z = 0$$

and $A_1x + B_1y + C_1z = \xi$ is easily expressed by means of a known formula of analytic geometry of space, it follows finally that

$$x' = \lambda \cdot O'Q' = \lambda \frac{\xi}{\sqrt{A_1^2 + B_1^2 + C_1^2} \cdot \sin \theta_1 \cdot \sin \alpha}.$$

Similarly, we find as the y' coordinate of the points of intersection of $A_2x + B_2y + C_2z = \eta$ and E',

$$y' = \lambda \cdot \frac{\eta}{\sqrt{A_2^2 + B_2^2 + C_2^2} \cdot \sin \theta_2 \cdot \sin \alpha}.$$

Now, since we wish each parallel ray determined by the parameter values ξ, η to pierce the plane E' in the point $x' = \xi$, $y' = \eta$, we must have

(b) $\quad \lambda = \sqrt{A_1^2 + B_1^2 + C_1^2} \cdot \sin \theta_1 \cdot \sin \alpha = \sqrt{A_2^2 + B_2^2 + C_2^2} \cdot \sin \theta_2 \cdot \sin \alpha,$

from which we get the second equation for θ_1, θ_2:

(c) $\qquad \sin \theta_1 \cdot \sqrt{A_1^2 + B_1^2 + C_1^2} = \sin \theta_2 \sqrt{A_2^2 + B_2^2 + C_2^2}.$

A simple calculation shows that the equations (a) and (c) have only one real pair of solutions for ctn θ_1 and ctn θ_2, determined except for the sign; i.e., *there is essentially only one position (of course symmetric to the common normal plane of $\xi = 0$, $\eta = 0$) of the plane E', in which the affine transformation $x' = \xi$, $y' = \eta$ is axonometrically realized*, insofar as we choose the scale of the rectangular coordinate system in E according to (b). We can give this whole argument a more geometric form if we start from the condition that the unit points of the x' and y' axes fall upon the lines $\xi = 1$, $\eta = 0$ and $\xi = 0$, $\eta = 1$. Then the problem is to find a plane E' which cuts a given triangular prism in an isosceles right triangle.

After this detailed presentation, I hardly need to discuss further the converse theorem, already mentioned, *that every axonometric projection represents an affine transformation with a vanishing determinant*. This converse can be verified by using first, as we did earlier (p. 78), the oblique coordinate system in the plane of projection E' which arises by parallel projection from the x and y axes in R and then, by means of a linear substitution, going over to the initially given rectangular coordinate system in E'.

In closing this chapter on affine transformations, I should like to remind you that we can get an illustration of axonometric representation experimentally by using a projection lamp (one must think of it as infinitely remote) *to throw shadow pictures of simple models* (square, circle, ellipse, cube) upon a projection screen. We should get, in this way, a confirmation of our results and our figures; and, in particular, we could easily check experimentally the theorem of Pohlke, by subjecting the shadow picture of three mutually perpendicular rods to all sorts of change by movements of the model as well as of the screen.

We go over, now, to a new chapter, which treats of more general transformations, including affine transformations as special cases, namely, the *projective transformations*.

II. PROJECTIVE TRANSFORMATIONS

In this chapter also, I should like to deal with space of three dimensions from the first.

1. I shall begin with the *analytic definition of the projective transformation.* We now take x', y', z', no longer as integral, but as *fractional linear functions* of x, y, z, but with the condition, which is essential, that they all have the same denominator:

(1)
$$\begin{cases} x' = \dfrac{a_1x + b_1y + c_1z + d_1}{a_4x + b_4y + c_4z + d_4}, \\[2mm] y' = \dfrac{a_2x + b_2y + c_2z + d_2}{a_4x + b_4y + c_4z + d_4}, \\[2mm] z' = \dfrac{a_3x + b_3y + c_3z + d_3}{a_4x + b_4y + c_4z + d_4}. \end{cases}$$

To every point x, y, z there corresponds, accordingly, a definite finite point x', y', z', provided only that the common denominator is not zero. If, however, the point x, y, z approaches the plane $a_4x + b_4y + c_4z + d_4 = 0$, the corresponding point x', y', z'—this is the novelty, as compared with the affine transformation—moves to infinity: it "vanishes," in a sense. We call that plane, therefore, the *vanishing plane*, its points *vanishing points*, and we say that it corresponds, in the projective transformation, to the part of space at infinity, or to the points at infinity.

2. In the treatment of the problems arising here, it is very convenient, as you know, to use *homogeneous coordinates*, i.e., in place of the three point coordinates x, y, z, to use four quantities ξ, η, ζ, τ, defined by the equations

$$x = \frac{\xi}{\tau}, \qquad y = \frac{\eta}{\tau}, \qquad z = \frac{\zeta}{\tau}.$$

These four quantities are to *vary independently of each other, but not all four are to vanish simultaneously*, and *none of them is to become infinite.* To every point x, y, z there will then belong infinitely many systems of values $\rho\xi$, $\rho\eta$, $\rho\zeta$, $\rho\tau$, where ρ is an arbitrary factor $(\neq 0)$. Conversely, every system of values ξ, η, ζ, τ where $\tau \neq 0$, determines a definite finite point x, y, z (all systems $\rho \cdot \xi$, $\rho \cdot \eta$, $\rho \cdot \zeta$, $\rho \cdot \tau$ give the same point). When $\tau = 0$, one, at least, of the quotients x, y, z becomes infinite, and we stipulate, accordingly, that *every system of values ξ, η, ζ, $\tau = 0$ shall signify an "infinitely distant point*," and, indeed, all systems $\rho\xi$, $\rho\eta$, $\rho\zeta$, 0 represent the same point at infinity. In this precise way we introduce the points which, as "infinitely distant," are added to the ordinary finite points.

Experience shows that operation with homogeneous coordinates produces, at least with beginners, something like physical discomfort. I believe that the somewhat indefinite, fluid, quality of these quantities, which the arbitrary factor ρ brings in, is the cause of this feeling, and I hope that such a statement may help to allay this discomfort.

With the same end in view, some incidental remarks may be helpful about *certain geometric representations* which can be associated with homogeneous coordinates. I shall speak first only of a *plane E*. In this case, let us write for the two rectangular coordinates

$$x = \frac{\xi}{\tau}, \qquad y = \frac{\eta}{\tau}.$$

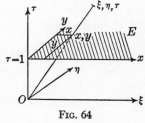

FIG. 64

We now interpret ξ, η, τ as *rectangular coordinates in space* and, in this space, we choose the plane $\tau = 1$, parallel to the ξ, η plane, as the plane E (see Fig. 64). In this plane E, put $x = \xi$, $y = \eta$. If we now join the point x, y of E to O by a straight line, then, for points on this line, ξ/τ and η/τ are constant and we may write

$$\frac{\xi}{\tau} = x, \qquad \frac{\eta}{\tau} = y,$$

since, for $\tau = 1$, we have $\xi = x$, $\eta = y$. *Accordingly, the introduction of homogeneous coordinates signifies simply the representation of the plane E into that space pencil of rays with the origin O as center, of which E is a section. The homogeneous coordinates of a point are the space coordinates of the points of the projecting ray of that point.* Since to each point of E there correspond the infinitely many points of the ray, the significance of the indefiniteness of the homogeneous coordinates is made clear. The exclusion of the system of values $\xi = \eta = \tau = 0$ has its geometric basis in the fact that the point O determines no ray, and hence no point in E. Moreover, it is obvious that we need no infinite values of ξ, η, τ, since we get all rays by joining O with finite points. Finally, it is clear that we avoid infinitely large values of the coordinates by replacing the infinite region of the plane E by the parallel rays through O given by $\tau = 0$.

Moreover, the common expression "the line at infinity" finds here its clear geometric connotation. Analytically, it is only the expression of the abstract analogy that all "infinitely distant points" satisfy the linear equation $\tau = 0$, just as every finite line has a linear equation. But now we can say geometrically that to every line of E there belongs a plane pencil of the space pencil O; and, conversely, every plane pencil in the space pencil O determines a line in E, except the plane pencil $\tau = 0$. Hence it seems appropriate to designate as a line the aggregate of points in E that correspond to this pencil $\tau = 0$, and so we have "the infinitely distant line."

We can form similar representations if we introduce homogeneous coordinates into *space of three dimensions*. We think of the space as a section $\tau = 1$ of a four-dimensional auxiliary space ξ, η, ζ, τ, and we relate it to the space pencil which projects it from the origin in the auxiliary space. We can then carry through without difficulty all the other considerations in almost word-for-word analogy with what precedes, and, in particular, we can carry over the interpretation of the infinitely distant elements. In this, the use of four-dimensional space is only a convenient means of expression, to which no mystical significance is to be attached.

3. If we now introduce into the equations (1) of the projective transformation *homogeneous coordinates for both* spaces R and R', we can separate them, by introducing an arbitrary proportionality factor ρ', since they all have the same denominator, into the following four equations:

(2)
$$\begin{cases} \rho'\xi' = a_1\xi + b_1\eta + c_1\zeta + d_1\tau, \\ \rho'\eta' = a_2\xi + b_2\eta + c_2\zeta + d_2\tau, \\ \rho'\zeta' = a_3\xi + b_3\eta + c_3\zeta + d_3\tau, \\ \rho'\tau' = a_4\xi + b_4\eta + c_4\zeta + d_4\tau. \end{cases}$$

Leaving out of account the arbitrary factor ρ', we see that this is the most general homogeneous linear transformation in four variables; hence it represents an *affine relation of the two four-dimensional auxiliary spaces* $\mathbf{P_4}, \mathbf{P'}$, in which we can interpret the homogeneous coordinates in the manner explained in No. 2. All this can be represented more concretely if we again limit ourselves to the *plane. We obtain the most general projective transformation of a plane if we apply an arbitrary affine transformation to the space of that space pencil, with fixed center O, which projects this plane, and then cut the plane with the transformed pencil.* We always get, in this way, the same projectivity of our space, corresponding to the factor ρ', if we add a similarity transformation from O. For this transforms into itself each of the rays through O, and the projectivity depends solely upon the intersections of these with the plane.

The procedure which we have followed, in using the auxiliary spaces

P, P′, is called the *principle of projection and section*. It is often very useful in that, generally speaking, it *makes complicated relations in space of n dimensions appear simpler and easier to understand, through auxiliary considerations in space of n + 1 dimensions.*

4. We shall now solve the transformation equations (2) for ξ, η, ζ, τ. The theory of determinants shows *that ξ, η, ζ, τ are likewise linear homogeneous combinations of $\xi', \eta', \zeta', \tau'$*, of course with a proportionality factor ρ:

$$(3) \quad \begin{cases} \rho\xi = a_1'\xi' + b_1'\eta' + c_1'\zeta' + d_1'\tau', \\ \rho\eta = a_2'\xi' + b_2'\eta' + c_2'\zeta' + d_2'\tau', \\ \rho\zeta = a_3'\xi' + b_3'\eta' + c_3'\zeta' + d_3'\tau', \\ \rho\tau = a_4'\xi' + b_4'\eta' + c_4'\zeta' + d_4'\tau', \end{cases}$$

provided only that the determinant

$$\Delta = \begin{vmatrix} a_1 & b_1 & c_1 & d_1 \\ a_2 & b_2 & c_2 & d_2 \\ a_3 & b_3 & c_3 & d_3 \\ a_4 & b_4 & c_4 & d_4 \end{vmatrix}$$

of (2) does not vanish. The systems of values ξ, η, ζ, τ and $\xi', \eta', \zeta', \tau'$ are thus in one-to-one correspondence (to within those arbitrary common factors).

Let me say, however, as you might expect after our experience with the affine transformations, that the case $\Delta = 0$ is here also especially interesting, and that it may not be disregarded. It represents the mapping of space upon a plane, as in every central projection, e.g., in photography. For the present, however, we shall consider the general case $\Delta \neq 0$.

5. It follows at once from (2) and (3) that, when a linear relation exists between ξ, η, ζ, τ, there is also one between $\xi', \eta', \zeta', \tau'$, and conversely. *To every plane there corresponds a plane;* in particular, to the infinitely distant plane of R' there corresponds a definite and, in general, a finite plane in R, i.e., the *vanishing plane* mentioned above. Thus the conventional introduction of the plane at infinity serves a purpose, since it permits the statement of the preceding theorem as valid without exception. It follows, further, that *to every line there corresponds a line*. In the terminology of Möbius (p. 71), *every projective transformation is a collineation*.

6. Now it is remarkable that the converse is also true: *Every collineation of space, i.e., every reversibly unique transformation such that to every line there corresponds a line, and which satisfies certain other almost self-evident conditions, is a projectivity*, i.e., a transformation defined analytically by equations (1) or (2).

For the sake of convenience, I shall give here Möbius' proof only for the plane; for space we should proceed similarly. The *plan of the proof* is as follows. From an arbitrary collineation, we select two corresponding point quadruples and we shall show (a) that there is always a projectivity which transforms two such quadruples into each other. However, a projectivity is also a collineation; and we shall prove (b) that, under certain conditions, there can be only *one* collineation in which these quadruples can correspond to each other. Thus the projectivity must, in fact, be identical with the given collineation, which proves the theorem. We shall now give the *details* of these two steps.

(a) We remark that the equations of the projectivity in the plane:

$$\rho'\xi' = a_1\xi + b_1\eta + d_1\tau,$$
$$\rho'\eta' = a_2\xi + b_2\eta + d_2\tau,$$
$$\rho'\tau' = a_3\xi + b_3\eta + d_3\tau$$

contain $9 - 1 = 8$ constants. (A change in ρ' does not alter the transformation.) That two given points may correspond to each other in a projectivity requires two linear equations for the constants of the projectivity, since we are concerned only with the *ratios* of the three homogeneous coordinates. The correspondence of two point quadruples represents thus $2 \times 4 = 8$ linear conditions, or, more precisely, eight linear homogeneous equations for the nine quantities $a_1, \cdots, d_3$. Such equations always have a solution, as you know; hence *we have found in this manner the constants of a projectivity which transforms the given quadruples into each other.* We can guarantee, to be sure, that this is a *proper* projectivity with a *non-vanishing* determinant, and that it is uniquely determined, only if each of the given point quadruples is "in general position," i.e., if no three points of a quadruple are collinear; but it is only for this case that we need the theorem.

(b) We now think of an arbitrary collineation of the planes E and E'. If, then, 1, 2, 3, 4 are any four points of E, of which no three are collinear, and

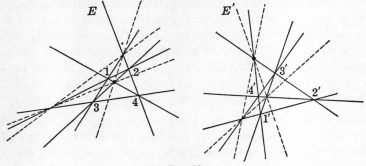

FIG. 65

if $1'$, $2'$, $3'$, $4'$ are the corresponding points in E', satisfying the same condition, then our assertion is *that the collineation is completely determined by the correspondence between these two quadruples of points.* We shall give this proof by showing that this collineation can be built up in one and only one way from these two corresponding quadruples by using solely their two characteristics properties (uniqueness, and the mutual correspondence of straight lines). As our chief aid, we shall use the so-called *Möbius' net*, which we spread over the plane after the manner of a spider's web. To begin with, we draw, in each plane (see Fig. 65) the six lines joining the four points by pairs. These must correspond in the collineation, for, to the line 1 2 there must correspond a line in E' which must contain $1'$ as the image of 1, as well as $2'$, the image of 2; and that could be only the line $1'$ $2'$. Similarly, the points arising as intersections of corresponding lines must themselves correspond, e.g., the points (1 4, 2 3) and ($1'$ $4'$, $2'$ $3'$): this follows immediately from the collinearity and the uniqueness. If we join the new points by lines, extend these to intersection with the earlier lines, join the resulting points of intersection again, and continue this process, there will appear in *each plane a net of points and lines which gets denser and denser, and these points and lines must correspond in pairs in the desired collineation.*

If we now select an arbitrary point in E, say, either it will be itself one of the corners of the net, or else it is easy to show that we can enclose it in a mesh which can be made as small as we please, i.e., we can make it a limit point of corners. In the first case the corresponding point in E' is uniquely determined as the corresponding net corner. In order to take care of the second case, we must make an *addition to the definition* of collineation, one which to Möbius seemed so self-evident that he did not think it required explicit statement. It is, namely, *that the mapping shall be continuous, i.e., each limit point of a point set in E shall be in correspondence with the limit point of the corresponding point set in E'.* From this, and from the preceding remarks, it follows also in the second case that the corresponding point in E' is uniquely determined. We have established then the *correctness of our assertion 6, insofar as the collineation is continuous.* In the same way we could prove that a continuous collineation in ordinary space is determined by five pairs, and in space of n dimensions by $n + 2$ pairs, of corresponding points.

Returning to the considerations at the beginning of No. 6 (p. 89), we have, as one result, the following precise theorem. *Projective transformations are the only continuous reversibly unique transformations which always carry lines into lines.*

After this digression, let us resume the investigation begun in No. 5 (p. 89) of *the behavior of the fundamental geometric manifolds* under projective transformations, or, as we can now say, under *collinear transformation.* We saw there that an unlimited plane or straight line is carried over by projection into a figure of the same sort, so that these concepts have a definite invariable significance with respect to projectivities. In this property, the general projectivities agree with the affine transformations. They differ from them however in their behavior with respect to parallelism.

7. *Behavior with respect to the concept of parallelism.* Indeed, the parallelism of two straight lines is not necessarily maintained under projective transformations, as it was under affine transformation (p. 72). On the contrary, the infinitely distant plane of one space can go over into any finite plane whatever (the vanishing plane), of the other, and there will correspond, thereby, in general, to the point at infinity common to two parallels, a finite point of the vanishing plane in which the two lines intersect that correspond to the parallels. By the aid of homogeneous coordinates we can follow this exactly. To be sure, we see here, also, that the concept of parallelism is not ruthlessly disturbed, but that it becomes a part of a perfectly definite general concept. *The infinitely distant points of space constitute a plane, which can be carried over by projection into any other (finite) plane of space, and which, to this extent, has equal justification with all these planes.* It is characterized as *arbitrary*, only to a certain degree, by the descriptive phrase "*the infinitely distant.*" *Lines (and planes also) are then called parallel if their intersection lies on this special plane.* By a projective transformation they may be carried into lines (or planes) which meet on *another* fixed plane, in which case the new lines (or planes) are said to be no longer parallel.

With this property there is connected the fact *that the fundamental manifolds of Grassmann, likewise, have no invariant significance under projection.* The free vector is by no means carried over into another free vector, the line-bound vector into another such, etc. In fact, let us look at a line-segment of space R, with the six coordinates.

$$X = x_1 - x_2, \qquad \cdot Y = y_1 - y_2, \qquad Z = z_1 - z_2,$$
$$L = y_1 z_2 - y_2 z_1, \qquad M = x_2 z_1 - z_2 x_1, \qquad N = x_1 y_2 - y_1 x_2$$

and let us set up the analogous quantities $X', \cdots, N'$ out of the coordinates of the points (x_1', y_1') and (x_2', y_2') which correspond to (x_1, y_1) and (x_2, y_2) under the projective transformation (1) (p. 86):

$$x_1' = \frac{a_1 x_1 + b_1 y_1 + c_1 z_1 + d_1}{a_4 x_1 + b_4 y_1 + c_4 z_1 + d_4} \text{ etc.}, \qquad x_2' = \frac{a_1 x_2 + b_1 y_2 + c_1 z_2 + d_1}{a_4 x_2 + b_4 y_2 + c_4 z_2 + d_4} \text{ etc.}$$

By these formulas, $X', \cdots, N'$ become fractions whose numerators, to be sure, appear as linear combinations solely of the six quantities $X, \cdots, N$, with constant coefficients, while the denominator common to all of them, $(a_4 x_1 + b_4 y_1 + c_4 z_1 + d_4)(a_4 x_2 + b_4 y_2 + c_4 z_2 + d_2)$, contains the point coordinates themselves and cannot be expressed in terms of $X, \cdots, N$ alone. Thus the coordinates of the transformed line-segment depend not only on those of the original segment but also on the special position of its end points. If we slide the segment (1 2) along its line, so that $X, \cdots, N$ do not change, $X', \cdots, N'$ will change, in general, i.e., *the segment (1' 2') is not a line-segment in the Grassmann sense.*

That the *unlimited straight line* persists as such, nevertheless, under projective transformation, follows from the fact that it is represented by the *ratios* of the quantities $X' : Y' : \cdots N'$, from which the disturbing common denominator disappears by cancellation. Thus these ratios are actually expressed solely in terms of the ratios $X : Y : \cdots : N$.

8. There remain still some important *manifolds which go over into manifolds of the same sort under projective transformation.* In the first place, every quadratic equation in x', y', z' arises from a quadratic equation in x, y, z, as we see by multiplying through by the square of the common denominator $a_4x + b_4y + c_4z + d_4$, and conversely. This shows *that every surface of the second degree in a space R corresponds to one of the same nature in R'*. Therefore every intersection of such a surface with a plane, i.e., every *curve of order two in a space R corresponds to one of the same nature in R'. In the same way, any algebraic manifold, defined by one or several equations in the coordinates, will be transformed into a manifold of the same sort;* the nature of these manifolds is thus invariant under projective change.

9. Along with these invariant manifolds, defined by equations, I must mention a *numerical quantity* whose value remains unchanged under all projective transformations. It offers a certain substitute for the concepts *distance* and *angle*, whose values, as you know, are not invariant even under affine transformations, to say nothing of projective transformations. Speaking first of the *straight line*, let us consider a *certain function of the distances among four arbitrarily selected points* 1, 2, 3, 4, namely, the *cross ratio* mentioned on page 6:

$$\frac{\overline{12}}{\overline{14}} : \frac{\overline{32}}{\overline{34}} = \frac{\overline{12} \cdot \overline{34}}{\overline{14} \cdot \overline{32}}.$$

In fact we can easily verify (by calculation), the invariance of this quantity under projective transformation, and we shall actually do so later in another connection. (See p. 146 et seq.)

The case is quite similar for *pencils of rays*, except that we use, not the angles themselves, but their *sines*. Thus, if 1, 2, 3, 4 are rays or planes of a pencil, their cross ratio is the expression

$$\frac{\sin (1, 2)}{\sin (1, 4)} : \frac{\sin (3, 2)}{\sin (3, 4)} = \frac{\sin (1, 2) \sin (3, 4)}{\sin (1, 4) \sin (3, 2)}.$$

Since these cross ratios were the first numerical invariants of projective transformations to be discovered, many students of projective geometry thought it a praiseworthy goal to reduce all other invariants to cross ratios, even though the reduction was sometimes very artificial. Later on we shall consider these questions more thoroughly.

These few indications will suffice to show how we can distinguish sharply between the various concepts of geometry according to their behavior under projective transformation. Everything that remains unchanged by such transformation constitutes the subject matter of *projective geometry*, which arose during the last century, of which I have already spoken, and which we shall discuss more thoroughly later on. This name, which is used now quite generally, is better than *geometry of position* (Geometrie der Lage), which was much used earlier, and by which mathematicians wished to indicate the contrast to *geometry of measure* or *elementary geometry*, which embraced all geometric properties, including those that are not invariant under projective transformation. The older name conceals entirely the fact that many properties of measurement, in particular the values of the cross ratio, are included.

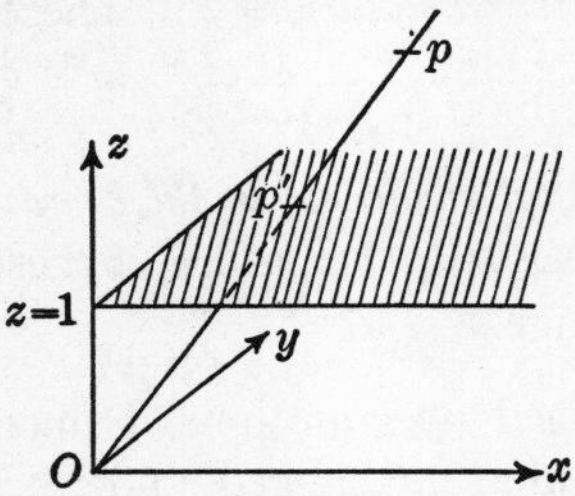

I should like to discuss now the *applications of projective transformations*, just as I did earlier with affine transformations.

1. Starting with *descriptive geometry*, and making no attempt to be systematic, I shall discuss some characteristic examples.

(a) The first is the *mapping of space upon a plane by means of central perspective*, which is the direct generalization of axonometry (parallel perspective). The projecting rays proceed here from a finite point instead of from an infinitely distant one. We select the center of projection at the origin of coordinates O and the plane of projection as $z = 1$. (See Fig. 66.) Then, for the image $p'(x', y', z')$ of any point $p(x, y, z)$ we always have $z' = 1$, and, since p and p' lie on the same ray through O, we have

$$x' : y' : z' = x : y : z.$$

Hence the equations for our mapping are

$$x' = \frac{x}{z}, \qquad y' = \frac{y}{z}, \qquad z' = \frac{z}{z}.$$

This is a *special projective transformation*, and the analogy with what happens in axonometry leads us to suspect that its *determinant vanishes*. In fact, going over to homogeneous coordinates, we get

$$\rho'\xi' = \xi, \qquad \rho'\eta' = \eta, \qquad \rho'\zeta' = \zeta, \qquad \rho'\tau' = \zeta,$$

and the determinant of the substitution is

$$\Delta = \begin{vmatrix} 1 & 0 & 0 & 0 \\ 0 & 1 & 0 & 0 \\ 0 & 0 & 1 & 0 \\ 0 & 0 & 1 & 0 \end{vmatrix} = 0.$$

FIG. 66

You can readily derive the various properties of this transformation by analogy with our earlier discussions, provided you note that, in general, every plane is connected with the plane of projection by a projective (two-dimensional) transformation with a non-vanishing determinant. It follows from this, in particular, that the cross ratio of any four points on a line, or of any four rays through a point, is unchanged by the transformation.

(b) The second example concerns a projectivity which includes the central perspective as limiting case, one with a non-vanishing determinant, the so-called *relief perspective*. The relief of an object is to be so formed that it will send the same rays to an observer's eye, placed at a definite point, which the original would send to an observer correspondingly placed. This means that, with an appropriately oriented system of coordinates, the original point and its image should lie on the same ray through the origin:

$$(1) \qquad\qquad x':y':z' = x:y:z.$$

The difference between this and the previous case is that the original is not mapped upon a plane but is compressed into a certain narrow space segment of finite width.

I assert that this is accomplished by the formulas

$$(2) \qquad x' = \frac{(1+k)x}{z+k}, \qquad y' = \frac{(1+k)y}{z+k}, \qquad z' = \frac{(1+k)z}{z+k},$$

which, in the first place, give at least a projectivity and also obviously satisfy equations (1). Let us form their *determinant*, using the corresponding homogeneous equations

$$\rho'\xi' = (1+k)\xi, \qquad \rho'\eta' = (1+k)\eta, \qquad \rho'\zeta' = (1+k)\zeta, \qquad \rho'\tau' = \zeta + k\tau.$$

It will be

$$\Delta = \begin{vmatrix} 1+k & 0 & 0 & 0 \\ 0 & 1+k & 0 & 0 \\ 0 & 0 & 1+k & 0 \\ 0 & 0 & 1 & k \end{vmatrix} = k(1+k)^3$$

and is thus different from zero, except when $k = 0$ or $k = -1$.

For $k = 0$, (2) goes over precisely into the previous formulas of central perspective, i.e., the relief degenerates completely into a plane. The value $k = -1$ gives $x' = y' = z' = 0$, i.e., every point in space is represented by the origin, which is obviously a useless and trivial degeneration.

For the sake of definiteness, we choose $k > 0$. In order to make the transformation (2) clear geometrically, we notice, first, that every plane $z = $ const. goes over into a parallel plane:

$$(3) \qquad\qquad z' = \frac{(1+k)z}{z+k}.$$

The resulting mapping of the two planes upon each other by the rays proceeding from O is perfectly clear, and we now need only interpret the law (3).

For $z = \infty\,(\tau = 0)$, $z' = 1 + k$. *The plane parallel to the xy plane and at a distance $1 + k$ is the vanishing plane of the space of the image, and at the*

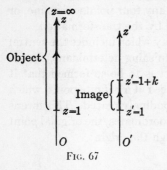

FIG. 67

same time it forms, in a sense, the background of the relief upon which the infinitely distant background of the space of the object appears to be mapped. The plane $z = 1$ plays also an important role, since object and image coincide for that plane. This follows from the fact that if $z = 1$, then $z' = 1$ also. If, now, z increases from 1 to ∞, z' increases monotonically from 1 to $1 + k$, i.e., *if we restrict ourselves to objects behind the plane $z = 1$, we obtain actually, as image, a relief of finite depth k.* In practice, there can and must always be such a restriction. (See Fig. 67.)

Examining again the relation (3), we find for the cross ratio of the points z, 1, z', 0, the relation

$$\frac{z-1}{z-0} \cdot \frac{z'-0}{z'-1} = \frac{z-1}{z} \cdot \frac{(1+k)z}{k(z-1)} = \frac{1+k}{k}\,.$$

In general, those two values z and z' correspond to each other which form with the points 1 and 0 a cross ratio of constant value.

We have a model in our mathematical collection which represents, in relief perspective, a sphere on a cube, a cone of revolution, and a cylinder of revolution. Examined at the proper distance, the model actually gives a very clear impression of the original bodies. Of course, psychological reactions play an important part. The isolated fact that the same light rays enter an eye does not suffice to determine the spatial impression; habit must certainly play an important part. Indeed, since we have seen a sphere on a cube much oftener than we have seen a narrow ellipsoid on a narrow hexahedron (that is the form of the image in relief perspective), we are disposed, from the start, to refer the light impression to the first source. A closer examination of the reactions that enter here may be left to the psychologists.

This will suffice to give you a first glimpse of the application of projective transformations to descriptive geometry. Of course, these theorems demand further consideration, and I cannot leave this field without urging you to make a thorough study of descriptive geometry, which is, I think, indispensable for every teacher of mathematics.

2. The second application of projective transformations of which I wish to talk is the *derivation of geometric theorems and points of view.* You will

recall that we discussed affine transformations with a similar purpose (p. 76 et seq.).

(a) We start from the theorem that *when we subject a circle to a projective transformation or to a central perspective transformation, it goes over into a "conic section,"* i.e., into the intersection by a plane of the cone whose surface is formed by the projecting rays drawn to the points of the circle. I have here a model which shows how an ellipse, a hyperbola, or a parabola can arise in this way. (See Fig. 68.)

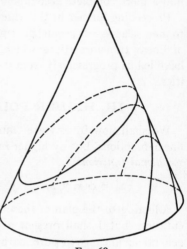

(b) *It follows that, for projective geometry, there is only a single conic section,* since any two can be transformed into a circle and therefore into each other. The division into ellipse, parabola, hyperbola indicates, from this standpoint, no really fundamental difference, but reflects merely the accidental position with reference to that line which is ordinarily called "infinitely distant."

FIG. 68

(c) Let us now derive the following *fundamental cross-ratio theorem for conics: Any four fixed points* 1, 2, 3, 4 *on a conic are projected from a fifth movable point P of the same conic by four rays whose cross ratio is independent of the position of P.*

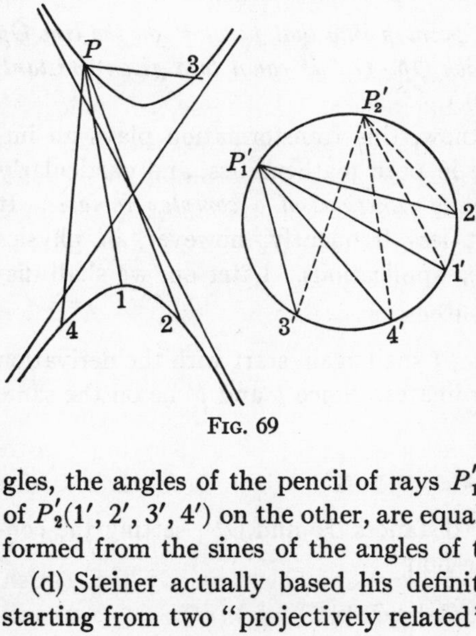

To prove this, we go back to the circle from which the conic in question arose by central perspective. Since, in this, the cross ratio is unchanged, our theorem will be true, in general, if only we can show that the four corresponding points 1′, 2′, 3′, 4′ on the circle are projected from two other arbitrary points P_1', P_2', by rays which have the same cross ratio. But this is at once evident, for, by the theorem on inscribed an-

FIG. 69

gles, the angles of the pencil of rays $P_1'(1', 2', 3', 4')$ on the one hand, and of $P_2'(1', 2', 3', 4')$ on the other, are equal in pairs; hence the two cross ratios formed from the sines of the angles of the two ray quadruples are equal.

(d) Steiner actually based his definition of conics on this theorem by starting from two "projectively related" pencils of rays, in which two corresponding ray quadruples have the same cross ratio. *A conic is then the locus of the intersections of corresponding rays of these projectively related pencils.*

These few remarks will suffice to make clear to you the great significance of projective transformations for the theory of conic sections. You can find a more complete account in any textbook on projective geometry.

Proceeding further in the wide range of this chapter, we shall now come to new classes of geometric transformations not belonging to the class of linear transformations which we have thus far considered and which have led us progressively from displacements to the most general projectivities.

III. HIGHER POINT TRANSFORMATIONS

We shall now investigate transformations that are represented, not by linear functions, but by higher *rational algebraic functions, or even by transcendental functions:*

$$x' = \phi(x, y, z), \qquad y' = \chi(x, y, z), \qquad z' = \psi(x, y, z).$$

Adhering to the plan of these lectures, I shall not give a systematic presentation, but I shall present a series of particular examples which have general significance in pure mathematics and, above all, in its applications.

First of all, I shall discuss that one of these transformations which is most frequently used: the *transformation by means of reciprocal radii.*

1. The Transformation by Reciprocal Radii

This transformation *carries each point p into that point p' on the line Op joining p with the origin O, for which Op · Op' is equal to a given constant.*

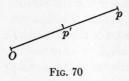

FIG. 70

(See Fig. 70.)

As you know, this transformation plays an important role in pure mathematics, and particularly in *the theory of functions of a complex variable.* It appears not less frequently, however, in physics and in other applications. Later on, we shall discuss at length *one* particular application.

1. In treating this transformation, I shall again start with the derivation of its equations in rectangular coordinates. Since p and p' lie on the same line through O, we have

(1)
$$x' : y' : z' = x : y : z,$$

and from the relation between the distances Op and Op', setting the constant equal to 1, for simplicity, we find

(2)
$$(x^2 + y^2 + z^2)(x'^2 + y'^2 + z'^2) = 1.$$

Therefore, the equations of the transformation are

(3) $\quad x' = \dfrac{x}{x^2 + y^2 + z^2}, \qquad y' = \dfrac{y}{x^2 + y^2 + z^2}, \qquad z' = \dfrac{z}{x^2 + y^2 + z^2}.$

In the same way, we obtain, conversely,

(4) $\quad x = \dfrac{x'}{x'^2 + y'^2 + z'^2}, \qquad y = \dfrac{y'}{x'^2 + y'^2 + z'^2}, \qquad z = \dfrac{z'}{x'^2 + y'^2 + z'^2}.$

Thus not only are the coordinates of p' expressed rationally in terms of those of p, but also the coordinates of p are expressed rationally in terms of those of p'; and the functions that occur are the same in both cases. The denominator in each case is a quadratic expression. We have here *a particular case of what is called a quadratic birational transformation.* There is, moreover, an extensive class of such birational transformations (in general uniquely reversible), which are expressed, in both directions, by rational functions. Under the name *Cremona transformations* they are the object of a widely developed theory, to which I must at least allude as I discuss the simplest one of them.

2. Equations (3) and (4) show that to every point p in space there corresponds a point p', and, conversely, to every point p' there corresponds a point p, if we except (for the present) the origin. However, if we let x, y, and z approach zero simultaneously, the denominator of (3) becomes small, of higher order than the numerator, and x', y', and z' become infinite. We could call the origin, therefore, a *vanishing point* of the transformation. Conversely, if x', y', and z' become infinite in any way, then, by (4), x, y, and z all approach zero. If, then, we were to use our earlier terminology, we should say that a single point corresponds to the whole infinitely distant plane. However, this "infinitely distant plane" was merely a convenient expression which was suitable for the projective transformation. It signified that, under that transformation, the infinitely remote part of space behaved as though it were a plane, i.e., it went over into the points of some finite plane, and this made it possible to enunciate theorems without making exceptions, and without introducing several cases. There is nothing to hinder us from employing here a different form of expression, and from stating, by means of it, for our present purpose, theorems likewise valid without exception. By our transformation, the infinitely remote in space is transformed into a point; hence we say, simply, *there is only one infinitely distant point, and it corresponds, under our transformation, to the origin of coordinates.* Then our transformation in fact is *uniquely reversible without exception.*

It is impossible to overemphasize that here, as well as in our earlier remarks, we are not thinking, in the remotest sense, of metaphysical representations of the true nature of infinity. There are, of course, always people, who, partial by habit to the one or to the other form of expression, would like to assign a transcendental meaning to infinity. Such advocates of these two points of view sometimes fall into controversy. Of course they are both wrong. They forget that we are really concerned merely with an arbitrary convention which is appropriate for the one purpose or for the other.

3. The principal property of our transformation is that (speaking generally) it *transforms spheres into spheres*. Indeed, the equation of a sphere has the form

(5) $$A(x'^2 + y'^2 + z'^2) + Bx' + Cy' + Dz' + E = 0.$$

Substituting for x', y', z' their values in (3), replacing the quadratic term $x'^2 + y'^2 + z'^2$ by means of (2), and multiplying through by $x'^2 + y'^2 + z'^2$, we get $A + Bx + Cy + Dz + E(x^2 + y^2 + z^2) = 0$, which is indeed the equation of a sphere. To be sure, it should be noticed that the equation (5) (for $A = 0$), includes also planes, which we can appropriately consider here as *special spheres;* they are in fact those spheres which contain the point at infinity. Under our transformation they go over into spheres that pass through the point which corresponds to the point at infinity, that is, the origin. Conversely, any spheres that go through the origin go over into spheres through the point at infinity, that is, into planes. With this convention, the theorem that spheres correspond to spheres is valid without exception.

Since two spheres (likewise a sphere and a plane) intersect in a circle, it follows also that *to a circle there corresponds always a circle*, whereby, in particular, *straight lines* are included as "*circles through the point at infinity*." Conversely, to a straight line corresponds, under our transformation, a circle through the origin.

4. This last theorem is, of course, still valid if we restrict the transformation to a *plane*. This gives rise to an elegant solution of the problem of generating a straight line which is very elementary and which belongs really to the field of interests of the non-mathematician. The problem is to guide a point, by means of a linkage of rigid rods, so that it will describe a straight line. Formerly, in the construction of steam engines, particular importance was placed upon mechanisms that would effect the transmission between the piston, which moves rectilinearly, and the end of the crank, which describes a circle.

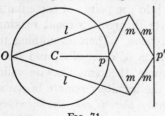

Fig. 71

This directs our interest to the *inversor* which Peaucellier, a French officer, constructed in 1864, and which caused a sensation then, although the construction is very simple and fairly obvious. The apparatus consists of six jointed rods. (See Fig. 71.) Two of the rods, of length l, are attached at a fixed point O; the other four rods, all of length m, form a rhombus whose opposite vertices are the ends of the rods l. Call the two free corners of this rhombus p and p'. The apparatus has two degrees of freedom: First, one can incline the two rods l to each other at will, and, second, one can rotate them together about O. With every such motion, however, Opp' remains a straight line, as it is easy to prove geometrically, and the product

$$Op \cdot Op' = l^2 - m^2 = \text{const.}$$

is independent of the position of p. Thus *the apparatus actually effects a transformation by reciprocal radii with O as center.* We need only move p on a circle through O, in order to force p'—according to the theorems of § 3—to move actually on a straight line. This result is secured at once if we attach at p a seventh rod pC, whose other end, C, is fixed at the midpoint between O and the initial position of p. Then there remains but one degree of freedom, and p' *will, in fact, be carried along a line.* It should be noticed that the point p' cannot traverse the entire unlimited line, but that its freedom to move is limited by the fact that its distance from O remains always less than lm, because the given lengths of the rods do not permit more extended motion. In some models, the point C is displaced a little, so that the circle which p traverses passes close to O, and p' moves, therefore, not in a straight line but on a *circle of large radius.* This application of the apparatus also may be useful at times.[1]

5. Of the general properties of the transformation by reciprocal radii, I will emphasize, lastly, that of the *preservation of angles.* This means that *the angle which two surfaces make with each other at any point of their curve of intersection is the same before and after the transformation.* I shall omit the proof since I am not concerned, in this survey, with carrying out the details.

6. We can look upon *stereographic projection,* which also plays an important role in the applications, as a special chapter of the transformations by reciprocal radii. It is obtained as follows. Let us consider the sphere which is carried by our transformation into the *fixed plane* $z' = 1$. By the third of the formulas (3) the equation of this sphere is

$$1 = \frac{z}{x^2 + y^2 + z^2},$$

which may be written in the form

$$x^2 + y^2 + (z - \tfrac{1}{2})^2 = \tfrac{1}{4}.$$

---

[1] [See also A. B. Kempe, *How to Draw a Straight Line,* London, 1877; and G. Hessenberg, *Gelenkmechanismen sur Kreisverwandtschaft,* Heft 6 der Naturwissenschaftlich-medizinischen Abhandlungen der Württembergischen Gesellschaft zur Förderung der Wissenschaften, Abteilung Tübingen, 1924.]

Thus the sphere which is transformed into the plane $z' = 1$ has a *radius* $\frac{1}{2}$, *and has its center at the point* $z = \frac{1}{2}$ on the z axis. It passes through the origin,

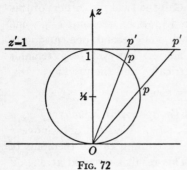

FIG. 72

and is tangent to the image plane $z' = 1$. (See Fig. 72.) We can at once make clear the details of the relation between the plane and the sphere if we use the space pencil of rays through the center O, and discover the corresponding points. I shall state the following theorems without proof.

1. The mapping is, *without exception, reversibly unique*, if we think of the infinitely distant part of the plane as a point, which is then mapped upon the point O on the sphere.

2. Circles on the sphere correspond to circles in the plane; in particular, circles through O correspond to circles through the point at infinity, i.e., to straight lines.

3. The relation between the two surfaces *preserves angles*, or, as it is customary to say, *the transformation is conformal.*

You know, of course, that stereographic projection has great significance in *the theory of functions of a complex variable.* Indeed, I used it to advantage frequently in my lectures last semester.[1] Of other applications in which it plays an equally important role, I would mention *geography* and *astronomy.* Stereographic projection was known to the ancient astronomers; even today, you find in every atlas representations of the hemispheres, and of the polar regions of the earth, in stereographic projection.

I shall now present a few more examples from the last-mentioned field of application.

2. Some More General Map Projections

A digression in this direction seems to me especially appropriate for the present lectures. The *theory of geographic maps* is, after all, a subject which is of great importance in school instruction. It will interest every boy to hear from what point of view the maps in his atlas were drawn. The teacher of mathematics can put more feeling into his instruction, if he can give the desired information, than he can if he discusses only abstract questions. Thus every prospective teacher should be informed in this field, which, moreover, furnishes the mathematician with interesting examples of point transformations.

It will serve our purpose best if, at the outset, we think of the earth as

---

[1] See Part I, p. 105 et seq.

projected stereographically from, say, the south pole, upon the xy plane. Then, with respect to that pole, any other mapping upon a $\xi\eta$ plane will be given by the two equations $\xi = \phi(x, y)$, $\eta = \chi(x, y)$.

Among the first representations, much used in practice, are those in which *angles are preserved.* We obtain these, as is taught in the theory of functions of a complex variable, if we *think of the complex variable $\xi + i\eta$ as an analytic function of the complex variable $x + iy$:*

$$\xi + i\eta = f(x + iy) = \phi(x, y) + i\chi(x, y).$$

I should like to emphasize, however, that precisely in geographic practice use is often made of *representations in which angles are not preserved,* so that conformal transformations should not be regarded, as is often done, as the only important ones.

Under the *conformal* representations there appears prominently the so-called *Mercator projection,* which was discovered about 1550 by the mathematician Gerhard Mercator, whose real name, by the way, was the good German name Kremer. You will find mercator maps of the earth in every atlas.

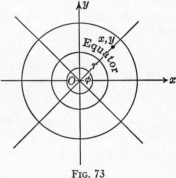

FIG. 73

The mercator projection is determined by choosing our analytic function f as the logarithm. It is given by the equation $\xi + i\eta = \log(x + iy)$.

As mathematicians, we can at once deduce the properties of the projection from this short formula, whereas for the geographer without mathematical training, the treatment of the mercator projection is, of course, rather difficult. Introducing polar coordinates into the xy plane (see Fig. 73), i.e., putting $x + iy = r \cdot e^{i\phi}$, we get

$$\xi + i\eta = \log(r \cdot e^{i\phi}) = \log r + i\phi,$$

so that $\xi = \log r$, $\eta = \phi$.

We assume that the south pole of the earth is the center of our stereographic projection. Then the origin O of the xy plane corresponds to the north pole of the earth, and the rays $\phi = $ const. in the xy plane correspond to meridians. Consequently, in the mercator projection (see Fig. 74) the meridians become $\eta = $ const., i.e., parallels to the ξ axis. The north pole ($r = 0$, $\xi = -\infty$) lies on them to the left, the south pole ($r = +\infty$, $\xi = +\infty$), to the right, at infinity. Since the angle ϕ is undetermined to within multiples of 2π, the mapping is infinitely many-valued, and each strip of width 2π, parallel to the ξ axis, gives an image of the entire surface of the earth. The circles of latitude, $r = $ const., become, in the mercator map, the parallels ξ = const., i.e., since angles are of course preserved, they are the orthogonal trajectories of the images of the meridians. To the equator $(r = 1)$, there corresponds the η axis $(\xi = 0)$.

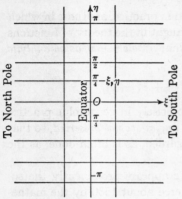

FIG. 74

This one example may serve to arouse you to further study of the numerous transformations in the geographical theory of mapping. Let me now pass on, rather, to a *more general theorem* of this theory. Those of you who have busied yourselves with geography have heard, certainly, of the *Tissot theorems* which Tissot developed in his book, translated by Hammer in Stuttgart.[1] It is very easy to make its contents clear, from our standpoint.

Let there be *two geographic maps*, representations of the earth's surface upon an xy plane and a $\xi\eta$ plane, each of which may be arbitrary and not necessarily conformal. The two will stand in some relation to each other, which we may write in the form $\xi = \phi(x, y)$, $\eta = \chi(x, y)$.

We shall examine the neighborhood of two corresponding positions (x_0, y_0) and (ξ_0, η_0), where $\xi_0 = \phi(x_0, y_0)$, $\eta_0 = \chi(x_0, y_0)$. For this purpose we introduce new variables (x', y') and (ξ', η') by means of the equations

$$x = x_0 + x', \qquad y = y_0 + y';$$
$$\xi = \xi_0 + \xi', \qquad \eta = \eta_0 + \eta'.$$

We obtain then, by development according to Taylor's theorem,

$$\xi' = \left(\frac{\partial \phi}{\partial x}\right)_0 \cdot x' + \left(\frac{\partial \phi}{\partial y}\right)_0 \cdot y' + \cdots,$$

$$\eta' = \left(\frac{\partial \chi}{\partial x}\right)_0 \cdot x' + \left(\frac{\partial \chi}{\partial y}\right)_0 \cdot y' + \cdots,$$

where the derivatives are to be taken for $x = x_0$, $y = y_0$, and where terms of higher order are indicated by dots. We restrict ourselves, now, to *such a small neighborhood of* (x_0, y_0) that the indicated linear terms give a sufficient approximation to the actual values of (ξ', η'). This means, of course, that we exclude singular positions (x_0, y_0) for which such a neighborhood does not exist. Thus we exclude a point at which all four partial derivatives vanish simultaneously, so that the linear terms would not give a usable approximation. Then if we look at the linear equations thus obtained between (x', y') and (ξ', η'), we have at once the fundamental theorem which

[1] *Die Netzenentwürfe geographischer Karten nebst Aufgaben über Abbildungen beliebiger Flächen auf einander*, Stuttgart, 1887.

forms the basis of Tissot's reflections: *Two geographic maps of the same terrain are connected, in the neighborhood of a non-singular position, approximately, by an affine transformation.* If we now apply our earlier theorems on affine transformations, we obtain actually all of the so-called Tissot theorems.

I shall merely remind you of a few principal points. We know that everything depends on the determinant of the affine transformations, i.e., here, on the determinant

$$\Delta = \begin{vmatrix} \left(\dfrac{\partial \phi}{\partial x}\right)_0 & \left(\dfrac{\partial \phi}{\partial y}\right)_0 \\ \left(\dfrac{\partial \chi}{\partial x}\right)_0 & \left(\dfrac{\partial \chi}{\partial y}\right)_0 \end{vmatrix},$$

which is called the *functional determinant of the functions ϕ and χ, for the position $x = x_0$, $y = y_0$.* We always avoid the case $\Delta = 0$ in these applications, for in that case the neighborhood of (x_0, y_0) in the xy plane would be mapped upon a curve segment of the $\xi\eta$ plane, and the geographer would hardly consider such a map as usable. We are thus to *consider here $\Delta \neq 0$.* In our earlier discussions (see p. 73 et seq.) we made clear how such an affine transformation comes about; hence we can now take over the theorem: *The neighborhood of the point $(\xi_0 \, \eta_0)$ is obtained from that of the point (x_0, y_0), with the accuracy which here concerns us, by subjecting the latter to a pure deformation in two mutually perpendicular directions and by then turning it through a suitable angle.* You will find in Tissot's book that he actually gives a clear ad hoc deduction of this theorem, and you have here an interesting example of how those concerned with the applications manage to meet the mathematical needs of their own subject. To the mathematician, the thing always seems very simple, but it is still instructive for him to know what these applications require.

I shall now pass to the consideration of a general class of point transformations.

3. The Most General Reversibly Unique Continuous Point Transformations

All of the mapping functions which we have thus far considered were continuous and successively differentiable, indeed they were analytic (developable into a Taylor series). However, we admitted multiple, even infinitely many-valued functions (e.g., the logarithm). We shall now set down as precisely our chief requirement *that our mapping functions shall be without exception reversibly one-valued. We shall assume also that they are continuous.* We shall make no assumptions, however, as to the existence of derivatives, etc. We inquire as to the properties of geometric figures which remain unchanged under these most general reversibly unique and continuous transformations. Let us think, say, of a surface or a solid made of rubber, with figures marked upon it. What is preserved in these figures if the rubber is arbitrarily distorted without being torn?

The totality of properties which we find in the treatment of this question makes up the field that is called *analysis situs*. We might call it the *science of those properties which depend upon position and not at all upon size*. The name comes from Riemann, who, in his famous paper of 1857, *Theorie der Abelschen Funkionen,*[1] was drawn into such investigations by function-theoretical interests. Since that time, moreover, it has often happened that analysis situs is not mentioned in books on geometry, and is left for discussion in the theory of functions when it is needed. It was not so, however, with Möbius, who, in a paper written in 1863,[2] discussed analysis situs from its purely geometric interest. He calls those figures which transform into each other through reversibly unique continuous distortion *elementarily related* figures, because the properties which are invariant under these transformations are the simplest possible properties.

We shall restrict ourselves here to the *investigation of surfaces*. To begin with, we should note a property which was first discovered by Möbius, and which Riemann had missed entirely: the *distinction, namely, as to whether a surface is one-sided or two-sided*. Indeed we have discussed (p. 18 et seq.) the *one-sided* Möbius band, upon which, by continuous movement, one can come unawares from the one side to the other, so that a distinction between the two sides no longer has any meaning. It is clear that this property persists through all continuous distortions and that therefore, *in analysis situs, we must actually distinguish, from the beginning, between one-sided and two-sided surfaces*.

For the sake of simplicity we shall concern ourselves here *only with two-sided surfaces*, especially since they alone are ordinarily considered in the theory of functions of a complex variable. However, the theory of one-sided surfaces is not essentially more difficult. It turns out that for a surface, in the sense of analysis situs, there are two *natural numbers* which are *completely characteristic:* The *number μ of its boundary curves* and the *number p of closed cuts which do not separate it into parts* (the so-called genus). More precisely, *a necessary and sufficient condition that two two-sided surfaces be applicable to each other reversibly uniquely, and continuously (that they be "elementarily related" or, as we say today, they be homeomorphic) is that these two numbers μ and p shall be the same for both surfaces*. The proof of this theorem would

[1] Journal für die reine und angewandte Mathematik, vol. 54 = *Gesammelte mathematische Werke* (2nd edition, Leipzig, 1892), p. 88.—Riemann, following Leibniz, uses here the word "analysis" in its original methodological sense, not with the meaning which it has taken on as a mathematical term.

[2] *Theorie der elementaren Verwandtschaft*, Berichte über die Verhandlungen der Königlich Sächsischen Gesellschaft der Wissenschaften, mathematischphysikalische Klasse, vol. 15, p. 18 ff. = *Gesammelte Werke*, vol. 2 (Leipzig, 1886), p. 433 ff.

carry us too far afield. I can merely illustrate these numbers μ and p by a *few examples*.

Let us think of *three surfaces* placed alongside of one another, a *sphere*, a *torus*, and a *double torus* (shaped like a pretzel), as they appear schematically in Fig. 75. Each is a closed surface, i.e., it has no boundary curve; hence

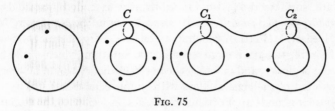

FIG. 75

$\mu = 0$. In the first example, every closed cut divides the surface into two separate parts, so that $p = 0$. In the second example, a meridian curve C represents a closed cut which does not separate the surface into parts. After the curve C has been drawn, however, every additional closed cut actually divides the surface into parts. This is precisely what we mean when we say $p = 1$. In the third example, $p = 2$, as is shown by the two different meridian curves C_1 and C_2, on the two separate handles. By the addition of more handles, we can create surfaces with any desired value of p. On the other hand, we can give μ any desired integral value different from zero by making in these surfaces small holes or *punctures*, each of which adds a boundary. Thus we can actually set up surfaces with arbitrary values of p and μ, and all other surfaces with the same values of p and μ must then be homeomorphic with them, no matter how different they may be in appearance. The theory of functions offers many examples of such surfaces.

I must explain here also the term *connectivity*, which Riemann introduced. By it he means the number $2p + \mu$, and he calls the surface $(2p + \mu)$-*ply connected*. A surface is *simply-connected* if $2p + \mu = 1$, so that $p = 0$ and $\mu = 1$; that is, it is homeomorphic to a sphere with one puncture, which we could deform continuously into a *circular disk* by enlarging the hole. (See Fig. 76.)

Riemann also introduces the notion of *crosscut*, i.e., a cut which joins one

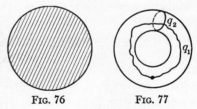

FIG. 76   FIG. 77

boundary point with another. Thus we can speak of crosscuts only if boundary curves actually exist, that is, only if $\mu > 0$. We can then prove the following theorem. *Each crosscut reduces the connectivity by 1, so that, in particular, any surface for which $\mu > 0$ can be changed into a simply-connected surface by $2p + \mu - 1$ crosscuts.* Let us consider a torus (see Fig. 77) with one puncture ($p = \mu = 1$), and let us draw the first crosscut q_1 from this puncture and necessarily back to the same puncture. Then let us draw the second crosscut q_2, which starts and also ends in the first cut and resembles precisely the closed cut in the torus of Fig. 76. Then the connectivity is actually reduced from $2 \cdot 1 + 1 = 3$ to 1.

As to literature concerning analysis situs, there is a comprehensive list, not merely for surfaces, but also for arbitrarily extended manifolds, in the *Enzyklopädie der mathematischen Wissenschaften* in the Report by M. Dehn and P. Heegard (III AB3), which is, to be sure, very abstract. It would be highly desirable to have a more readable presentation, which would be accessible to the beginner, and in which the abstract theory would be preceded by a development of the general ideas with simple examples.[1]

Analysis situs finds applications in physics, especially in potential theory. But it reaches also into *school instruction*, in *the polyhedron theorem of Euler*, concerning which I shall say a word. Euler observed that if *an ordinary polyhedron* has E corners, K edges, and F faces *we always have the relation* $E + F = K + 2$. Now if we deform the polyhedron in any way which is reversibly unique and continuous, these numbers, and hence the equation, will remain unchanged, so that the latter will still hold when E, F, K are the numbers of corners, faces, and edges of an *arbitrary division of the sphere* or, indeed, of any *surface homeomorphic to it*, provided only that *each subdivision is simply-connected*. We can generalize this theorem at once to surfaces of arbitrary genus, as follows. *If we divide a surface which admits p closed cuts without dismemberment, into F simply-connected parts by means of K line-segments*, and if *E corners are created, then we shall have $E + F = K + 2 - 2p$.* I leave it to you to set up illustrative examples and to ponder over the proof of the theorem, or to read it in the Dehn-Heegard report. Of course, there are still broader generalizations of this theorem.

With this we shall leave altogether the theory of point transformations, and we shall try to obtain a view of the most important classes of those transformations which carry points over into other space elements.

IV. TRANSFORMATIONS WITH CHANGE OF SPACE ELEMENT

1. Dualistic Transformations

The most obvious cases are those correspondences which interchange *point* and *line* in a two-dimensional region, or *point* and *plane* in a three-dimensional region. I shall restrict myself to the first case, and I shall follow the line of thought which Plücker first used in 1831 in the second part of his

---

[1] [A more recent work is B. v. Kerékjartó, *Vorlesungen über Topologie* (vol. 1, only, has appeared), Berlin, Springer, 1923. Another article on analysis situs will appear soon in the Enzyklopädie der mathematischen Wissenschaften, by H Tietze.]

Analytisch-geometrische Entwickelungen, which we mentioned earlier (p. 57). We shall begin with the analytic formulation.

The first idea used by Plücker, which I have discussed already (p. 59 et seq.), is to place on an equal footing with ordinary coordinates the constants u and v in the equation of the straight line,

$$(1) \qquad\qquad ux + vy = 1,$$

to regard u and v as *line coordinates,* and to build up the structure of analytic geometry by using these two sorts of coordinates in analogous "dual" ways. Thus, in the plane, there correspond to each other the *curve as a locus of points given* by the point equation $f(x, y) = 0$, and the *curve as the envelope of a single infinity of lines of a family defined* by the line equation $g(u, v) = 0$.

A proper *transformation,* such as we now wish to consider, will be obtained, of course, only when we add to our plane E a second plane E', and set up a relation between the line coordinates u and v in E and the point coordinates x' and y' in E'. Thus the most general transformation of this kind would be given by the two equations

$$(2) \qquad\qquad u = \phi(x', y'), \qquad v = \chi(x', y')$$

i.e., to each point (x', y') in E' there will correspond the line in E whose equation is obtained by substituting these values (2) in (1).

1. To begin with, let us consider the *simplest example of such a transformation,* which is given by the equations

$$(3) \qquad\qquad u = x', \qquad v = y'.$$

By means of this transformation, to the point (x', y') in E', there will correspond in E the line

$$(3a) \qquad\qquad x'x + y'y = 1.$$

If we now superimpose the planes E and E' so that their coordinate systems coincide, we see that this equation represents the polar of the point (x', y') with respect to the unit circle about the origin, $(x^2 + y^2 = 1)$, so that our *transformation is the familiar polar relation for the circle.* (See Fig. 78.)

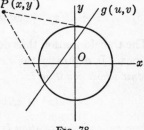

FIG. 78

We notice that, in place of the two equations (3), the *one* equation (3a) suffices to define the relation, since it is the equation of the line corresponding to any point (x', y'). Since it is completely symmetrical in x and y on one hand and in x' and y' on the other, *the two planes E and E' must play the same role in our relation,* i.e., to every point in E there must also correspond a line in E'. It makes no difference, when the two planes coincide, whether we think of the point as in E or in E'.

With respect to the first property, we call the transformation *dual in the narrower sense;* with respect to the second, *reciprocal.* Thus, without making any distinction between the two planes, we can speak simply of the correspondence of a definite polar to a pole, and then express the reciprocal property in the manner stated on page 57.

As for other properties of this transformation, I remark merely that, to a curve traced by the point (x', y') in the plane E', there would correspond, by the principle of duality, the curve in the plane E enveloped by the corresponding line (u, v).

2. By analogy with our earlier discussion of the most general "collineation," it can be proved easily that the *most general dual relation* is obtained if we generalize the assumption (3) and set u and v equal to *linear fractional functions of x' and y' with the same denominator:*

(4)
$$\begin{cases} u = \dfrac{a_1 x' + b_1 y' + c_1}{a_3 x' + b_3 y' + c_3}, \\[2mm] v = \dfrac{a_2 x' + b_2 y' + c_2}{a_3 x' + b_3 y' + c_3}. \end{cases}$$

Substituting these values for u and v in (1), multiplying by the common denominator, and noting that the nine coefficients $a_1, \cdots, c_3$ are arbitrary, we obtain the *most general linear equation in x and y as well as in x' and y':*

(4a) $a_1 xx' + b_1 xy' + c_1 x + a_2 yx' + b_2 yy' + c_2 y - a_3 x' - b_3 y' - c_3 = 0.$

Conversely, every such "bilinear" equation in x, y and x', y' represents a dual transformation between the planes E and E'. For, if we assume that one pair of coordinates are constant, i.e., if we think of a fixed point in one of the planes, the equation is linear in the other two coordinates and represents a *line* in the other plane, corresponding to that fixed point.

3. This relation, however, is not in general *reciprocal* in the sense defined above, unless two symmetrical terms in (4a) always have the same coefficient, in which case the equation is

(5) $Axx' + B(xy' + yx') + Cyy' + D(x + x') + E(y + y') + F = 0.$

The transformation thus determined is familiar from the theory of conic sections. It expresses the *correspondence of pole and polar with respect to the conic whose equation is*

$$Ax^2 + 2Bxy + Cy^2 + 2Dx + 2Ey + F = 0.$$

Every such polar relation is dual and reciprocal.

We can pass immediately from this to the consideration of an essentially more general class of transformations with a change of the space element, namely, the contact transformations.

2. Contact Transformations

These transformations, so named by Sophus Lie, are obtained if, instead of the bilinear equation (4a), we start with an arbitrary higher equation in the four point coordinates of the two planes:

(1) $$\Omega(x, y; x', y') = 0.$$

We shall assume that this equation satisfies the requisite conditions of continuity. It is called, after Plücker, the *aequatio directrix* or *directrix equation*. For plane geometry, all the relevant developments are found in Plücker's work mentioned above.[1] To begin with, we keep x and y fixed, i.e., we consider a definite point $P(x, y)$ in E. (See Fig. 79.) Then the equation $\Omega = 0$ represents, in the running coordinates x' and y', a definite curve C' in the plane E', and we make this curve correspond, as a new element of the plane E', to the point P, as we did earlier with the straight line. If, however, we now take a fixed point $P'(x', y')$ in E', say on the curve C', then the same equation $\Omega = 0$, in which we now think of x' and y' as fixed and of x and y as running coordinates, represents a definite curve C in E. Of course, the curve C must pass through the first point P. In this way, we have established a correspondence between the points P in E and the ∞^2 curves C' in E', and between the points P' in E' and

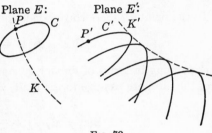

FIG. 79

the ∞^2 curves C in E, just as we established earlier a correspondence between points and straight lines.

If, now, a point P in E moves on an arbitrary curve K (indicated by a broken line), there will correspond to each position of P a definite curve C' in E'. In order to obtain from the simply infinite family made up of the curves C', a single curve in E' which we can set into correspondence with the curve K in E, we apply to the present case the *envelope principle* already used in the relation of duality: *We place in correspondence with K that curve K' in E' which is enveloped by the curves C' that correspond to the points of K by means of the equation $\Omega = 0$.* Evidently, we could repeat the same argument, starting with an arbitrary curve K' in E'. Thus we have finally derived from the directrix equation $\Omega = 0$, a transformation of the two planes by which to every curve in the one plane, there corresponds a definite curve of the other plane.

In order to follow this discussion *analytically*, let us replace the curve K by a rectilinear polygon with short sides, as we habitually do in differential

---

[1] *Loc. cit.*, pp. 259–265.

calculus for the sake of clearness, and let us ask what corresponds to a single such polygonal side. We always have in mind, of course, a passage to the curve as a limit, so that by the polygon side we understand, really, *a point P and its direction of motion* (the direction of the tangent to K at P); together these form a so-called *line-element*. We now choose, in this direction from P, a point P_1 (see Fig. 80) with coordinates $x + dx$ and $y + dy$, where dx and dy are small

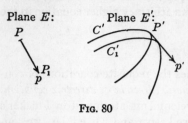

Plane E:

Plane E':

FIG. 80

and are ultimately to approach zero, but where dy/dx always has the definite value p which characterizes the given direction at P. To the point P' corresponds the curve C' in E' whose equation in the running coordinates x' and y' is

$$\Omega(x, y; x', y') = 0.$$

To the point P_1 there corresponds the curve C_1' whose equation is

$$\Omega(x + dx, y + dy; x', y') = 0.$$

Expanding in terms of dx and dy, and retaining only linear terms because of the ultimate passage to the limit, we obtain

$$\Omega(x, y; x', y') + \frac{\partial \Omega}{\partial x} dx + \frac{\partial \Omega}{\partial y} dy = 0.$$

These two equations give the coordinates x' and y' of the intersection of C' and C_1', which, in the limit, is the point of contact of C' with the envelope K'. Since $dy/dx = p$, we may write these equations in the form

$$(2) \qquad \begin{cases} \Omega(x, y; x', y') = 0, \\ \dfrac{\partial \Omega}{\partial x} + \dfrac{\partial \Omega}{\partial y} p = 0. \end{cases}$$

Moreover, C' and C_1' have, in the limit, a common tangential direction in P' given by the equation $dy'/dx' = p'$, which is also the direction of the envelope K' in P'. Since $\Omega = 0$ is the equation of C' in the running coordinates x' and y', this tangent direction is determined by the equation

$$\frac{\partial \Omega}{\partial x'} dx' + \frac{\partial \Omega}{\partial y'} dy' = 0$$

or

$$(3) \qquad \frac{\partial \Omega}{\partial x'} + \frac{\partial \Omega}{\partial y'} p' = 0.$$

Thus, if we know a point P of K and the direction p of the tangent at P, then a point P' on the corresponding curve K' is determined, together with the direction p' at P'. We say, therefore, that *our transformation establishes a correspondence between every line-element x, y, p of the plane E and a definite line-element x', y', p' of the plane E', by means of equations* (2) *and* (3).

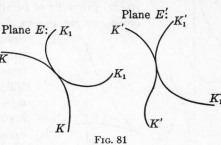

FIG. 81

If we apply this argument to each side of the polygon which approximates the corresponding curve K (or to each of the line-elements of K), we get in E' the sides of the polygon which approximates the corresponding curve K' (or the line-elements of K'). Hence *the equations* (2), *solved for x' and y', give the analytic representation of the curve K', when we let x, y, and p, the coordinates and the slope, run through the values given by all the points on K*. (See Fig. 81.)

It now becomes clear why Lie called these transformations *contact transformations*. For, if two curves in E touch each other, this means that they have a line-element in common; hence the corresponding curves in E' must have a common line-element, i.e., a common point and a common direction through that point. *The tangency of two curves is thus an invariant under the transformation*, which is what the name implies. Lie developed extensively the theory of these contact transformations also for *space*. He began in 1896, together with G. Scheffers, a comprehensive presentation in his work entitled *Geometrie der Berührungstransformationen*, which unfortunately was not continued much beyond the first volume.[1]

Having given this brief discussion of the *theory* of transformations with a change of the space element, I shall try to enliven it with a few concrete examples, in order to show what can be done with these things in the applications.

3. Some Examples

Let me speak first of the *dual transformations* and of the role which they play in the *theory of the forms of algebraic curves*. We shall inquire how typical curve-forms change under dual transformation, as in the reciprocal polar relation with respect to a conic. We must restrict ourselves, of course, to a few characteristic cases. Thus I shall examine first, under *curves of third degree*, the type which has an *odd number of branches*, and which is cut by every line either in one or in three real points. In the adjacent sketch (Fig. 82) there is one *asymptote;* but we can immediately obtain from this a form with three *asymptotes* by transforming the curve projectively so that a line which cuts it in three points is thrown to infinity. In any event, the curve has three real points of *inflection*, and these have the

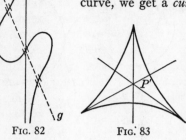

FIG. 82

special property of being *collinear*. By dualization of this curve, we get a *curve of class three*, to which there can be drawn from any point either one or three tangents. To the point of inflection there must correspond a cusp, as will become clear upon careful reflection. Moreover, you will find these matters discussed thoroughly in my earlier lectures on geometry. The curve of the third class which arises here (Fig. 83) has thus three cusps, and the

FIG. 83

tangents at those cusps must go through a point P' which corresponds to the line g on which the three points of inflection lie.

I shall now make similar brief statements concerning the *curves of degree four and those of class four*. A curve of fourth degree can appear in the form

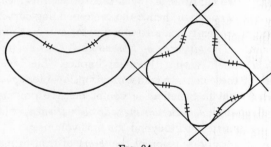

FIG. 84

of an *oval with an indentation;* indeed, there exist also *forms with two, three, or four indentations*. (See Fig. 84.) In the first case, there will be two real points of inflexion and one double tangent; in the others there can be as many as eight inflexions and four double tangents. If we dualize, we must add to what was said above that the dual of a double tangent is a double point. There will arise, therefore, types of *curves of fourth class* with from two to eight cusps and from one to four double points, as sketched in Fig. 85. There is a special charm in carefully working out the forms of algebraic

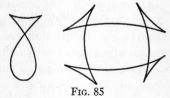

FIG. 85

curves. Unfortunately, I cannot here follow them in more detail and I must content myself with these brief indications.[1] These examples amply

[1] [See F. Klein, *Gesammelte mathematische Abhandlungen*, vol. 2, p. 89 et seq., p. 136 et

illustrate, however, how duality transformations bring under the same law things which at first glance seem as unlike as possible.

I come now to the *applications of the theory of contact transformations*. It turns out here, interestingly enough, that the idea of contact transformations, like most really good theoretical ideas, has a wide field of application. Indeed, mathematicians were making use of them long before the theory was worked out. It is the old *principle of cog wheels, or gears*, that I now have in mind particularly. It constitutes a *special chapter of kinematics*, of the general science of the mechanisms of motion, which is of central importance, for example, in the construction of machines. The devices for drawing a straight line, of which we recently discussed an example, also belong to kinematics. What I have so often said in these lectures holds likewise here: I can of course only pick out small parts of each discipline and endeavor to make their meaning and significance as obvious as possible by means of simple examples. With the stimulation that I have supplied, I trust that you will try to fill in the details from special presentations. As chief means of orientation in the whole field of kinematics, I recommend the report by A. Schoenflies in the *Enzyklopädie* (IV$_3$), which also gives information concerning the extensive literature.

The *problem* of constructing gears is to *transfer uniform motion from one wheel to another*. However, since forces are also to be transferred at the same time, it is not enough to let the wheels roll upon each other (see Fig. 86). It is necessary to provide one of the wheels with projections (teeth) which fit into depressions on the other. The problem is, therefore, to form the profiles or faces of these teeth so that *uniform rotation of the one wheel will bring about uniform rotation of the other*. That is certainly a very interesting problem, even from the geometric side. I shall give the most important part of its solution.

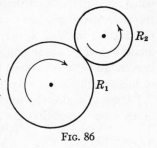

Fig. 86

The teeth of one of the wheels can be chosen, in the main, arbitrarily, with restrictions imposed by practical usableness, such as that the individual teeth should not collide with one another. *The teeth of the second wheel are then necessarily fully determined, and, in fact, they are derived from the teeth of the first wheel by a definite contact transformation.*

I need only explain briefly how this theorem comes about, without giving a full proof. We note first that we are concerned only with the motion of the two wheels relatively to each other. We may think, therefore, of one of them R_1 as fixed, while the other R_2, in addition to its own rotation, travels around R_1. Thus every point on R_2 describes in the fixed plane of

seq., p. 99 et seq., Berlin, Springer, 1922, the two papers *Über eine neue Art Riemannscher Flächen* and the first paper *Über den Verlauf der Abelschen Integrale bei den Kurven 4 Grades*.]

R_1 an epicycloid which is prolate, has cusps, or is curtate, according as the tracing point is inside, on, or outside the periphery of R_2. It follows that to

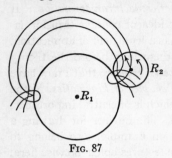

FIG. 87

every point of the moving plane of R_2 there corresponds a definite curve in the plane of R_1. If we derive, by the method already discussed, the *contact transformation* from the equation which expresses this correspondence, we shall have precisely the contact transformation for the gears in question. It is easy to show that two curves which correspond to each other under this transformation actually mesh into one another in this motion.

Finally, a word as to how the theoretical principle, thus outlined, actually takes form in the practical construction of gears. I shall mention only the simplest case, the toothing of the driving pinion. Here the teeth of R_2 are simply *points* (see Fig. 88) or, rather, since points could not transfer force, small circular pivots, the pinions. To every such small circle there corresponds, under the contact transformation, a curve which differs only slightly from an epicycloid, namely, a curve parallel to it and distant from it by the radius of the pinion. The circles roll upon these curves when R_2 turns, so that these curves are the flanks of the teeth which must be erected upon R_1 in order that the circular teeth of R_2 may clutch properly. In this model which I show you, the beginnings of these

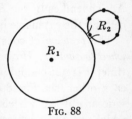

FIG. 88

curves can be seen realized as profiles of the teeth of R_1, each curve being of such width that one tooth after another clutches.

I show you also the models of two other types of gear teeth which are much used in practice, the *involute and the cycloid gear teeth*.[1] For the first

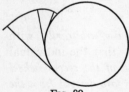

FIG. 89

type, the tooth profiles of both wheels are involutes of circles (see Fig. 89), curves which arise when a thread is unwound from a circle, and whose evolutes are therefore circles. For the second type mentioned, the teeth are made up of arcs of cycloids.

I hope that I have succeeded in giving you at least a preliminary orientation concerning the problems with which the theory of transformations with a change of the space element is concerned. Before we leave this second major part concerning transformations, I must supplement what I have said by a discussion of an important chapter which should not be omitted in a cyclopedia of geometry, namely, the use of imaginary elements.

---

[1] All these models are made by F. Schilling (firm of M. Schilling, Leipzig).

V. THEORY OF THE IMAGINARY

As you know, the theory of imaginary quantities was first developed in algebra and analysis, especially in the theory of equations and in the theory of functions of a complex variable, where, indeed, it has celebrated its greatest triumph. In addition to this, however, at an early date, mathematicians had assigned to the variables x and y in analytic geometry *complex values* $x = x_1 + ix_2$, $y = y_1 + iy_2$, and had thus added to the real points a large manifold of *complex points* without, at first, assigning any proper geometric meaning to this manner of speaking, which had been borrowed from analysis.

The usefulness of this new introduction was, of course, that it made superfluous those distinctions of cases which were imposed by a restriction to real variables, and that it made it possible to enunciate theorems in a general way, without exceptions. Entirely analogous considerations in projective geometry led us to the introduction of infinitely distant points as well as the infinitely distant line and plane. What we did is appropriately called the *"adjoining of improper points"* to the proper points of space which are conceived intuitively.

We shall now undertake both extensions at the same time. To that end, we shall introduce, as before, *homogeneous coordinates*. Remaining, for the present, in the plane, we put $x : y : 1 = \xi : \eta : \tau$ and we admit *complex values* for ξ, η, τ. We exclude the system of values $(0, 0, 0)$. Let us consider now, for example, a homogeneous *quadratic equation*

$$(1) \qquad A\xi^2 + 2B\xi\eta + C\eta^2 + 2D\xi\tau + 2E\eta\tau + F\tau^2 = 0,$$

and let us call the totality of systems (ξ, η, τ) which satisfy it (no matter whether they represent finite or infinitely distant points) a *curve of second degree*. The term *conic section* is sometimes used, but this can lead to misunderstanding, if not by those who know the subject, at least by those who are not familiar with the consideration of imaginary elements. The curve, under this definition, need not have a single real point.

We now combine (1) with a *linear equation*

$$(2) \qquad \alpha\xi + \beta\eta + \gamma\tau = 0,$$

which we look upon as the definition of a *curve of first degree*, i.e., a *straight line*. These equations then have just two sets of values $(\xi : \eta : \tau)$ in common, i.e., a *curve of the first degree and one of the second degree intersect always in two points, which may be real or complex, at a finite or at an infinite distance, separate or coincident*. To be sure, degenerations are thinkable which would furnish exceptions to this theorem. If the left side of (1) breaks up into two linear factors, one of which is identical with (2), i.e., if the curve of second degree is a pair of straight lines, and if (2) is identical with one of them, then every point of (2) is a common point. This amounts to saying that the quadratic equation which we get by eliminating one variable from the two given equations has only vanishing coefficients. Other degenerations appear, of course, when the left side of one of the given equations, or, indeed, of both of them, vanishes identically ($A = B = \cdots = F = 0$, or $\alpha = \beta = \gamma = 0$). However, I shall ignore all such particular situations as being essentially trivial. Passing to the consideration of *two curves of second degree*, we may then enunciate the theorem that they always have *four common points*.

Let us now introduce homogeneous coordinates $x : y : z : 1 = \xi : \eta : \zeta : \tau$ in space, and let us assign to them arbitrary complex values, excluding the system of values $(0 : 0 : 0 : 0)$. The totality of solutions of a linear homogeneous equation in these four variables is called a *surface of the first degree* (a *plane*); of a quadratic homogeneous equation, a *surface of second degree*. Then, if we ignore trivial exceptions, it is true that, in general, a *surface of second degree is cut by a plane in a curve of second degree;* and *that two surfaces of second degree intersect in a space curve of order four*, which *itself is cut by any plane in four points*. In this it is left undetermined whether or not these curves of intersection have real branches, or whether they lie wholly in a finite region.

In his *Traité des propriétés projectives des figures*, Poncelet had already applied these notions, as early as 1822, to *circles and spheres*. To be sure, he did not use homogeneous coordinates and the precise formulations which they make possible. Instead, he followed his strong feeling for geometric continuity. In order to become acquainted with his remarkable results in exact form, let us start with the *equation of the circle*

$$(x - a)^2 + (y - b)^2 = r^2,$$

which we shall write in the homogeneous form

$$(\xi - a\tau)^2 + (\eta - b\tau)^2 - r^2\tau^2 = 0.$$

The intersection with the line at infinity $\tau = 0$ will thus be given by the equations

$$\xi^2 + \eta^2 = 0, \qquad \tau = 0.$$

The constants a, b, and r, which characterize the preceding circle, do not appear in this result. Hence, *every circle cuts the line at infinity in the same two fixed points:*

$$\xi : \eta = \pm i, \qquad \tau = 0,$$

which are called the *imaginary circular points*. In the same way one can show *that every sphere cuts the plane at infinity in the same imaginary conic:*

$$\xi^2 + \eta^2 + \zeta^2 = 0, \qquad \tau = 0,$$

which is called the *imaginary spherical circle*.

The converse is also true: *Every curve of second degree which passes through the imaginary circular points in its plane is a circle; and every surface of second order which contains the imaginary spherical circle is a sphere.* These are, then, characteristic properties of the circle and the sphere.

I have purposely avoided using the expressions "infinitely distant" circular points and "infinitely distant" spherical circle, which are sometimes used. Indeed, the *distance from the origin to the imaginary circular points* is not definitely infinite, as might perhaps at first be believed. Instead, that distance has the form $\sqrt{x^2 + y^2} = \sqrt{\xi^2 + \eta^2}/\tau = 0/0$, and is therefore *indeterminate*. Any desired limiting value may be assigned to it according to the way in which we approach the imaginary circular points. Similarly, the distance from *any* finite point to the imaginary circular points is indeterminate, and the same is true of the distance from any point in space to a point of the imaginary spherical circle. This is not surprising, for we have required of these imaginary circular points that they should be at a distance *r* from a finite point (lie on the circle with an arbitrarily given radius *r*), and at the same time that they should be at an infinite distance from it. This apparent contradiction can be relieved in the analytic formula only by its yielding this indeterminateness. It is necessary to make these simple things clear, especially since untruths are often spoken and written about them.

The imaginary circular points and the imaginary spherical circle make it possible to include the theory of circles and spheres very elegantly under the general theory of manifolds of the second degree, whereas, in the elementary treatment, certain differences seem to exist. Thus, in elementary analytic geometry, it is customary to speak always of only *two* points common to two circles, since the elimination of one unknown from their equations leads to only a quadratic equation. The elementary presentation takes no account of the fact that the two circles have in common also the two imaginary circular points on the line at infinity. The preceding general theorem actually furnishes us *four intersections*, the requisite number for two curves of the second degree. Similarly, it is customary to speak always of only *one* circle in which two spheres meet, and moreover that one may be real or imaginary. However, we know now that the spheres have in common also the imaginary *spherical circle* on the plane at infinity, and this, together with the finite circle, makes the curve of order four in which the general theorem requires them to intersect.

In this connection, I should like to say a few words about the so-called *imaginary transformation*. By this is meant a *collineation with imaginary coefficients* which carries imaginary points in which we are interested over into real points. Thus, in the theory of the imaginary circular points, we can use to advantage the transformation

$$\xi' = \xi, \qquad \eta' = i\eta, \qquad \tau' = \tau.$$

This transformation sends the equation $\xi^2 + \eta^2 = 0$ into the equation $\xi'^2 - \eta'^2 = 0$ and *changes the imaginary circular points* $\xi : \eta = \pm i$, $\tau = 0$ *into the real infinitely distant points*

$$\xi' : \eta' = \pm 1, \qquad \tau = 0$$

which are the points at infinity in the two directions that make an angle of 45° with the axes. Thus all circles are transformed into conics which go

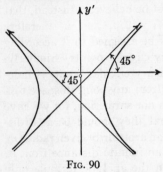

through these two real infinitely distant points, i.e., into *equilateral hyperbolas whose asymptotes make an angle of* 45° *with the axes.* (See Fig. 90.) By means of the picture of these hyperbolas, all of the theorems on circles can be explained. This is very useful for some purposes, especially for the corresponding developments in space. I must content myself with these brief remarks if I am not to overstep the limits of these lectures.

FIG. 90   More complete discussions are given in lectures and books on projective geometry.

The question arises as to whether or not a *pure geometric* approach might be made to these imaginary points, planes, conics, etc., without drawing them by force from the formulas of analysis, as we have done thus far. The older geometers, Poncelet and Steiner, were never clear on this point. To Steiner, imaginary quantities in geometry were ghosts, which made their effect felt in some way from a higher world without our being able to gain a clear notion of their existence. It was von Staudt who first gave a complete answer to the question, in his works *Geometrie der Lage* [1] and *Beiträge zur Geometrie der Lage*,[2] which we have mentioned before. We must now give some attention to his reflections. These books of von Staudt are quite hard to read, since his theories are developed at once deductively in their final form without reference to analytic formulas and without inductive hints. One can grasp with comfort only the genetic presentation which follows the path probably taken by the author in the development of his ideas.

Corresponding to the two works of von Staudt, there are two different steps in the development of his ideas which I shall now present briefly. The work of 1846 is concerned primarily with the consideration of *manifolds of order two with real coefficients*—I say manifolds, because I wish to leave undetermined the number of dimensions (straight line, plane, or space). Let us consider, say, a *curve* of the second degree in the plane, i.e., a homogeneous quadratic equation in three variables with real coefficients:

$$A\xi^2 + 2B\xi\eta + C\eta^2 + 2D\xi\tau + 2E\eta\tau + F\tau^2 = 0.$$

---

[1] Nürnberg, 1846.   [2] Nürnberg, 1856–1860.

For the analytic treatment, it is a matter of indifference whether or not this equation has real solutions, i.e., whether or not the curve of the second degree has a real branch or has only complex points. The question is how a pure geometer, in the latter case, should visualize such a curve; how he should define it by geometric means. The same question arises in the one-dimensional region, when we cut the curve by a straight line, say by the x-axis $\eta = 0$. The intersections, whether they are real or not, are then given by the equation with real coefficients

$$A\xi^2 + 2D\xi\tau + F\tau^2 = 0$$

and the question is whether or not, in the case of complex roots, one can attach a geometric meaning to them.

Von Staudt's idea is, in the first place, as follows. He considers, instead of the curve of second degree, its *polar system*, which we have dicussed (p. 110), i.e., a dual reciprocal relation given by the equation

$$A\xi\xi' + B(\xi\eta' + \xi'\eta) + C\eta\eta' + D(\xi\tau' + \xi'\tau) + E(\eta\tau' + \eta'\tau) + F\tau\tau' = 0.$$

Because of the reality of the coefficients, this is a *thoroughly real relation, which creates a correspondence between every real point, and a real line*, whether the curve itself is real or not. The polar system, on the other hand, completely determines the curve as the *totality of those points which lie on their own polars*. The question is left open as to whether or not such points have a real existence. In any case, however, *the polar system supplies always a real representative of the curve of second degree defined by the preceding equation*, and one which can be used, instead of the curve itself, as the object of the investigation.

If we now cut the curve by the x axis, i.e., set η and η' equal to zero, we have on it, by analogy, *a one-dimensional real polar relation*, given by the equation

$$A\xi\xi' + D(\xi\tau' + \xi'\tau) + F\tau\tau' = 0,$$

which always sets two real points in reciprocal relation to each other. The intersections of the x axis with the curve are the two self-corresponding points in this polar relation, the so-called *fundamental or order points*. They can be real or imaginary, but they will be only of secondary interest; the chief thing is, again, the polar relation as their real representative.

To designate the two points $(\xi/\tau, \xi'/\tau')$, which correspond to each other in such a one-dimensional polar relation, we use the expression *point pairs in involution*, which originated with Desargues in the seventeenth century, and we distinguish *two principal kinds* of such involutions, according as the *fundamental points are real or imaginary*, and a *transition case* in which they coincide. The chief thing here for us, however, is the notion of involution itself; the distinction as to cases, i.e., the question as to the nature of the roots of the quadratic equation, is of secondary interest only.

These considerations, which can easily be carried over into three dimensions, of course, do not afford, indeed, an interpretation of the imaginary, but still they supply, insofar as manifolds of order two are concerned, a *standpoint for the distinction between real and imaginary*. *Each manifold of second order is represented by a real polar system* and we can operate geometrically with this polar system as we can operate analytically with the real equations of the manifold.

An *example* will show this more fully. Consider a curve of the second degree, i.e., of a polar system given in the plane, and consider also a straight line. This offers intuitively many possible cases according as the curve has or has not any real points whatever, and, if it has, whether the line cuts it in real points or not. In any case, the plane

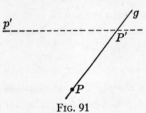

FIG. 91

polar system will establish on the line g (see Fig. 91) a linear polar system, i.e., an involution. To every point P on g there corresponds in the first system a polar p', and this meets g in a point P'. The points (P, P') traverse the involution in question. We may enquire also about the fundamental points, and determine whether they are real or imaginary. In all this, we have put into geometric language just what we inferred from the equations in the beginning of this discussion.

We shall apply these considerations, in particular, to the *imaginary circular points and the imaginary spherical circle.* We said earlier that any two circles cut the line at infinity in the same two points, the imaginary circular points. This means now, geometrically, *that their polar systems set up on the line at infinity one and the same one-dimensional polar system, the same involution.* In fact, if we draw the tangents (see p. 57) from an infinitely distant point P to a circle, then its polar p'_1, as the join of the points of tangency of these tangents from P, will be perpendicular to their common direction (see Fig. 92). Since all lines to the same point at infinity are parallel, the polar p'_2 of P, with respect to a second circle, will be perpendicular to the same direction as p'_1 and therefore parallel to p'_1. In other words, p'_1 and p'_2 meet the line at infinity in the same point P'. *Thus the polar systems of all circles cut the line at infinity in one and the same polar system, the so-called "absolute involution,"* whose *pairs of points, looked at from any finite point, appear in directions at right angles to each other.*

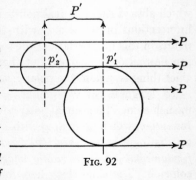

FIG. 92

Let us now put these thoughts into analytic language. If we start from the homogeneous equation of the circle:

$$(\xi - a\tau)^2 + (\eta - b\tau)^2 - r^2\tau^2 = 0,$$

or

$$\xi^2 + \eta^2 - 2a\xi\tau - 2b\eta\tau + (a^2 + b^2 - r^2)\tau^2 = 0,$$

then the corresponding polar relation is

$$\xi\xi' + \eta\eta' - a(\xi\tau' + \xi'\tau) - b(\eta\tau' + \eta'\tau) + (a^2 + b^2 - r^2)\tau\tau' = 0.$$

From this we get the relation generated on the line at infinity if we put $\tau = \tau' = 0$:

$$\xi\xi' + \eta\eta' = 0, \qquad \tau = 0, \qquad \tau' = 0.$$

These equations are, in fact, independent of the special constants a, b, and r of the initial circle. Furthermore, it follows from analytic geometry that, because of the first equation, two lines drawn to the points $(\xi, \eta, 0)$ and $(\xi', \eta', 0)$ are perpendicular to each other, so that we have actually obtained the theorem stated above.

Entirely analogous results hold for the *spheres of space*. They all generate on the plane at infinity one and the same, the so-called *absolute polar relation*, which is given by the equations

$$\xi\xi' + \eta\eta' + \zeta\zeta' = 0, \qquad \tau = 0, \qquad \tau' = 0.$$

Since the first equation says that the directions $\xi : \eta : \zeta$ and $\xi' : \eta' : \zeta'$ are perpendicular to each other, then *there corresponds to every point at infinity P that line at infinity which is cut out by the plane perpendicular to the direction toward P from a finite point*. Thus we have a real geometric equivalent of the theorems concerning the imaginary spherical circle.

It may be said, to be sure, that the imaginary is avoided rather than interpreted in this discussion. An actual interpretation of individual imaginary points, lines, and planes was first given by von Staudt in his *"Beiträge"* of 1856–60, by an extension of this theorem. I shall give this interpretation, also, because it is actually simple and ingenious; it seems strange and difficult only in von Staudt's abstract presentation. I shall follow the analytic presentation given by Stolz in 1871.[1] Stolz and I were then together in Göttingen. He had read von Staudt, which I could never bring myself to do; hence I learned in personal intercourse with him not only these but many other interesting ideas of von Staudt with which I myself later worked a good deal. I wish here to give only the most important features of the train of thought, without carrying out the details fully. It will suffice if I confine myself to the plane.

---

[1] *Die geometrische Bedeutung der complexen Elemente in der analytischen Geometrie*, Mathematische Annalen, vol. 4, p. 416, 1871.

Let us assume, to start with, *an imaginary point P*, given by its complex coordinates (ξ, η, τ). Let these be separated into their real and imaginary parts

(1) $$\xi = \xi_1 + i\xi_2, \qquad \eta = \eta_1 + i\eta_2, \qquad \tau = \tau_1 + i\tau_2.$$

Now we wish to construct a *real figure* by means of which this point P can be interpreted, and the *connection is to be projective*, i.e., speaking more precisely, it is to remain unchanged under arbitrary real projective transformation.

1. The first necessary step for this is to fix attention upon the two real points P_1, P_2 whose homogeneous coordinates are, respectively, the real parts of the coordinates of P and the imaginary parts multiplied by $-i$:

(1a) $$P_1: \ \xi_1, \eta_1, \tau_1; \qquad P_2: \ \xi_2, \eta_2, \tau_2.$$

These two points are different, i.e., the relation $\xi_1 : \eta_1 : \tau_1 = \xi_2 : \eta_2 : \tau_2$ cannot obtain, otherwise $\xi : \eta : \tau$ would behave like three real quantities and would represent therefore one real point. Hence P_1, P_2 determine a real straight line g whose equation is

(2) $$\begin{vmatrix} \xi & \eta & \tau \\ \xi_1 & \eta_1 & \tau_1 \\ \xi_2 & \eta_2 & \tau_2 \end{vmatrix} = 0.$$

This line contains the given imaginary point P, as well as the *conjugate imaginary point* $\overline{P}$, whose coordinates are

($\overline{1}$) $$\overline{\xi} = \xi_1 - i\xi_2, \qquad \overline{\eta} = \eta_1 - i\eta_2, \qquad \overline{\tau} = \tau_1 - i\tau_2,$$

since both coordinate triples (1), ($\overline{1}$) satisfy the equation of the line.

2. Of course the pair of points P_1, P_2, so constructed, can by no means pass as the representative of the imaginary point P, for they depend essentially upon the separate values of ξ, η, and τ, whereas, for the point P, it is only the ratios of these values which count. The same point P will therefore be represented if, instead of ξ, η, and τ, their products by an arbitrary complex constant $\rho = \rho_1 + i\rho_2$ are written in the form

(3) $$\begin{cases} \rho\xi = \rho_1\xi_1 - \rho_2\xi_2 + i(\rho_2\xi_1 + \rho_1\xi_2), \\ \rho\eta = \rho_1\eta_1 - \rho_2\eta_2 + i(\rho_2\eta_2 + \rho_1\eta_2), \\ \rho\tau = \rho_1\tau_1 - \rho_2\tau_2 + i(\rho_2\tau_1 + \rho_1\tau_2); \end{cases}$$

but then we get, if we separate the real parts from the imaginary, instead of the points P_1, P_2, *other* real points P_1', P_2', whose coordinates are

(3a) $$\begin{cases} P_1': & \xi_1' : \eta_1' : \tau_1' = \rho_1\xi_1 - \rho_2\xi_2 : \rho_1\eta_1 - \rho_2\eta_2 : \rho_1\tau_1 - \rho_2\tau_2, \\ P_2': & \xi_2' : \eta_2' : \tau_2' = \rho_2\xi_1 + \rho_1\xi_2 : \rho_2\eta_1 + \rho_1\eta_2 : \rho_2\tau_1 + \rho_1\tau_2. \end{cases}$$

If we consider the totality of pairs of points P'_1 and P'_2, given by all the values of ρ_1 and ρ_2, we have a geometric manifold in which only the ratios $\xi : \eta : \tau$ count, i.e., the "geometric" point P, which is therefore fitted to serve as representing P. Moreover, the connection with P is, in fact, projective, for, if we transform ξ, η, τ in any real linear manner, then ξ'_1, η'_1, τ'_1, and ξ'_2, η'_2, τ'_2 suffer the same substitution.

3. In order, now, to study the geometric nature of this totality of pairs of points, we note first that, whatever the value of ρ, the points P'_1 and P'_2 *lie on the line* P_1P_2 (see Fig. 93), since their coordinates obviously satisfy equation (2). Moreover, if we allow ρ to assume all complex values, i.e., ρ_1 and ρ_2 all real values (a common real factor makes no essential difference), then P'_1 runs through all the real points of g, and P'_2 represents always a second real point on g in unique correspondence with P'_1.

FIG. 93

Thus, for $\rho_1 = 1$, $\rho_2 = 0$, we have P_1 and P_2 as corresponding points. The correspondence stands out more clearly if we introduce the ratio

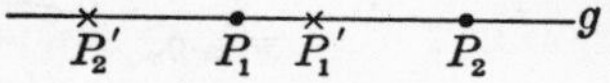

$$\frac{\rho_2}{\rho_1} = -\lambda.$$

Then we have

(3b)
$$\begin{cases} \text{for } P'_1: & \xi'_1 : \eta'_1 : \tau'_1 = \xi_1 + \lambda\xi_2 : \eta_1 + \lambda\eta_2 : \tau_1 + \lambda\tau_2; \\ \text{for } P'_2: & \xi'_2 : \eta'_2 : \tau'_2 = \xi_1 - \frac{1}{\lambda}\xi_2 : \eta_1 - \frac{1}{\lambda}\eta_2 : \tau_1 - \frac{1}{\lambda}\tau_2. \end{cases}$$

4. From these formulas we can infer also that, when λ varies, the points P_1 and P_2 become all the *point pairs of an involution on the line g*. For if we introduce a one-dimensional coordinate system on g, the homogeneous coordinates of the points P_1 and P_2 become linear integral functions of the parameters $\lambda'_1 = \lambda$ and $\lambda'_2 = -1/\lambda$, respectively, of the equations (3b). Hence the equation $\lambda'_1 \cdot \lambda'_2 = -1$ between the two parameters yields a symmetrical bilinear relation between the linear coordinates of P'_1 and P'_2, and consequently, in view of the definition on page 121 (see also p. 110), the assertion is proved.

5. The *fundamental points of this involution*, i.e., the points which correspond to each other, are given by $\lambda = -1/\lambda$, or $\lambda = \pm i$. They are both imaginary, one being the point P with which we started, the other the conjugate imaginary $\overline{P}$. Thus far we have given only a new presentation of von Staudt's old theory. *Besides P we have considered the point $\overline{P}$, which, together with P, forms a one-dimensional manifold of the second degree, determined by a real quadratic equation, and we have then constructed the resulting involution as its real representative.* I remind you that such an involution is determined if we know *two of its point pairs*, say P_1, P_2 and P'_1, P'_2. If this

involution is to have imaginary fundamental points, it is necessary and sufficient that these point pairs should *overlap*, i.e., that one of the points P_1' and P_2' should lie between P_1 and P_2 and the other outside of them.

6. In order to solve our problem completely, we need only a means for transforming the common representative of P and $\overline{P}$ into a *representative of P alone* (or of $\overline{P}$ alone). Von Staudt discovered such a means in 1856 as the result of a brilliant thought. The point P_1', with the coordinates $\xi_1 + \lambda\xi_2 : \eta_1 + \lambda\eta_2 : \tau_1 + \lambda\tau_2$ traverses, namely, the line g in a *perfectly definite direction* (see Fig. 94) if λ runs through all real values from 0 to $+\infty$ and back through negative values to 0. It is easy to show that we

FIG. 94

should be led to just the same sense on g if we started with the coordinates of P multiplied by an arbitrary ρ, i.e., if we considered the point $\xi_1' + \lambda\xi_2', \cdots$. Moreover, under real projective transformation of P, the direction of the arrow for the image point would follow from the one just determined, as a result of the same transformation. We shall, then, satisfy our requirements *if we make this arrow direction correspond, once for all, with the original point P* $(\xi_1 + i\xi_2, \cdots)$. Since the conjugate imaginary point $\overline{P}$ has the coordinates $\xi_1 + i(-\xi_2), \cdots$, we must, accordingly, assign as the sense of motion of P for positive increasing λ, the opposite of the sense just determined for the line g, thus achieving the desired distinction: *We distinguish between $+i$ and $-i$ simply by distinguishing between the positive and the negative traversing of the real values of λ.*

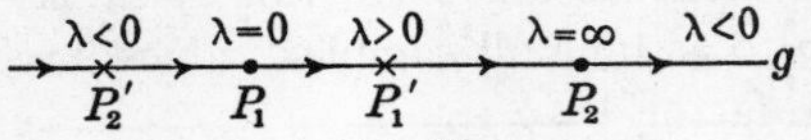

Thus we have, at last, the following *rule for the construction of a unique and projectively invariant real geometric figure to represent the imaginary point* $\xi_1 + i\xi_2, \eta_1 + i\eta_2, \tau + i\tau_2$: *Construct the points* $P_1(\xi_1 : \eta_1 : \tau_1)$ *and* $P_2(\xi_1 : \eta_2 : \tau_2)$, *their join g, and that point involution* on g (or another point pair on g) *in which the points*

$$P_1'(\xi_1 + \lambda\xi_2 : \eta_1 + \lambda\eta_2 : \tau_1 + \lambda\tau_2) \text{ and } P_2'\left(\xi_1 - \frac{1}{\lambda}\xi_2 : \eta_1 - \frac{1}{\lambda}\eta_2 : \tau_1 - \frac{1}{\lambda}\tau_2\right)$$

are always paired. Finally, we add the arrow, giving it the direction in which P_1' moves with positive increasing λ.

7. It remains for us still to show *that, conversely, every such real figure, consisting of a straight line, two overlapping point pairs on it P_1, P_2 and P_1', P_2' (or an involution range without real double points), together with a direction arrow, represents one and only one imaginary point.* I need not carry this proof out in detail. However, by choosing a suitable real constant factor, it is easy to give the coordinates of P_2 such values ξ_2, η_2, τ_2 that the coordinates of P_1' and P_2' are proportional to

$$\xi_1 + \lambda\xi_2 : \eta_1 + \lambda\eta_2 : \tau_1 + \lambda\tau_2 \quad \text{and} \quad \xi_1 - \frac{1}{\lambda}\xi_2 : \eta_1 - \frac{1}{\lambda}\eta_2 : \tau_1 - \frac{1}{\lambda}\tau_2,$$

or, what is the same thing, that the double points of the assumed involution range have the coordinates $\xi_1 \pm i\xi_2, \cdots$. The sign of λ, which is thus far arbitrary, is to be chosen so that the direction of motion of the point $\xi_1 + \lambda\xi_2 : \eta_1 + \lambda\eta_2 : \tau_1 + \lambda\tau_2$, when λ increases positively from zero on, shall agree with the direction arrow. Then the point P, with coordinates $\xi_1 + \lambda\xi_2, \cdots$, in view of the preceding developments, will actually represent the given involution with the given direction of the arrow. Moreover, it can be shown, that we are led to the same co-ordinate ratios, i.e., to the same point P, if we start from another point pair of the involution.

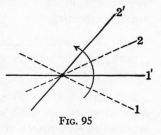

FIG. 95

Having completed the discussion of our problem for the *point*, we can carry over the solution to the *straight line* in the plane by the principle of duality. *Accordingly, we have a real unique representation of a complex line* by means of a real point (or a pencil involution without real double rays), together with a definite sense of rotation in the pencil. (See Fig. 95.)

These results permit also the representation of all relations between complex and real elements, by means of tangible properties of real geometric figures. This fact constitutes the real value of these results. In order to make this clear by a concrete example, I shall show you the meaning, in this representation, of the statement *that a point P* (real or imaginary) *lies on a line g* (real or imaginary). Here we have, of course, to distinguish four cases:

1. Real point and real line.
2. Real point and imaginary line.
3. Imaginary point and real line.
4. Imaginary point and imaginary line.

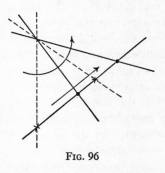

FIG. 96

Case 1 needs no special explanation; it constitutes a fundamental relation of the usual geometry. In case 2, the given real point must lie also on the conjugate imaginary line; hence it *must be identical with the vertex of the pencil* which we use to represent the imaginary line. Similarly, in case 3, the real line must be identical *with the range which carries the point involution* that represents the given imaginary point. Case 4 is the most interesting. (See Fig. 96.) Obviously, in this case, the conjugate imaginary point must lie on the conjugate imaginary line, from which it follows that each point pair of the involution range which represents P

must lie on a pair of lines of the involution pencil which represents g, i.e., that *these two representing involutions must be perspective to each other;* moreover, it turns out that *the arrows of the two involutions are also in perspective.*

Summing up this discussion, we may say that we have *a complete real picture of the plane of analytic geometry, one which takes account also of the complex elements, if we adjoin to the totality of the real points and lines of the plane, as new elements, the totality of given involution figures together with the direction arrows.* It will suffice, perhaps, if I indicate in outline how we should construct this real picture of complex geometry. In this I shall follow the order in which the earlier theorems of elementary geometry are now usually presented.

1. We start with the *existence theorems* which take accurate account of the presence of the elements we have just considered in the extended field of ordinary geometry.

2. Then follow the *theorems of connection*, which state that *through two points there goes one and only one line* and that *two straight lines have one and only one common point*, even in the extended region defined in 1. There are four cases to be distinguished here, just as above, according to the reality of the given elements, and it is interesting to determine in what point and line involutions these complex relations find their image.

3. As to the *laws of order*, there arises here, in contrast with real relations, an *entirely new situation*. In particular, the totality of real and complex points on a straight line constitute a *two-dimensional continuum*, as do also all the lines through a fixed point. Everyone, indeed, is accustomed, from the theory of functions of a complex variable, to represent the aggregate of values of a complex variable by all the points of a plane.

4. Concerning the *theorems of continuity*, I shall only point out how we represent the complex points which lie arbitrarily near a real point. For this purpose, we draw a real line through the real point P (or through a neighboring real point) and we take upon it two overlapping point pairs P_1, P_2 and P_1', P_2' (see Fig. 97) such that two points P_1, P_1' of different pairs lie close to each other and to P. If we now let P_1 and P_1' move into coincidence, the involution determined by these pairs degenerates, i.e., the two double points which were complex coincide with

FIG. 97

$P_1 = P_1'$. Each of the two imaginary points represented by the involution (with the one or the other arrow) thus goes continuously into a point near P or, indeed, into P itself. We must, of course, work our way carefully into these representations of continuity in order to use them with profit.

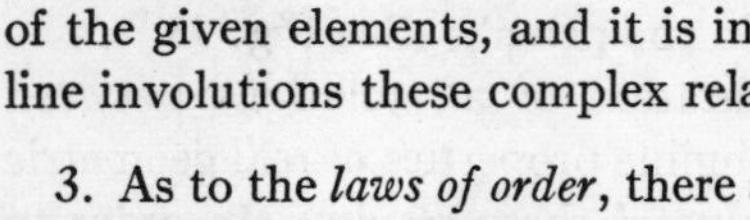

If this entire construction is prolix and bothersome, in comparison with the ordinary real geometry, it can, on the other hand, supply incomparably more. In particular, it completely clarifies algebraic manifolds, from a geometric standpoint, as the totality of their real and complex elements. With it, we can make geometrically obvious, with figures, such theorems as the *fundamental theorem of algebra*, or the *theorem of Bezout* that two curves of degrees m and n have, in general, $m \cdot n$ common points. To achieve this, we should have to work out the theorems much more carefully than has yet been done. However, all the essential material for such an investigation can be found in the literature.

In most cases, to be sure, the application of this geometric interpretation, notwithstanding its theoretical advantages, might create such complications that we should be satisfied with its theoretical possibilities and return actually to the more naive standpoint: a complex point is the aggregate of complex coordinate values with which, to a certain extent, one can operate as with real points. As a matter of fact, this use of imaginary elements, in complete disregard of all questions of theory, has always proved fruitful in dealing with the imaginary circular points and the imaginary spherical circle. As we saw, Poncelet was the first to use the imaginary in this sense. Other French geometers followed, notably Chasles and Darboux. In Germany, this conception of the imaginary was used particularly by Lie with great success.

With this digression on the imaginary, I bring to a close the second main division of this course and turn to a new chapter.

PART THREE

SYSTEMATIC DISCUSSION OF GEOMETRY AND ITS FOUNDATIONS

I. THE SYSTEMATIC DISCUSSION

In this chapter, we shall use geometric transformations to bring about a division of the entire field of geometry, one which will enable us, from *one* standpoint, to see the separate parts and their interrelations.

1. Survey of the Structure of Geometry

We are concerned here with ideas such as those that I developed systematically in my *Erlanger Programm* [1] of 1872. You will find information as to the development of these ideas since that time in the encyclopedia report by G. Fano: *Die Gruppentheorie als geometrisches Einteilungsprinzip* (Enz. III A.B. 4b).

1. As in the past, we shall consistently make use of analysis to gain mastery of geometric relations by *thinking of the totality of points in space as represented by the totality of values of the three "coordinates" x, y, and z.* To every transformation of space there corresponds, then, a certain transformation of these coordinates. From the beginning of our discussions we have recognized four kinds of transformations of particular significance, which are represented by certain *special linear substitutions of x, y, and z: Parallel displacements, rotations about the origin O, reflections in O, and similarity transformations with O as center.*

2. It might be supposed that the introduction of coordinates would bring about complete identity between analysis of three independent variables (x, y, z) and geometry. Such is not the case, however, at least in a specific sense. As I have already emphasized (p. 25 et seq.), geometry is concerned only with those relations between the coordinates which remain unchanged by the linear substitutions mentioned in 1, regardless of whether these are thought of as changes in the system of coordinates or as transformations of space. *Thus geometry is the invariant theory of those linear substitutions.* All non-invariant equations between coordinates, on the other hand, e.g., the statement that a point has the coordinates (2, 5, 3), have reference only

---

[1] *Vergleichende Betrachtungen über neuere geometrische Forschungen*, Erlangen, 1872. Reprinted in Mathematische Annalen, vol. 43, p. 63 et seq., 1893; and F. Klein, *Gesammelte mathematische Abhandlungen*, vol. 1, p. 460 et seq., Berlin, Springer, 1921.

to a definite coordinate system, fixed once for all. Such a discussion would belong to a science which must individualize each point for itself and consider its properties separately: to *topography*, or, if one prefers, *geography*. As an aid to understanding, I call to your attention several *examples of geometric properties:* The statement that two points are separated by a *distance*, when once a unit of length is chosen, means for us that we can construct from their coordinates (x_1, y_1, z_1) and (x_2, y_2, z_2) an expression $\sqrt{(x_1 - x_2)^2 + (y_1 - y_2)^2 + (z_1 - z_2)^2}$ which remains unchanged under all those linear substitutions, or is multiplied by a factor that is independent of the special location of the points. A similar meaning must be given to the statements that two lines are inclined at a certain *angle*, that a conic has certain *principal axes* and *foci*, etc.

The totality of these geometric properties we shall call *metric geometry*, in order to distinguish it from other *kinds of geometry*. We shall obtain the latter by separating out for consideration by themselves, according to a definite principle, certain groups of theorems of metric geometry. Accordingly, all these newer kinds of geometry are, at least for the immediate purpose, parts of metric geometry as the most inclusive "kind of geometry."

3. We start with the *affine transformations*, which we have studied carefully, i.e., with the integral linear substitutions in x, y, and z:

$$
\begin{cases}
x' = a_1x + b_1y + c_1z + d_1, \\
y' = a_2x + b_2y + c_2z + d_2, \\
z' = a_3x + b_3y + c_3z + d_3.
\end{cases}
$$

Under this transformation all the transformations mentioned in 1 are embraced as special cases, and we select from among the totality of geometric concepts and theorems the narrower group of those which remain unchanged under all affine transformations. This aggregate of concepts and theorems we consider as the first new kind of geometry, the so-called *affine geometry* or the *invariant theory of affine transformations*.

From the knowledge we have acquired of affine transformations, we can select, at once, the concepts and the theorems of this geometry. I recall here only a few: In affine geometry, we cannot discuss distance and angle. The notion of principal axes of a conic, and the distinction between circle and ellipse likewise disappear. There remains, however, the distinction between *finite* and *infinite* space and everything which depends upon it, such as the notion of *parallelism of two lines*, the division of conics into *ellipses*, *hyperbolas*, *parabolas*, etc. Moreover, the notions of *center* and *diameter of a conic*, and particularly the relation of *conjugate* diameters, remain.

4. We shall now proceed to *projective changes*, i.e., we shall introduce the linear fractional transformations

$$x' = (a_1x + b_1y + c_1z + d_1) : (a_4x + b_4y + c_4z + d_4),$$
$$y' = (a_2x + b_2y + c_2z + d_2) : (a_4x + b_4y + c_4z + d_4),$$
$$z' = (a_3x + b_3y + c_3z + d_3) : (a_4x + b_4y + c_4z + d_4),$$

which include the affine transformations as special cases. Geometric properties that remain unchanged under these transformations must certainly belong also to affine geometry. Thus, from affine geometry, we separate out the so-called *projective geometry* as the *invariant theory of projective transformations*. The step-by-step sifting of affine and projective geometry from metric geometry can be compared to the procedure of the chemist, who, by applying ever stronger reagents, isolates increasingly valuable ingredients from his compound. Our reagents are first affine transformations, and then projective transformations.

As to the theorems of projective geometry, it should be emphasized that the exceptional role of infinity and the concepts connected with it in affine geometry all now fall away. There is only *one kind of proper conic*. There still remains, however, for example, the *relation between pole and polar*, and likewise the *generation of the conic by means of projective pencils*, which we discussed earlier (p. 96 et seq.).

By means of the same principle, we may now pass *from metric geometry also to other kinds of geometry*. One of the most important is the geometry of reciprocal radii.

5. *The geometry of reciprocal radii*. This comprises the aggregate of those theorems of metric geometry which retain their validity under all *transformations of reciprocal radii*. In this geometry, the concepts of straight line or plane have no independent meaning; they appear as special cases in the notion of *circle or sphere*, respectively.

6. Finally, let me propose still another kind of geometry, which, in a sense, is obtained by the most careful sifting process of all, and which, therefore, includes the fewest theorems. This is *analysis situs*, which I mentioned earlier (p. 105 et seq.). Here one is concerned with the *aggregate of properties which persist under all transformations which are reversibly unique and continuous*. In order to avoid assigning an exceptional place to infinity, which would go into itself in all such transformations, we can adjoin either the *projective transformations*, or the *transformations by means of reciprocal radii*.

We shall define still more sharply the scheme thus outlined, by introducing the *concept of a group*. As we have already seen, *an aggregate of transformations is called a group if the combination of two of its transformations gives again a transformation of the aggregate, and if the inverse of every transformation also belongs to the aggregate*. Examples of groups are the totality of *all movements*, or that of *all collineations* (projective transformations);

for two movements combine into a movement, two collineations into a collineation, and in both cases there exists an inverse to every transformation.

If we look back at our different kinds of geometry, we see that the transformations which play a role in each case always form a group. In the first place, all linear substitutions which leave unchanged the relations of *metric geometry*—displacements, rotations, reflections, similarity transformations—obviously form a group, which one calls the *principal group of the transformations of space*. It is easy to establish the analogous significance of the *affine group* of all affine transformations for *affine geometry*, and of the *projective group* of all collineations for *projective geometry*. The theorems of the *geometry of reciprocal radii* remain valid under all transformations that are obtained by combining any reciprocal radii transformations with substitutions of the principal group. All these form again a group, namely, that of *reciprocal radii*. For *analysis situs*, finally, one has to do with the *group of all continuous reversibly unique distortions*.

We wish now to determine upon how many independent parameters a single operation in each of these groups depends. In the principal group, the motions involve six parameters, to which one must add one parameter for the change in unit length, so that altogether there are *seven parameters*. We express this by calling the *principal group a* G_7. The equations of the general affine transformation contain $3 \cdot 4 = 12$ arbitrary coefficients; those of the projective $4 \cdot 4 = 16$, whereby a factor common to all is unessential. It follows that the *affine group is a* G_{12}, and that the *projective group is a* G_{16}. The *group of the reciprocal radii* turns out to be a G_{10}. Finally, the *group of all continuous distortions* has no finite number of parameters whatever; the operations of this group depend, rather, upon arbitrary functions, or, if one wishes, upon infinitely many parameters. We may say that it is a G_∞.

In the connection between different kinds of geometry and groups of transformations, which we have just discussed, there appears a *fundamental principle* which can serve to characterize all possible geometries. It was just this which constituted the leading thought of my *Erlanger Programm: Given any group of transformations in space which includes the principal group as a sub-group, then the invariant theory of this group gives a definite kind of geometry, and every possible geometry can be obtained in this way.* Thus each geometry is characterized by its group, which, therefore, assumes the leading place in our considerations.

This principle has been completely carried through in the literature only for the first three cases of our outline. We shall devote some time to these as the most important or the best known, and we shall pay special attention to the passage from one of them to the other.

We shall adopt an order opposite to that just followed, and start with projective geometry, that is, with the G_{16} *of all projective transformations,* which we may write in the homogeneous form

$$
(1) \quad
\begin{cases}
\rho'\xi' = a_1\xi + b_1\eta + c_1\zeta + d_1\tau, \\
\rho'\eta' = a_2\xi + b_2\eta + c_2\zeta + d_2\tau, \\
\rho'\zeta' = a_3\xi + b_3\eta + c_3\zeta + d_3\tau, \\
\rho'\tau' = a_4\xi + b_4\eta + c_4\zeta + d_4\tau.
\end{cases}
$$

In order to get from this to the affine group, we begin with the remark that a projectivity is an affine transformation if it sends the plane at infinity into itself, i.e., if to every point with vanishing τ there corresponds a point with vanishing τ'. This will happen if $a_4 = b_4 = c_4 = 0$; hence, if we divide each of the equations (1) by $\rho'\tau'$ in order to get non-homogeneous equations, and replace $a_1 : d_4, \cdots$ simply by $a_1, \cdots$, we obtain

$$
(2) \quad
\begin{cases}
x' = a_1x + b_1y + c_1z + d_1, \\
y' = a_2x + b_2y + c_2z + d_2, \\
z' = a_3x + b_3y + c_3z + d_3.
\end{cases}
$$

These are, in fact, the old affine formulas: *The condition that the plane at infinity shall remain unchanged separates out of the projective G_{15} a twelve-parameter sub-group, namely, the affine group.*

Similarly, we obtain the *principal group G_7* by selecting out the projectivities (*or the affine transformations*) which leave invariant *not only the plane at infinity but also the imaginary spherical circle*, i.e., under which, to every point which satisfies the equations $\xi^2 + \eta^2 + \zeta^2 = 0$ and $\tau = 0$, there corresponds a point which satisfies the same equations. This assertion is easily verified. You need only bear in mind that our condition fixes, to within a constant factor, the six (homogeneous) constants of the conic which corresponds to the imaginary spherical circle by virtue of an affine transformation in the plane $\tau' = 0$. Hence it imposes upon the twelve constants of the affine transformation $6 - 1 = 5$ conditions, so that precisely the $12 - 5 = 7$ parameters of the G_7 remain.

This whole manner of viewing the subject was given an important turn by the great English geometer A. Cayley [1] in 1859. Whereas, up to this time, it had seemed that affine and projective geometry were poorer sections of metric geometry, Cayley made it possible, on the contrary, *to look upon affine geometry as well as metric geometry as special cases of projective geometry.* "*projective geometry is all geometry.*" This apparently paradoxical connection arises from the fact that one adjoins to the figures under investigation certain manifolds, namely, the *plane at infinity*, or, as the case may be, the imaginary *spherical circle* which lies in it; hence *the affine or the metric properties, respectively, of a figure are nothing but the projective properties of the figure thus extended.*

---

[1] In *A sixth memoir upon quantics*, Philosophical Transactions of the Royal Society of London, 1859 = *Collected Mathematical Papers*, vol. 2 (Cambridge, 1889), p. 561 et seq.

Let me illustrate this by two very simple examples, in which I shall present well-known facts in a somewhat altered form. The statement that two straight lines are parallel has no immediate meaning in projective geometry. However, if we add the plane at infinity to the given manifold (the two lines), we have the purely projective statement (see p. 92) that two given lines intersect on a given plane. We have a similar situation if a line is perpendicular to a plane. We can resolve this (see p. 122 et seq.) into a polar relation (a projective property) of the given figure extended by the addition of the imaginary spherical circle (see Fig. 98): The point trace P_∞ of the line and the line trace g_∞ of the plane, in the plane at infinity, are pole and polar with respect to the imaginary spherical circle.

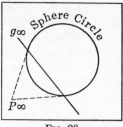

FIG. 98

I should like to carry out more fully the line of thought which I have indicated briefly here and show how it leads to a *completely systematic structure of geometry*. The greatest credit for this belongs to the English mathematicians. I have already mentioned Cayley. Next to him I should place J. J. Sylvester and G. Salmon of Dublin. These men, *beginning in* 1850, created the algebraic discipline which is called, in a narrower sense, *the invariant theory of linear homogeneous substitutions*,[1] and which, under the guidance of Cayley's principle, makes possible a complete *systematic structure of geometry on an analytic basis*. In order to understand this system, it will be necessary for us to devote a little time to the theory of invariants.

2. Digression on the Invariant Theory of Linear Substitutions

Of course, I shall be able to present only the main results and lines of thought, without going into details and proofs. As to the *literature* of this wide field, I refer you, above all, to the report by W. Franz Meyer: *Die Fortschritte der projectiven Invariantentheorie im letzten Vierteljahrhundert* in the first volume of *Jahresberichte der deutschen Mathematiker-Vereinigung* (1892), as well as to the report on *Invariantentheorie* in the *Enzyklopädie* by the same author (Enz. Bd. I B 2). All that is needed in the geometry of invariant theory especially is to be found in the textbooks of G. Salmon,[2] which have contributed most to spread the ideas which arise here. The German edition of Salmon's book by W. Fiedler has always enjoyed an

---

[1] The words "invariant theory" are used also in a wider sense with reference to arbitrary transformation groups. In the narrower sense, as we shall use them in these pages, they were first applied by Sylvester.

[2] *Analytic Geometry* I. *Conic Sections;* II. *Higher Plane Curves;* III. *Space;* IV. *Lectures on the Algebra of Linear Transformations.* German by W. Fiedler, Leipzig (Teubner). Each volume in several editions. [I newly edited by F. Dingeldey; III by K. Kommerell and A. Brill.]

unusually wide use. The lectures of A. Clebsch,[1] which Lindemann edited, are in the same category.

1. Going over now to our subject, let us think of any number of given variables, and let us speak, accordingly, of a *binary, ternary, quaternary,* . . . *region*. To enable us to consider the variables in the first three cases ultimately as homogeneous coordinates in a line, a plane, or in space, we designate them by the symbols

$$\xi, \tau; \qquad \xi, \eta, \tau; \qquad \xi, \eta, \zeta, \tau,$$

where $\tau = 0$ will always characterize the infinitely distant elements.

2. We consider the *groups of all homogeneous linear substitutions of these variables*. At present we shall have in mind not merely the ratios of the variables, as will be the case later in projective geometry, but also their individual values. We may write these substitutions in the form

$$
\begin{aligned}
&\xi' = a_1\xi + d_1\tau, \\
&\tau' = a_4\xi + d_4\tau;
\end{aligned}
\qquad
\begin{aligned}
&\xi' = a_1\xi + b_1\eta + d_1\tau, \\
&\eta' = a_2\xi + b_2\eta + d_2\tau, \\
&\tau' = a_4\xi + b_4\eta + d_4\tau;
\end{aligned}
\qquad
\begin{aligned}
&\xi' = a_1\xi + b_1\eta + c_1\zeta + d_1\tau, \\
&\eta' = a_2\xi + b_2\eta + c_2\zeta + d_2\tau, \\
&\zeta' = a_3\xi + b_3\eta + c_3\zeta + d_3\tau, \\
&\tau' = a_4\xi + b_4\eta + c_4\zeta + d_4\tau.
\end{aligned}
$$

The number of parameters in these three groups is 4, 9, and 16, respectively.

For convenience, we shall use habitually in the formulas only the variables ξ and τ, and we shall write out only the terms involving these two, with dots between them. If we are dealing then with the binary region, we simply ignore these dots; for the ternary and quaternary regions, we replace the dots by terms in η, or in η and ζ, analogous to terms already written out. In general, then, we speak of the variables $\xi, \cdots, \tau$ and of the linear substitutions in them

$$
(1) \qquad
\begin{cases}
\xi' = a_1\xi + \cdots + d_1\tau, \\
\quad\cdot\quad\cdot\quad\cdot\quad\cdot\quad\cdot\quad\cdot\quad\cdot \\
\tau' = a_4\xi + \cdots + d_4\tau.
\end{cases}
$$

3. As to the objects of the invariant theory, we shall consider the question in two different forms. In the first form we think of *any individual systems of values of the variables* $\xi_1, \cdots, \tau_1; \xi_2, \cdots, \tau_2; \xi_3, \cdots, \tau_3; \cdots$, which, in the spirit of geometry, we may designate outright as *points* $1, 2, 3, \cdots$. Each of these systems of values is subjected to the substitutions of the group (1), and we are concerned with *setting up combinations of our systems of values which remain invariant under these simultaneous substitutions*.

---

[1] *Vorlesungen über Geometrie*, edited by F. Lindemann, Leipzig (Teubner), 1st ed., 1876 et seq., 2nd ed., 1906 et seq.

4. The second form of the problem considers, in addition to such points, also *functions of the variables*, and, primarily, *rational integral functions*. We may confine ourselves, indeed, to *homogeneous* rational integral functions (called *forms*), since the terms of like dimension substitute as such, anyway, by reason of the homogeneity of the substitutions. Thus we shall consider the *linear forms*

$$\phi = \alpha\xi + \cdots + \delta\tau$$

the quadratic forms

$$f = A\xi^2 + \cdots + 2G\xi\tau + \cdots + K\tau^2$$

and so on. We can also examine simultaneously *several forms* of like dimension, in which case we distinguish them by indices, e.g.,

$$\phi_1 = \alpha_1\xi + \cdots + \delta_1\tau; \qquad \phi_2 = \alpha_2\xi + \cdots + \delta_2\tau; \qquad \cdots.$$

Similarly, we could start with *forms in several variables*, e.g., with the bilinear forms

$$f = A\xi_1\xi_2 + \cdots + \Delta\xi_1\tau_2 + \cdots + N\tau_1\xi_2 + \cdots + \Pi\tau_1\tau_2.$$

In order to make clear the general problem which arises here, we must first inquire *how the coefficients of these forms are transformed* when we subject the variables to the substitutions of the group (1) and prescribe that the value of the form ϕ or f shall remain unchanged. Considering first the linear form, let us place

$$\phi = \alpha\xi + \cdots + \delta\tau = \alpha'\xi' + \cdots + \delta'\tau'.$$

If we introduce for $\xi', \cdots, \tau'$ the expressions (1), we get, in the variables $\xi, \cdots, \tau$, the identities

$$\alpha\xi + \cdots + \delta\tau = \alpha'(a_1\xi + \cdots + d_1\tau) + \cdots + \delta'(a_4\xi + \cdots + d_4\tau)$$
$$= (\alpha'a_1 + \cdots + \delta'a_4)\xi + \cdots + (\alpha'd_1 + \cdots + \delta'd_4)\tau,$$

from which we obtain

$$(2) \qquad \begin{cases} \alpha = a_1\alpha' + \cdots + a_4\delta', \\ \cdots \cdots \cdots \cdots \cdots \\ \delta = d_1\alpha' + \cdots + d_4\delta'. \end{cases}$$

Thus the new coefficients $\alpha', \cdots, \delta'$ of the linear form are connected with the old $\alpha, \cdots, \delta$ by *another linear substitution*, which is related in a simple way to (1): the vertical and the horizontal rows in the array of coefficients are interchanged (the substitution is "transposed") and, furthermore, the places of the old (unaccented) and the new (accented) magnitudes are interchanged. This new substitution (2) is called *contragredient* to the original substitution (1) and we say, briefly, that the coefficients $\alpha, \cdots, \delta$ of a linear form are contragredient to the variables $\xi, \cdots, \tau$. The sets of variables $\xi_1, \cdots, \tau_1; \xi_2, \cdots, \tau_2; \cdots$, which are all subjected to the same substitution (1), are called, in analogous terminology, *cogredient variables*.

Going over now to the *quadratic form f*, let us inquire first how the quadratic terms $\xi^2, \cdots, \xi\tau, \cdots, \tau^2$ behave under the linear substitution (1). From (1), we find at once, for the quadratic terms of the new variables, the formulas

(3)
$$\begin{cases} \xi'^2 = a_1^2\xi^2 + \cdots + 2a_1d_1\xi\tau + \cdots + d_1^2\tau^2, \\ \cdots \cdots \cdots \cdots \cdots \cdots \cdots \\ \xi'\tau' = a_1a_4\xi^2 + \cdots + (a_1d_4 + a_4d_1)\xi\tau + \cdots + d_1d_4\tau^2, \\ \cdots \cdots \cdots \cdots \cdots \cdots \cdots \cdots \\ \tau'^2 = a_4^2\xi^2 + \cdots + 2a_4d_4\xi\tau + \cdots + d_4^2\tau^2. \end{cases}$$

We can express these relations briefly as follows. The quadratic terms of the variables undergo, simultaneously with the variables themselves, a homogeneous linear substitution which can be derived immediately from (1). Since *f* is a *linear* form in these quadratic terms, we infer, by repetition of the foregoing reasoning, that the *coefficients* $A, \cdots, 2G, \cdots, K$ *undergo a transformation which is linear and homogeneous, and which is, indeed, contragredient to the substitution* (3) *of the terms* $\xi^2, \cdots, \xi\tau, \cdots \tau^2$; i.e., the equations between $A, \cdots, 2G, \cdots, K$ and $A', \cdots, 2G', \cdots, K'$ are obtained from (3) just as (2) are from (1).

5. We can now formulate the *general problem of the theory of invariants*. Given any set of points $1, 2, \cdots$, and also certain linear, quadratic, or even higher forms $\phi_1, \phi_2, \cdots, f_1, f_2, \cdots$, then we mean by an *invariant* a function of the coordinates $\xi_1, \cdots, \tau_1; \xi_2, \cdots, \tau_2; \cdots$, and of the coefficients $\alpha_1, \cdots, \delta_1; \alpha_2, \cdots, \delta_2; \cdots; A_1, \cdots, K_1; A_2, \cdots, K_2; \cdots$, which remains unchanged under the linear substitutions (1) of the variables and the associated substitutions of the systems of coefficients which we have just determined. *The aggregate of all possible invariants is to be studied.*

The words *covariant* and *contravariant* are used sometimes for particular kinds of what are designated above in general as invariants. If the variables $\xi_1, \cdots, \tau_1; \xi_2, \cdots, \tau_2; \cdots$ themselves occur in the invariant expression, we speak of *covariants*, and if coefficients of linear forms $\alpha_1, \cdots, \delta_1; \alpha_2, \cdots, \delta_2; \cdots$ appear in it, we say *contravariant*. The word *invariant* is then confined to the expressions which contain neither such coordinates $\xi_1, \cdots$ nor coefficients $\alpha_1, \cdots$, but are made up only of coefficients of quadratic or higher forms. The reason why these two cases are emphasized and contrasted is that the sets of variables $\xi, \cdots, \tau$ on the one hand, and $\alpha, \cdots, \delta$ on the other, show a certain reciprocal behavior: if one of them undergoes a linear substitution, the other experiences the contragredient substitution, no matter with which set we start. Hence we can derive from every invariant expression of the one sort, by suitable rearrangement, a similar one of the other sort. As for the geometric interpretation, we have here obviously an expression of the *principle of duality*, for $\alpha, \cdots, \delta$ become homogeneous line or plane coordinates if we think of $\xi, \cdots, \tau$ as point coordinates. However, the distinction as to whether or not $\xi, \cdots, \tau$, or $\alpha, \cdots, \delta$, actually appear in the expressions in question has, of course, no fundamental significance. We shall, in general, from now on, use the word *invariant* in the wider sense.

6. We shall now define the notion of invariant more sharply in another direction, so as to make it possible to build up the theory in an orderly way. From now on, we shall think of invariants only as *rational functions of the coordinates and the coefficients* and which, moreover, are *homogeneous* in the coordinates of every point and in the coefficients of every form that occurs. We can express each such rational function as the *quotient of two integral rational homogeneous functions*, and we shall investigate these by themselves. Since a factor common to numerator and denominator does not alter the value of the quotient, these terms need not be invariants, in the sense thus far used, but may possibly take on a certain factor under each linear substitution.

It can be shown that this factor depends only on the coefficients of the substitution, and that it is necessarily a *power of the determinant of the substitution:*

$$r = \begin{vmatrix} a_1 \cdots d_1 \\ \cdots \cdots \\ a_4 \cdots d_4 \end{vmatrix}$$

We come thus finally to the *consideration of those rational integral homogeneous functions of the given sets of quantities* which, under linear substitution of the *variables and the coefficients (as we have set them up) are multiplied by a power r^λ of the determinant of the substitution*. These we call *relative invariants*, since the changes they undergo are always unessential and they remain entirely unchanged under all substitutions for which $r = 1$. The exponent λ is called the *weight of the invariant*. By contrast, we call that which we have heretofore designated as invariant an *absolute invariant*. *Thus every absolute invariant is the quotient of two relative invariants of the same weight.*

7. With this we have actually gained a *point of view for the systematization of the theory of invariants*. The simplest relative invariants will be polynomials of the *lowest possible degree* in the given sets of variables. Starting with them, we should ascend to those of higher degree. If j_1, j_2 are any two relative invariants, then every product of their powers $j_1^{\kappa_1} \cdot j_2^{\kappa_2}$ will also be a relative invariant. For, if the substitution brings to j_1 the factor r^{λ_1} and to j_2 the factor r^{λ_2}, then $j_1^{\kappa_1} \cdot j_2^{\kappa_2}$ will reproduce itself except for the factor

$r^{\kappa_1\lambda_1 + \kappa_2\lambda_2}$. If we now construct a sum of such terms, each multiplied by a constant factor

$$\sum_{(\kappa_1,\ \kappa_2,\ \ldots)} c_{\kappa_1,\ \kappa_2,\ \ldots} j_1^{\kappa_1} j_2^{\kappa_2} \ldots,$$

and if we make sure that the individual summands are all multiplied by the same power of r, i.e., that they all have the same weight (are "isobaric"), then we have again, obviously, a relative invariant of higher degree, since the factor of the individual terms can be placed before the summation sign.

The *central problem* of the theory of invariants is, naturally, the question as to whether or not we can always get *all* the invariants in this way. *What is, in each given case, the complete system of lowest invariants from which one can build up, rationally and integrally, in the way indicated, all relative invariants?* The principal theorem, however, is that *to every finite number of given quantities there is always a finite "complete invariant system," i.e., a finite number of invariants from which all others can be built up rationally and integrally.* The credit for these definitive results in the systematic theory of invariants goes to the German investigators P. Gordon and D. Hilbert. The memoir by Hilbert in volume 36 of the Mathematische Annalen [1] is especially noteworthy.

I shall now take up some simple examples, such as we shall use afterward in geometry, in order to make clear the abstract development which we have been considering. Here, of course, I shall give outlines rather than proofs.

1. Let us assume, first, that we have merely a *number of points in a binary region:*

$$\xi_1, \tau_1; \qquad \xi_2, \tau_2; \qquad \xi_3, \tau_3; \qquad \cdots.$$

Here we have the interesting theorem that *the simplest invariants are furnished by the two-rowed determinants which can be formed from these coordinates, and that these determinants constitute the complete invariant system.*

With two points 1 and 2, we can set up a two-rowed determinant

$$\Delta_{12} = \begin{vmatrix} \xi_1 & \tau_1 \\ \xi_2 & \tau_2 \end{vmatrix}.$$

This is actually an integral rational function of the variables, and is also homogeneous both in (ξ_1, τ_1) and (ξ_2, τ_2). We recognize the invariant nature of this determinant at once if we apply the rule for multiplying determinants to the calculation:

$$\Delta_{12}' = \begin{vmatrix} \xi_1'\tau_1' \\ \xi_2'\tau_2' \end{vmatrix} = \begin{vmatrix} a_1\xi_1 + d_1\tau_1, & a_4\xi_1 + d_4\tau_1 \\ a_1\xi_2 + d_1\tau_2, & a_4\xi_2 + d_4\tau_2 \end{vmatrix} = \begin{vmatrix} a_1 d_1 \\ a_4 d_4 \end{vmatrix} \cdot \begin{vmatrix} \xi_1\tau_1 \\ \xi_2\tau_2 \end{vmatrix} = r \cdot \Delta_{12}.$$

Thus the invariant has the *weight* 1.

[1] *Über die Theorie der algebraischen Formen*, vol. 36, p. 473 et seq., 1890.

In the same way, n points $1, 2, \cdots, n$ have altogether $n(n-1)/2$ invariants of weight 1:

$$\Delta_{ik} = \begin{vmatrix} \xi_i \tau_i \\ \xi_k \tau_k \end{vmatrix} \qquad (i, k = 1, 2, \cdots, n).$$

To prove that these determinants constitute the *complete* invariant system, i.e., that *every relative invariant of the n points can be expressed as a sum of isobaric terms:*

$$\Sigma C \cdot \Delta_{ik}^s \Delta_{lm}^t \cdots$$

would take us too far. We obtain the most general rational absolute invariants from the relative invariants, as quotients, where numerator and denominator are of equal weight; thus a simple example of an absolute invariant would be the quotient Δ_{ik}/Δ_{lm}.

In connection with this example, I should like to explain a finer abstraction which plays an important role in the theory, namely that of the *syzygy* (i.e., a coupling together, or connecting, of invariants). It can happen, namely, *that certain of those aggregates of the fundamental invariants vanish.* Thus we have, for example, with four points

$$\Delta_{12}\Delta_{34} + \Delta_{13}\Delta_{42} + \Delta_{14}\Delta_{23} = 0.$$

This amounts to nothing more than a known determinant identity, which we have used, in fact, on occasion (see p. 30). Such an identity between invariants of the complete system is called a *syzygy*. If we have several such syzygies, we can form new ones from them by multiplication and addition, and we may ask, as with determinants themselves, concerning the complete system of syzygies, out of which all the others can be formed in this way. The theory shows *that there is always a finite system of this sort.* In the case of four points, for example, this complete system consists of the single equation above, i.e., all identities obtaining between the six determinants $\Delta_{12}, \cdots,$ Δ_{34} are consequences of that one. In the case of five or more points, the complete system consists of all the equations of this type. Knowledge of these syzygies is, of course, of fundamental importance toward knowledge of the whole invariant system; for, if two isobaric aggregates of the simplest invariants differ by terms which have as a factor the left side of a syzygy, they are identical and do not need to be counted twice.

2. Similarly, *if we have single points in a ternary or quarternary region,* then the full invariant system consists, in precisely the same way, of the *three-rowed or four-rowed determinants formed from the coordinates.* In the ternary region, for example, the fundamental invariant of three points is again of weight 1:

$$\Delta_{123} = \begin{vmatrix} \xi_1 & \eta_1 & \tau_1 \\ \xi_2 & \eta_2 & \tau_2 \\ \xi_3 & \eta_3 & \tau_3 \end{vmatrix}.$$

I shall leave to you all the rest of the details; in particular, how the syzygies are set up here.

3. Let us now consider a *quadratic form*, in, say, a quartenary region:

$$f = A\xi^2 + 2B\xi\eta + C\eta^2 + 2D\xi\zeta + 2E\eta\zeta + F\zeta^2 + 2G\xi\tau + 2H\eta\tau \\ + 2J\zeta\tau + K\tau^2.$$

We can write down at once *one invariant* which depends only on the ten coefficients $A, \cdots, K$, namely, the *determinant*

$$\Delta = \begin{vmatrix} A & B & D & G \\ B & C & E & H \\ D & E & F & J \\ G & H & J & K \end{vmatrix}.$$

Since the coefficients $A, \cdots, K$ transform contragrediently to the quadratic terms in $\xi, \cdots, \tau$, it is easy to show that the *weight of this invariant* is -2: $\Delta' = r^{-2} \cdot \Delta$. *The full system of invariants formed alone from the coefficients of the form consists solely of this* Δ, i.e., *every* integral rational invariant which contains only $A, \cdots, K$ is a multiple of a power of Δ.

If we add now the *coordinates* ξ, η, ζ, τ of a point to the coefficients of the former, the *simplest common invariant*, or (according to the terminology mentioned above) *covariant*, is the form f itself; for the transformations of the coefficients $A, \cdots, K$ are completely determined by the prescription of their invariance. Thus *every given form is of course its own covariant.* Indeed, by definition, it is entirely unchanged under our substitutions and is therefore an invariant of weight 0, or an *absolute invariant.* Moreover, if we employ two points $\xi_1, \cdots, \tau_1$ and $\xi_2, \cdots, \tau_2$, there will appear, as new covariant, the so-called *polar form:*

$$A\xi_1\xi_2 + B(\xi_1\eta_2 + \xi_2\eta_1) + C\eta_1\eta_2 + \cdots + K\tau_1\tau_2,$$

whose *weight is again 0*, i.e., it is likewise *absolutely invariant.*

Finally, if we consider, simultaneously with f, *also a linear form ϕ*, i.e., the totality of its coefficients $\alpha, \beta, \gamma, \delta$, we obtain the following *simultaneous invariant of weight* -2 which arises from the determinant through the so-called process of "bordering" with $\alpha, \beta, \gamma, \delta$:

$$\begin{vmatrix} A & B & D & G & \alpha \\ B & C & E & H & \beta \\ D & E & F & J & \gamma \\ G & H & J & K & \delta \\ \alpha & \beta & \gamma & \delta & 0 \end{vmatrix}.$$

According to what precedes, we can also call it a *contravariant*. This determinant, as you know, plays an important role in analytic geometry. We recognize that the pure analytic process of forming invariants is fundamental here.

If we have two linear forms ϕ_1, ϕ_2, with coefficients $\alpha_1, \cdots, \delta_1$ and $\alpha_2, \cdots, \delta_2$, we obtain, by a "double bordering" of the same determinant, another *invariant*:

$$\begin{vmatrix} A & B & D & G & \alpha_1 & \alpha_2 \\ B & C & E & H & \beta_1 & \beta_2 \\ D & E & F & J & \gamma_1 & \gamma_2 \\ G & H & J & K & \delta_1 & \delta_2 \\ \alpha_1 & \beta_1 & \gamma_1 & \delta_1 & 0 & 0 \\ \alpha_2 & \beta_2 & \gamma_2 & \delta_2 & 0 & 0 \end{vmatrix},$$

which likewise has the *weight* -2.

These few statements must suffice to give you a glimpse of the broad field of the theory of invariants. An unusually extensive doctrine has been developed here, and much acumen has been exercised, especially in devising methods for setting up the complete system of invariants and the complete system of syzygies for a given fundamental form. Let me make just one more remark of a general character. In our examples, we have always reached our invariants by setting up determinants, and in this we find justification for the *theory of determinants as the foundation for the theory of invariants*. Because of this connection, Cayley originally used the name hyperdeterminants for invariants. It was Sylvester who introduced the word *invariant*. It is interesting to raise the question as to the importance, in the field of mathematics as a whole, which should be assigned to a particular chapter of it, let us say to determinants. Cayley once said to me, in conversation, that if he had to give fifteen lectures on the whole of mathematics, he would devote *one* of them to determinants. Reflect, if you will, whether, according to your experience, your appraisal of the value of the theory of determinants would be so high. I find that in my own elementary lectures, I have, for pedagogical reasons, pushed determinants more and more into the background. Too often I have had the experience that, while the students acquired facility with the formulas, which are so useful in abbreviating long expressions, they often failed to gain familiarity with their *meaning*, and skill in manipulation prevented the student from going into all the details of the subject and so gaining a mastery. Of course, in general considerations, and consequently here in the theory of invariants, determinants are indispensable.

We come now, at last, to our real object, to obtain, by the aid of these reflections, a systematization of geometry.

3. Application of Invariant Theory to Geometry

We begin by using the variables $\xi, \cdots, \tau$ to represent *ordinary rectangular non-homogeneous coordinates:* (ξ, τ) in the plane, (ξ, η, τ) in three-dimensional space, (ξ, η, ζ, τ) in four-dimensional space, etc. The linear homogeneous substitutions of invariant theory

(1)
$$\xi' = \alpha_1 \xi + \cdots + d_1 \tau,$$
$$\cdots \cdots \cdots \cdots$$
$$\tau' = \alpha_4 \xi + \cdots + d_4 \tau$$

represent then the *totality of affine transformations of the space under consideration with fixed origin of coordinates.* Each relative *invariant* itself will be a geometric magnitude which, to within a factor, remains unchanged by these affine transformations, i.e., *a magnitude which has a definite meaning in the affine geometry defined by these transformations.*

If, for example, in the *binary case,* i.e., in the *plane,* two points 1 and 2 are given, then, as we have seen, the *fundamental invariant* Δ_{12} *represents twice the area of the triangle* (012), provided with a suitable sign. In fact, it is known (see the analogous situation for space, p. 73) that an affine transformation merely multiplies the area of a triangle by the determinant of the substitution, and this means precisely that Δ_{12} is a relative invariant of weight 1. The quotient Δ_{12}/Δ_{34}, of two areas, remains absolutely unchanged, but so also does the *equation* $\Delta_{12} = 0$, since multiplication by a factor would have no significance in this equation. Actually, this equation has the absolutely invariant meaning, with respect to our affine transformation, that the three points 0, 1, 2 lie on a straight line.

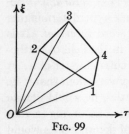

FIG. 99

If we have several points $1, 2, 3, 4, \cdots$ (see Fig. 99), their *complete invariant system* consists of all their determinants Δ_{ik}. Hence if it is possible to construct a quantity which is a rational integral function of the coordinates and which is relatively invariant under all affine transformations (1), i.e., *which has significance, at all, in our affine geometry,* it must be expressible as a *polynomial in the Δ_{ik}.* We can verify this at once geometrically in simple cases, e.g., every area in the plane, say that of the polygon (1, 2, 3, 4), is such an invariant, and the general formula which we gave earlier (p. 8) for the area of a polygon

$$(1, 2, 3, 4) = \Delta_{12} + \Delta_{23} + \Delta_{34} + \Delta_{41}$$

is actually nothing but the expression of the general theorem for this special case.

Finally let us consider the *syzygies* between the invariants. The fundamental syzygy

$$\Delta_{12}\Delta_{34} + \Delta_{13}\Delta_{42} + \Delta_{14}\Delta_{23} = 0$$

represents an identity between the areas of the six triangles formed by four arbitrary points and the origin, and therefore a general theorem of our affine geometry. Something similar holds, of course, for every syzygy. Conversely, every theorem of our affine geometry, insofar as it is a relation between invariants of the affine transformations (1), must be represented by a syzygy. Thus, according to our previous assertion (p. 141) about the *complete* system of syzygies in the case of four points, *all* the theorems of our affine geometry which are valid for a system of four points must follow from the one just given. In the same way, we can establish the correctness of the general assertion that *the theory of invariants permits the systematic enumeration of all possible magnitudes and theorems, without exception, since it supplies the complete system of invariants and syzygies.*

Again I shall refrain from carrying through this examination in detail. I mention merely that, along with points, one can consider also geometric manifolds determined by forms $\phi = \alpha\xi + \delta\tau, f = A\xi^2 + 2G\xi\tau + \kappa\tau^2, \cdots$. Such a form sets up a correspondence between each point of the plane and a number, i.e., it determines a *scalar field*. With this point of view, we can easily interpret geometrically the invariants of a given form, and each syzygy between the invariants will represent again a geometric theorem.

Alongside of what I may call the naive interpretation of invariant theory in geometry of n dimensions, which we have thus far considered, in which the n variables are thought of as rectangular coordinates, there is another *essentially different interpretation:* One can think of the variables *as homogeneous coordinates* in $(n-1)$-dimensional space R_{n-1}, whose non-homogeneous coordinates are $x = \xi/\tau, \cdots$, where a factor common to the n coordinates is unessential. We discussed earlier (p. 87 et seq.) the connection between the coordinates in R_{n-1} and R_n. We thought of R_{n-1} as the linear $(n-1)$-dimensional manifold $\tau = 1$ of R_n and projected its points by rays drawn from the origin of R_n. The aggregate, then, of all possible systems of values of the homogeneous coordinates of a point in R_{n-1} is identical with that of the coordinates of the points in R_n corresponding to it. Now the linear substitutions of the homogeneous variables in R_{n-1} represent *projective transformations.* Indeed, all substitutions of the form

$$\rho'\xi' = a_1\xi + \cdots + d_1\tau,$$
$$\cdots \cdots \cdots \cdots \cdots$$
$$\rho'\tau' = a_4\xi + \cdots + d_4\tau,$$

which differ from one another by an arbitrary factor ρ' produce one and the same projective change. The *group of all these projective transformations* contains not n_2 but only $n_2 - 1$ *arbitrary constants;* in R_2 and R_3, in particular, the number of such constants is 8 and 15, respectively.

If we wish, then, to interpret the theory of invariants of n variables $\xi, \cdots, \tau$ geometrically in the projective geometry of R_{n-1}, we must bear in mind, above all, that, just because we are using homogeneous coordinates, only those magnitudes and relations of the theory of invariants will be capable of interpretation which are *homogeneous of order zero* in the coordinates $\xi, \cdots, \tau$ of every point that occurs, and which have the same property also with respect to every system of coefficients of a linear, quadratic, or other form which may occur.

This will become clear if I carry it out in concrete *examples*. It will be sufficient to discuss the *binary field* ($n = 2$). We assume, then, two variables ξ and τ, and we think of $x = \xi/\tau$ as an *abscissa on the straight line.* If a series of systems of values (ξ_1, τ_1), (ξ_2, τ_2), $\cdots$, is given, we know that the determinants

$$\Delta_{ik} = \begin{vmatrix} \xi_i & \tau_i \\ \xi_k & \tau_k \end{vmatrix}, \qquad (i, k = 1, \cdots, p)$$

represent the complete system of fundamental invariants. Of all invariant statements, which ones have meaning in projective geometry? Among these is certainly not the statement that one of the Δ_{ik} has some definite numerical value, for if we multiply ξ_i, τ_i by a factor ρ, which would not change the point i, we multiply Δ_{ik} also by ρ. However, the vanishing of a Δ_{ik}, that is, the relation $\Delta_{ik} = 0$, has a meaning in projective geometry, for we can write it in the form $\xi_i/\tau_i = \xi_k/\tau_k$, so that actually only the ratios of the coordinates of the points appear, and the geometric significance—the *coincidence of the points i and k*—is evident.

In order, now, to get a *numerical invariant* which is itself of dimension zero in the coordinates of each point, we must combine more than two points. Trial shows that we need at least four points 1, 2, 3, 4, in which case each quotient of the form

$$\frac{\Delta_{12} \cdot \Delta_{34}}{\Delta_{14} \cdot \Delta_{32}}$$

is homogeneous of dimension zero in each of the four pairs of variables (ξ_1, τ_1), $\cdots$, (ξ_4, τ_4). It follows from this that its weight is 0, i.e., it is an *absolute invariant*. This quantity has, then, a projective meaning and represents a numerical value which is invariant under all projective transformations of the line. It is, of course, nothing other than the *cross ratio* of the four points written in a definite order. For it can be written, in non-homogeneous coordinates, in the form

$$\frac{x_1 - x_2}{x_1 - x_4} : \frac{x_3 - x_2}{x_3 - x_4}.$$

From the standpoint of the theory of invariants, we obtain the cross ratio of four points as the simplest invariant of a point range on the line which satisfies the homogeneity condition that is necessary in order that the invariant have a meaning in projective geometry.

I should like to add here a general remark. For many years I have thought about the widespread tendency in projective geometry to resolve all magnitudes which exhibit invariant character back to cross ratios. From the standpoint which we have reached, we can pronounce the judgment that such an effort only makes it more difficult to gain a deeper insight into the structure of projective geometry. It is better to begin with a search for all rational integral (relative) invariants and to form from them, first, the rational invariants, especially the absolute ones, and among these again those which satisfy the homogeneity condition of projective geometry. In this way we follow a systematic procedure which progresses from the simplest to the more complex. This procedure is obscured if we place in the foreground a special rational invariant, the cross ratio, and try to form the other invariants exclusively from it.

Let us now see to what kind of theorems of projective geometry the *syzygies* between the invariants Δ_{ik} give rise. Starting from the fundamental syzygy

$$\Delta_{12}\Delta_{34} + \Delta_{13}\Delta_{42} + \Delta_{14}\Delta_{23} = 0,$$

dividing through by the last summand of the left side, and noting that $\Delta_{23} = -\Delta_{32}$, and $\Delta_{24} = -\Delta_{42}$, we get

$$\frac{\Delta_{12}\Delta_{34}}{\Delta_{14}\Delta_{32}} = 1 - \frac{\Delta_{13}\Delta_{24}}{\Delta_{14}\Delta_{23}} .$$

Here we have, on the left, the cross ratio of the points 1, 2, 3, 4, according to the original definition. On the right, we have the cross ratio of the same points formed in the same way after the order of 2 and 3 has been changed. The cross ratios in still other orders are obtained if we divide by other terms. *Thus the fundamental syzygies between the invariants of four points find their geometric meaning in the known relations between the six values which their cross ratio can take according to the order in which the four points are taken.*

I shall not go any farther here in showing how the projective geometry of the straight line is built up on this foundation and how, in like manner, the *interpretation of the ternary and quaternary theory of invariants in the projective geometry of the plane and of space* proceeds. You will find that set forth in detail in, for example, the books of Salmon-Fiedler and Clebsch-Lindemann, already mentioned, where precisely this interpretation of the theory of invariants is used continually. There arises thus a *self-contained complete development of projective geometry*, not only with respect to the magnitudes which one can consider in it (corresponding to the invariants), but also with respect to the theorems which can be set up (corresponding to the syzygies). To be sure, this interpretation is less satisfying for the student of invariants than it is for the geometrician. For the former, the interpretation given in the study of affine geometry of R_{n+1} is more valuable, since in R_n only those invariants and syzygies are useful which satisfy the homogeneity condition, as we have seen.

I should like to consider in more detail one especially important point, in order to resume the discussion which we interrupted earlier (p. 135). I should like to show how the Cayley principle makes it possible by use of the theory of invariants to classify affine and metric geometry in the scheme of projective geometry.

4. The Systematization of Affine and Metric Geometry Based on Cayley's Principle

We are concerned here with *general* affine geometry, where we do not assume a special fixed point, the origin of coordinates, as was the case when the complete interpretation of the theory of invariants was first discussed.

We start at once, in three-dimensional space, with the non-homogeneous coordinates x, y, z or, as the case may be, with the homogeneous coordinates ξ, η, ζ, τ. Then the Cayley principle states that *affine* geometry or *metric* geometry arises from projective geometry when we adjoin to the given manifold the *plane at infinity*, $\tau = 0$, or this plane and also the *imaginary spherical circle* $\tau = 0$, $\xi^2 + \eta^2 + \tau^2 = 0$, respectively.

A *remark about the imaginary spherical circle* will simplify the following discussion. We have defined it here by two equations, as the intersection of the plane at infinity with a cone through the origin. But we can determine it, or, in fact, any conic, by *one equation in plane coordinates*, if we think of it as the *envelope* of all the planes which touch it. If, as before, we denote the "plane coordinates," i.e., the coefficients of a linear form ϕ, by $\alpha, \beta, \gamma, \delta$, then, as is easily verified, the equation of the imaginary spherical circle is $\alpha^2 + \beta^2 + \gamma^2 = 0$. In other words, this equation is the condition that the plane $\alpha\xi + \cdots + \delta\tau = 0$ shall be tangent to the imaginary spherical circle.

It is now easy to understand the transition by means of the theory of invariants to affine and to metric geometry, respectively. To the given systems of values—point coordinates, linear and quadratic forms, etc.—which describe the configuration under discussion, we add the *definite linear form* τ (i.e., the system of coefficients 0, 0, 0, 1), or *the quadratic form* $\alpha^2 + \beta^2 + \gamma^2$, *written in plane coordinates*, respectively. If, just as before, we treat the system of forms thus extended, i.e., if we set up the *full system of its invariants and of the syzygies between these*, and emphasize those among them which satisfy the *condition of homogeneity*, we obtain *all of the concepts and all of the theorems of affine and of metric geometry, respectively, of the elements originally given.* The development by means of the theory of invariants is thus carried over to affine and to metric geometry. I should like again to call your attention (see p. 147) to the fact that, by emphasizing in particular the forming of *rational integral* invariants and syzygies, a systematizing point of view comes into geometry which otherwise is not brought clearly to light.

Instead of talking abstractly about this, I prefer to make these relations clear at once by means of *simple examples* by showing how we can represent the most elementary fundamental magnitudes of affine and metric geometry as simultaneous invariants of the given systems of magnitudes and of the forms τ and $\alpha^2 + \beta^2 + \gamma^2$, respectively.

To start with, I choose from *affine geometry*, as an example, the *volume T of the tetrahedron formed by four points*, which, as you know, is expressed by the formula

$$T = \frac{1}{6}\begin{vmatrix} x_1 & y_1 & z_1 & 1 \\ x_2 & y_2 & z_2 & 1 \\ x_3 & y_3 & z_3 & 1 \\ x_4 & y_4 & z_4 & 1 \end{vmatrix} = \frac{1}{6\tau_1\tau_2\tau_3\tau_4}\begin{vmatrix} \xi_1 & \eta_1 & \zeta_1 & \tau_1 \\ \xi_2 & \eta_2 & \zeta_2 & \tau_2 \\ \xi_3 & \eta_3 & \zeta_3 & \tau_3 \\ \xi_4 & \eta_4 & \zeta_4 & \tau_4 \end{vmatrix}.$$

Let us inquire to what extent this expression has the asserted invariant property. In the first place, we know that this determinant is actually the fundamental relative invariant of four points (p. 141). Moreover, we find, in the denominator for these four points, the values of the linear form τ which we adjoined to our configuration, and these are the very simplest (absolute) invariants that can be constructed by the use of a form (p. 142). This means, of course, that, after a transformation, those values of the form into which the linear form τ goes over are to be written in the denominator, or that, if we adjoin in general the form $\alpha\xi + \beta\eta + \gamma\zeta + \delta\tau$, the product of the four values of this form for the points $1, \cdots, 4$ is to go into the denominator. *Thus T is itself also a rational invariant* and, indeed, it is homogeneous of dimension zero in the coordinates of each of the four points. To be sure, T has the dimension -4 with respect to the coefficients of our adjoined linear form $0, 0, 0, 1$ (or $\alpha, \beta, \gamma, \delta$, as the case may be) which appear in the denominator. Hence, since a common factor of these magnitudes is arbitrary, the absolute value of T can have no meaning in the projective geometry of our extended figure. In fact, there is also no way of assigning a definite numerical value to the volume of a tetrahedron in affine geometry, unless we have already selected a unit segment or a unit tetrahedron, as we always did when we were using non-homogeneous coordinates. But this would mean, from our present general point of view, that we should add to our figure other elements beside the "infinitely distant plane" $\tau = 0$. If we adjoin a fifth point, for example, and take the *quotient* of two expressions analogous to T, we have actually an expression that satisfies all of the conditions of homogeneity. This expression must be, then, an *absolute invariant* of affine geometry. The single expression T is only a *relative* invariant of *weight* 1, as indeed we learned earlier (see p. 73).

At this point we should refer again to the *developments of the first main part*, the essential meaning of which now appears more clearly. We recognized in our special study of affine transformations (see p. 72 et seq.) that the Grassmann elementary magnitudes of geometry which we deduced there belong entirely to affine geometry. The *Grassmann determinant principle*, however, which supplied those magnitudes, is by no means a haphazard device. To the contrary, as we can now see, it is a thoroughly *natural application of the theory of invariants in affine geometry*, i.e., projective geometry under adjunction of the plane at infinity. The appearance of the ordinary determinants—segment, area, volume—is sufficiently explained by the example just discussed. It remains to be shown how the development by the theory of invariants leads to the general Grassmann elements defined by the minors of *rectangular matrices*. That, again, will be made clear by means of an example. Given two points (ξ_1, η_1, τ_1) and (ξ_2, η_2, τ_2) in a plane, we wish to find the equivalent in the theory of invariants of the manifolds of affine geometry (line-segment, straight line, $\cdots$) which belong to them. This falls into orderly agreement with earlier results if we add a third "undetermined" point (ξ, η, τ) and consider again the fundamental invariant

$$\frac{1}{\tau\tau_1\tau_2} \begin{vmatrix} \xi & \eta & \tau \\ \xi_1 & \eta_1 & \tau_1 \\ \xi_2 & \eta_2 & \tau_2 \end{vmatrix}$$

as a linear form in ξ, η, τ. The three coefficients of these variables, that is, the determinants of the matrix

$$\frac{1}{\tau_1\tau_2} \begin{vmatrix} \xi_1 & \eta_1 & \tau_1 \\ \xi_2 & \eta_2 & \tau_2 \end{vmatrix} \quad \text{or} \quad \begin{vmatrix} x_1 & y_1 & 1 \\ x_2 & y_2 & 1 \end{vmatrix},$$

are thus the characteristic magnitudes for the newly defined manifold, and *we have actually been led precisely to the matrix which was used earlier to define the line-segment* 1 2. In exactly the same way, in space, we can set up, from three or from two points, by adjoining one or two quadruples of undetermined coordinates, respectively, a relatively invariant linear or bilinear form, whose coefficients then supply the coordinates of a plane-segment or a space line-segment, in entire agreement with our old definition. I cannot amplify these suggestions with further details; they will perhaps suffice as a first orientation and as a stimulation to further study.

Now that we have found an ordered place in the theory of invariants for the principle of Grassmann, it is important to raise the question as to its usefulness. In this connection, we should compare it especially with that principle of classification which was stated (p. 25 et seq.) for the particular case of the principal group, and which yielded for us there all the fundamental geometric manifolds. The appropriate extension of the principle of classification to the case of an arbitrary linear transformation group is obvious. According to it, we shall consider, in each "geometry," alongside of the *single* integral rational functions of the given series of magnitudes (coordinates, form coefficients, etc.) which thus far have furnished the invariants, also *systems* of such functions $\Xi_1, \Xi_2, \cdots$. If such a system is transformed into itself under all the substitutions of the pertinent group concerned, i.e., if the similarly formed functions $\Xi_1', \Xi_2', \cdots$ of the transformed series of magnitudes are expressed linearly in terms of $\Xi_1, \Xi_2, \cdots$ alone, with the aid of coefficients which arise in a definite and unique manner from those of the fundamental transformation, we say *that the system defines a manifold of the geometry in question.* The separate functions of which the system consists are called the *components* of the manifold. The property which determines the nature of a geometric manifold is the behavior of its components under the transformations of the group under consideration. Two geometric manifolds are said to be of the *same sort* when their components form two series of the same number of expressions, each of which, under change of coordinates, undergoes the *same* linear substitution, that is, they are *cogredient*, according to our earlier terminology. If the system which defines a geometric manifold consists of a single function, the linear substitution reduces to a multiplication by a factor, and the function is a relative invariant.

I shall make this abstract situation clear by means of a simple example from the invariant theory of the ternary field, which we shall interpret in the affine geometry of three-dimensional space with a fixed origin. If two points (ξ_1, η_1, τ_1) and (ξ_2, η_2, τ_2) are given, then the simplest system of functions in which both coordinate triples appear homogeneously and symmetrically is the system of nine bilinear terms

$$(1) \qquad \xi_1\xi_2, \, \xi_1\eta_2, \, \xi_1\tau_2, \, \eta_1\xi_2, \cdots, \tau_1\tau_2.$$

Under a linear transformation, in our customary notation (see p. 136), we get:

$$(2) \quad \begin{cases} \xi_1'\xi_2' = a_1^2\xi_1\xi_2 \ + a_1b_1(\xi_1\eta_2 + \eta_1\xi_2) \ + \cdots + d_1^2\tau_1\tau_2, \\ \xi_1'\eta_2' = a_1a_2\xi_1\xi_2 + a_1b_2\xi_1\eta_2 \ + a_2b_1\eta_1\xi_2 + \cdots + d_1d_2\tau_1\tau_2, \\ \cdot\ \cdot\ \cdot\ \cdot\ \cdot\ \cdot\ \cdot\ \cdot\ \cdot\ \cdot\ \cdot\ \cdot\ \cdot\ \cdot\ \cdot\ \cdot\ \cdot\ \cdot\ \cdot \\ \cdot\ \cdot\ \cdot\ \cdot\ \cdot\ \cdot\ \cdot\ \cdot\ \cdot\ \cdot\ \cdot\ \cdot\ \cdot\ \cdot\ \cdot\ \cdot\ \cdot\ \cdot\ \cdot \\ \tau_1'\tau_2' = a_4^2\xi_1\xi_2 \ + a_4b_4(\xi_1\eta_2 + \eta_1\xi_2) \ + \cdots + d_4^2\tau_1\tau_2, \end{cases}$$

i.e., these nine magnitudes form, in fact, a system of the sort just discussed. We shall look upon them as the determining elements of a manifold of our affine geometry. Such a manifold, and likewise any other system consisting of nine magnitudes which transform according to the equations (2), is called a *tensor*.

Upon examining equations (2), we notice that we can derive from the nine quantities (1), on the one hand six, and on the other hand three, simple linear combinations which are transformed into themselves under a linear substitution. Indeed, if we arrange the quantities (1) into a quadratic system

$$\begin{matrix} \xi_1\xi_2 & \xi_1\eta_2 & \xi_1\tau_2, \\ \eta_1\xi_2 & \eta_1\eta_2 & \eta_1\tau_2, \\ \tau_1\xi_2 & \tau_1\eta_2 & \tau_1\tau_2, \end{matrix}$$

the first set is the sums of the terms symmetric to the diagonal:

(3) $2\xi_1\xi_2, \quad \xi_1\eta_2 + \eta_1\xi_2, \quad \xi_1\tau_2 + \tau_1\xi_2, \quad \cdots, \quad 2\tau_1\tau_2,$

and the other is their differences:

(4) $\xi_1\eta_2 - \eta_1\xi_2, \quad \xi_1\tau_2 - \tau_1\xi_2, \quad \eta_1\tau_2 - \tau_1\eta_2.$

The substitution formulas for the systems (3) and (4) come immediately from equations (2). Thus we have secured two new manifolds for our affine geometry, of which the one, made up of the six magnitudes (3), is called a *symmetric tensor*, while that consisting of the three magnitudes (4) is the *plane-segment* already known to us. The name applies, of course, to any system of magnitudes which are transformed cogrediently. We shall consider directly the justification for the adjective "symmetric."

As to the geometric meaning of the three quantities (4), we know (see p. 29) that they are twice the projections upon the coordinate planes of the triangles formed by the points (ξ_1, η_1, τ_1) and (ξ_2, η_2, τ_2), and the origin of coordinates, each triangle contour being traversed in a suitable sense. We have here precisely one of the first manifolds which the Grassmann determinant principle yielded. Hence we may enunciate the following theorem. *The systematic search for manifolds of affine geometry by means of our principle of classification leads necessarily, among other things, to the Grassmann determinant principle and to the geometric manifolds determined by its use.* Of course, I cannot carry this out here in detail. It will suffice to state that all the manifolds can be derived which we discussed earlier if we treat the general affine geometry in a similar way by means of Cayley's principle, by means of the quaternary invariant theory (see p. 148 et seq.).

The important result of our examination, however, is the knowledge that *the Grassmann determinant principle is something special, and, in itself, does not at all yield all the manifolds of affine geometry.* We have, rather, in the tensors (1) and (3) *essentially new geometric magnitudes.*

Because of the great significance which these manifolds have for many fields of physics, as, for example, for the theory of elastic deformation and for the theory of relativity, I shall discuss them briefly. Above all, I shall make some remarks concerning the names of these quantities, which should help the reader to orient himself in the newer literature on tensor calculus.

I used the word *tensor* in volume 1 of this work, when I was discussing Hamilton's quaternion calculus, in a sense different from that which we are now using. If $q = a + bi + cj + dk$ is a quaternion, we called the expression $T = \sqrt{a^2 + b^2 + c^2 + d^2}$ its tensor. This name, introduced by Hamilton, is justified, since one can interpret multiplication by a quaternion, geometrically, as a rotation and a stretching, with a fixed origin, as we explained fully in volume 1 (p. 65 et seq.). The measure of the stretching turns out to be precisely the square root T which we called the tensor. W. Voigt, in his work on the physics of crystals,[1] used the word *tensor* in a manner closely related to this. Voigt denotes by it directed magnitudes which correspond to events, such as the longitudinal stretching or compression of a rod, at the ends of which pulls or pushes are applied in the direction of the axis of the rod, but in opposite senses. We could represent such a tensor pictorially by a segment which carries at its ends arrowheads oppositely directed (see Fig. 100).

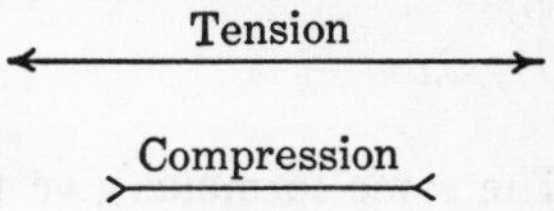

Tension

Compression

FIG. 100

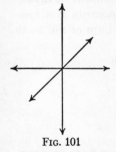

FIG. 101

We could designate the directional character of a tensor, thus understood, as "two-sided," and that of a vector, by contrast, as "one-sided." Such tensors arise often in physics as *tensor triples*, i.e., three of them at right angles to one another (see Fig. 101). We mentioned earlier (see p. 75) a pure strain (pure affine transformation) as a uniform stretching of space in three mutually orthogonal directions, with a fixed origin. Instead of this, we can say now that a pure strain is represented geometrically by a tensor triple. We reach a commonly used meaning of the word *tensor* if we think of the concept of those three stretchings of space as a single geometric quantity, and, dropping the word *triple*, call *this* magnitude a tensor. The tensor notion in this sense is precisely what we called above a "symmetric tensor."

In fact, a pure strain, with a fixed origin, is given by substitutions of the following form

$$(5) \quad \begin{cases} \xi = a_{11}x + a_{12}y + a_{13}z, \\ \eta = a_{12}x + a_{22}y + a_{23}z, \\ \tau = a_{13}x + a_{23}y + a_{33}z. \end{cases} \quad (a_{ik} = a_{ki}).$$

[1] See, for example, (a) *Der gegenwärtige Stand unserer Kenntnisse der Kristallelastizität;* (b) *Über die Parameter der Kristallphysik und über gerichtete Grössen höherer Ordnung.* Both memoires in the Göttinger Nachrichten 1900.

Let us interpret the number triples (x, y, z) and (ξ, η, τ) as point coordinates in one and the same rectangular coordinate system. The array of the coefficients of the transformation is symmetrical with respect to the principal diagonal. If we go over now to a new rectangular coordinate system with the same origin, we obtain, as a simple calculation shows, the following new representation for the strain in question:

$$(6) \qquad \begin{cases} \xi' = a'_{11}x' + a'_{12}y' + a'_{13}z', \\ \eta' = a'_{12}x' + a'_{22}y' + a'_{23}z', \\ \tau' = a'_{13}x' + a'_{23}y' + a'_{33}z'. \end{cases} \qquad (a'_{ik} = a'_{ki}).$$

The same formulas give the relations between x, y, z and x', y', z' as between ξ, η, τ and ξ', η', τ'. For the six coefficients $a_{11}, a'_{12}, \cdots, a_{33}$ it turns out that

1. They depend linearly upon the six coefficients $a_{11}, a_{12}, \cdots, a_{33}$, and upon these only, i.e., *they define a geometric magnitude.*

2. They transform precisely as do the expressions (3), bilinear in the coordinates, which we designated on page 152 as the components of a *symmetric tensor.* The adjective *symmetric* is justified by the form of the array of coefficients in the transformation formulas (5) and (6).

Let us now go over to the general affine transformation

$$(7) \qquad \begin{cases} \xi = a_{11}x + a_{12}y + a_{13}z, \\ \eta = a_{21}x + a_{22}y + a_{23}z, \\ \tau = a_{31}x + a_{32}y + a_{33}z, \end{cases}$$

where the origin is fixed. Then it develops, in a manner corresponding precisely to that just indicated, that in the geometry of the orthogonal transformations the nine coefficients $a_{11}, a_{12}, \cdots, a_{33}$ transform precisely as do the coordinate products (1); hence they form the components of a magnitude of the same sort. This means, in our terminology, according to which the word *tensor* is not restricted specially to pure strains, that the array of coefficients of a general affine transformation is a tensor.

A large number of other names for this concept are to be found in the literature. Some of the most common are the following.

1. *Affinor* (because of the connection with the affine transformation).

2. *Linear vector function* [since the linear substitutions (7) can be so interpreted that, by means of them, to a vector x, y, z, starting from the origin, another similar vector ξ, η, τ will be placed in linear correspondence].

3. *Dyad* and *dyadic.* However, the first of these two words is used originally only for a particular case, to be explained later.

The components of the plane-segment (4) also can be regarded as the co-efficients of a transformation, namely one of the type

(8)
$$\begin{cases} \xi = & 1 \cdot x - c \cdot y + b \cdot z, \\ \eta = & c \cdot x + 1 \cdot y - a \cdot z, \\ \tau = & -b \cdot x + a \cdot y + 1 \cdot z. \end{cases}$$

Indeed, it is easy to show that the coefficients of this substitution behave, under rectangular coordinate transformation, as do the bilinear expressions (4). Because of the structure of the array of coefficients in (8) (symmetry with respect to the main diagonal along with change of sign), the magnitude determined by it is also called an *antisymmetric tensor*.

Geometrically, the formulas (7) can be interpreted as a general homogeneous deformation, the formulas (6) as a pure deformation (without rotation), and the formulas (8) as an *infinitesimal* rotation. The *decomposition of a homogeneous infinitesimal deformation into a pure deformation and a rotation corresponds thus perceptually to the formal process (p. 151) in which we derived the symmetric tensor (3) and the antisymmetric tensor (4) from the coordinate products (1).*

Thus far, in changing the coordinate system, we have confined ourselves to orthogonal transformations. It remains to complete this for the case in which we pass from the rectangular to oblique coordinates, or, indeed, where both (ξ, η, τ) and (x, y, z) are, at the start, introduced as oblique parallel coordinates. We shall continue to think of the origin of coordinates as fixed. In making this change, we pass from the geometry of the principal group to that of the affine group. When we examine, for this group, the behavior of the substitution coefficients under transformation of the coordinates, it turns out that, although they again represent the components of a geometric magnitude, they are transformed, not as are the coordinate products (1), but contragrediently to them. The coefficients of (6) and (8) behave in a corresponding way. It can be shown that the same tensor (for example the same homogeneous deformation) with respect to a parallel coordinate system can be given by components of the sort (1), as also by such components as the coefficients of (7). The former are called *cogredient*, the latter are called *contragredient* components of the tensor. Instead of *cogredient* and *contragredient*, the terms *contravariant* and *covariant* are often used. Sometimes the last two expressions are interchanged in meaning. The difference between the two kinds of components is the same as that between point and plane coordinates.

Another meaning of the word *tensor*, and one that is much more general than the one we have favored, will become clear if we study the behavior of homogeneous forms under a change of coordinates. On page 138, we carried through this investigation for the case of a quadratic form

$$a_{11}\xi^2 + 2a_{12}\xi\eta + \cdots + a_{33}\tau^2,$$

using a somewhat different notation. We found that the form coefficients $a_{11}, 2a_{12}, \cdots, a_{33}$ transform linearly, homogeneously, and contragrediently to the terms $\xi^2, \xi\eta, \cdots, \tau^2$ of the point coordinates. The latter, however, transform cogrediently to the expressions (3), as it is easy to see. We can announce this result as follows. The coefficients $a_{11}, 2a_{12}, \cdots, a_{33}$ of a quadratic form are the contragredient components and the terms $\xi^2, \xi\eta, \cdots, \tau^2$ are the cogredient components, of a symmetric tensor. A corresponding result holds for a bilinear form. Of the latter, we may say, with Gibbs, that it forms a *dyad* when it can be written as a product of two linear forms. Finally if we have *a homogeneous n-tuple linear form* of the point coordinates, we can show, by a slight calculation, that its coefficients likewise substitute linearly and homogeneously under transformation of coördinates, and, indeed, contragrediently to the terms of the point coordinates.

The generalization of the tensor notion, which we have discussed, consists in calling every such magnitude a tensor, using this name not merely, as we did before, in connection with bilinear forms. It is in this general form that the name is used, in particular, by Einstein and his followers. In the older terminology it was customary to speak rather of linear, quadratic, bilinear, trilinear, cubic, etc., *forms*.

Along with this variety in terminology, there appears the tendency, in practice, to denote the system of components of a tensor by a *single* letter, and to indicate calculations with tensors, when they arise, by means of symbolic combinations of the letters. All these things are in themselves essentially very simple; if they seem difficult to the reader, it is only because different writers use different notations. The same unfortunate situation arises here that we mentioned when we were discussing the vector calculus, but here it is greatly exaggerated. However, it seems impossible to get rid of the confusion. We could not refrain from mentioning it, since the whole modern literature is controlled by it.

Let us now turn to *metric geometry* in order to select there a few characteristic examples. I shall show how the two most important fundamental notions "*distance r between two points* $x_1 = \xi_1/\tau_1, \cdots$, and $x_2 = \xi_2/\tau_2, \cdots$," as well as "*angle ω between two planes* $\alpha_1, \cdots, \delta_1$ and $\alpha_2, \cdots, \delta_2$" can be derived from the systematic procedure of the theory of invariants. From the well-known formulas of analytic geometry, we have

$$r = \sqrt{(x_1 - x_2)^2 + (y_1 - y_2)^2 + (z_1 - z_2)^2}$$
$$= \sqrt{\frac{(\xi_1\tau_2 - \xi_2\tau_1)^2 + (\eta_1\tau_2 - \eta_2\tau_1)^2 + (\zeta_1\tau_2 - \zeta_2\tau_1)^2}{\tau_1^2\tau_2^2}},$$
$$\omega = \arccos\left(\frac{\alpha_1\alpha_2 + \beta_1\beta_2 + \gamma_1\gamma_2}{\sqrt{(\alpha_1^2 + \beta_1^2 + \gamma_1^2)(\alpha_2^2 + \beta_2^2 + \gamma_2^2)}}\right)$$

These are algebraic and transcendental functions, respectively, of the parameter. We may call them *"algebraic"* and *"transcendental" invariants*, respectively, if we show that the rational integral parts of which they are formed are themselves invariants in the old sense.

We start with the angle ω. The figure, whose invariant it should be, consists of the two linear forms $\alpha_1, \beta_1, \gamma_1, \delta_1$ and $\alpha_2, \beta_2, \gamma_2, \delta_2$, and the quadratic form in plane coordinates

$$\alpha^2 + \beta^2 + \gamma^2 + 0 \cdot \delta^2,$$

which represents the imaginary spherical circle. We can of course construct invariants from this quadratic form in plane coordinates, just as we did earlier (p. 142 et seq.) from forms in point coordinates, by always interchanging point and plane coordinates ("dualizing"). In particular, the values of the form for the two given systems of values

$$\alpha_1^2 + \beta_1^2 + \gamma_1^2 + 0 \cdot \delta_1^2 \quad \text{and} \quad \alpha_2^2 + \beta_2^2 + \gamma_2^2 + 0 \cdot \delta_2^2$$

and also the value of the polar form constructed for these two systems

$$\alpha_1\alpha_2 + \beta_1\beta_2 + \gamma_1\gamma_2 + 0 \cdot \delta_1\delta_2$$

are all invariant. It is precisely out of these expressions that $\cos \omega$ is actually constructed. Furthermore, $\cos \omega$ is *homogeneous of dimension zero* in each of the two systems $\alpha_1, \cdots, \delta_1$ and $\alpha_2, \cdots, \delta_2$, and likewise in the coefficients 1, 1, 1, 0 of the given quadratic form, so that the expression has an independent meaning in metric geometry. There is, in fact, in metric geometry, an absolute angle measure which is independent of the arbitrary choice of the unit. This amounts to saying that our expression is an *absolute invariant*.

Next, as to the *distance r*, we recall that we constructed invariants of a quadratic form in point coordinates by bordering its determinant with the coordinates of one or of two planes (see p. 144 et seq.). In the same way we shall now obtain invariants for our figure, which consists of a quadratic form in plane coordinates and two points, if, proceeding precisely in a dual manner, we border the determinant of the form $\alpha^2 + \beta^2 + \gamma^2 + 0 \cdot \delta^2$:

$$\begin{vmatrix} 1 & 0 & 0 & 0 \\ 0 & 1 & 0 & 0 \\ 0 & 0 & 1 & 0 \\ 0 & 0 & \text{-}0 & 0 \end{vmatrix}$$

once and twice with the coordinates $\xi_1, \cdots, \tau_1$ and $\xi_2, \cdots, \tau_2$ of the given points. From the determinants thus obtained we form the quotient

$$\begin{vmatrix} 1 & 0 & 0 & 0 & \xi_1 & \xi_2 \\ 0 & 1 & 0 & 0 & \eta_1 & \eta_2 \\ 0 & 0 & 1 & 0 & \zeta_1 & \zeta_2 \\ 0 & 0 & 0 & 0 & \tau_1 & \tau_2 \\ \xi_1 & \eta_1 & \zeta_1 & \tau_1 & 0 & 0 \\ \xi_2 & \eta_2 & \zeta_2 & \tau_2 & 0 & 0 \end{vmatrix} : \left\{ \begin{vmatrix} 1 & 0 & 0 & 0 & \xi_1 \\ 0 & 1 & 0 & 0 & \eta_1 \\ 0 & 0 & 1 & 0 & \zeta_1 \\ 0 & 0 & 0 & 0 & \tau_1 \\ \xi_1 & \eta_1 & \zeta_1 & \tau_1 & 0 \end{vmatrix} \cdot \begin{vmatrix} 1 & 0 & 0 & 0 & \xi_2 \\ 0 & 1 & 0 & 0 & \eta_2 \\ 0 & 0 & 1 & 0 & \zeta_2 \\ 0 & 0 & 0 & 0 & \tau_2 \\ \xi_2 & \eta_2 & \zeta_2 & \tau_2 & 0 \end{vmatrix} \right\}.$$

If we develop these determinants, it is easy to show that this quotient is precisely the value given above for r, which is thus shown to be invariant. Like the fundamental invariant of affine geometry, which we considered earlier, this quotient is homogeneous and of dimension zero in the coordinates of the two points, but not in the coefficients of the given quadratic form, in which it is homogeneous and of dimension -4. Moreover it is *not an absolute invariant*, for each of the determinants has the weight 2, i.e., the quotient has the weight $2 - 4 = -2$, as we see from the fact that what we here have is the dual of the constructions considered on pages 142–143. Consequently the numerical value of r has no immediate significance in metric geometry. Indeed, we can measure the distance between two points only if we assume a further arbitrary (unit) segment, i.e., if we adjoin that segment to the figure, along with the fundamental quadratic form. Absolute invariants of metric geometry appear only if we construct quotients of expressions of the sort here considered.

Here again I must not go into further detail. These examples will give you, at least, some idea as to the appearance of the complete systematic development of affine and metric geometry which results from the systematic articulation of integral rational invariants. I hope that you will extend your knowledge by reading in the many textbooks already mentioned.[1]

I shall touch lightly one more simple example, which is treated in detail in the new edition of Clebsch-Lindemann; [2] I refer to the so-called *geometry of the triangle*. In the course of time, an extensive closed field has appeared here, due especially to the work of secondary teachers, devoted to the many *remarkable points, lines, circles*, which can be defined in connection with the triangle: the center of gravity, the altitudes, the bisectors of the angles, the incircles, the circumcircle, the Feuerbach circle, and so on. The countless relations, toward the discovery of which men have long striven, and are still striving, fall easily into orderly arrangement in our systematic development. Let there be *given*, as vertices of a triangle, *three points*

$$(\xi_1, \eta_1, \tau_1), \qquad (\xi_2, \eta_2, \tau_2), \qquad (\xi_3, \eta_3, \tau_3).$$

---

[1] [In connection with the above. attention should be called especially to an article by H. Burkhardt in vol. 43 (1893) of the Mathematische Annalen: *Über Funktionen von Vectorgrössen, welche selbst wieder Vectorgrössen sind. Eine Anwendung invariantentheoretischer Methoden auf eine Frage der mathematischen Physik.*]

[2] *Loc. cit.*, p. 321. I should mention, above all, the Enzyklopädie report (III A B 10).

Since we are concerned with metric relations, we adjoin the two *imaginary circular points*, whose line equation is $\alpha^2 + \beta^2 = 0$. We may simply adjoin the values $(1, i, 0)$ and $(1, -i, 0)$ of their point coordinates. (See Fig. 102.) Then the whole *geometry of the triangle is nothing else than the projective invariant theory of these* 5 *points*, i.e., five arbitrary points, two of which we denote by special terminology. This remark gives to geometry of the triangle the transparent character of a systematic structure which is otherwise lost to sight.

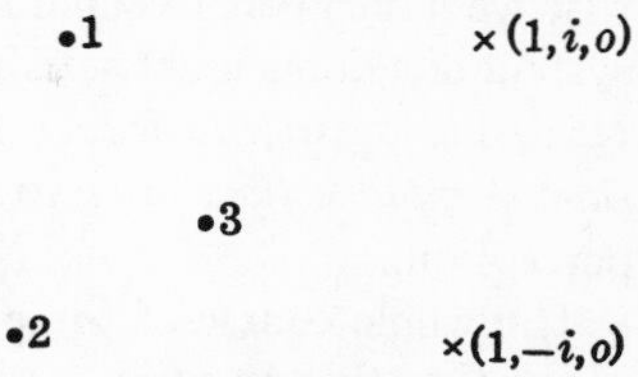

$\bullet 1 \qquad\qquad \times (1, i, o)$

With this I leave the consideration of the systematic development of geometry. It certainly satisfies the esthetic sense to have an orderly arrangement of the sort which I have described. Moreover, since this systematic

$\bullet 3$

$\bullet 2 \qquad\qquad \times (1, -i, o)$

FIG. 102

treatment alone permits a deeper insight into geometry, every mathematician, every prospective teacher, should know something about it. For this reason I felt compelled to include it in this course, although you will often find this point of view in the literature, but perhaps not always in such a consistent presentation. Of course it would be entirely perverse to tie ourselves dogmatically to this systematic procedure and to present geometry always in this light. The subject would soon become tedious and would lose all attractiveness. Above all, this would be a bar to investigative thought, which always functions independently of systematic planning.

Up to this point we have been considering, in a sense, the architecture of the structure of geometry. We shall now turn our attention to the no less important question of its foundations.

II. FOUNDATIONS OF GEOMETRY

A view of the very broad field which we now enter is afforded by the encyclopedia article by F. Enriques entitled *Prinzipien der Geometrie* (Enz. III A. B. 1). Investigations in the foundations of geometry often approach very closely the interests of the theory of knowledge and of psychology, which, from their viewpoints, study the origin of space perception and the justification of treating it by mathematical methods. We shall touch these questions very superficially, of course, and we shall treat essentially the *mathematical side of the problem*, assuming that space perception is to be taken for granted. We must also pass over the question that is so important in pedagogy, as to how space perception develops in the individual to the precise form to which we, as mathematicians, are accustomed.

Our problem, restricted in this manner, is to *erect the entire structure of geometry upon the simplest foundation possible, by means of logical operations*.

Pure logic cannot, of course, supply the foundation. Logical deduction can be used only after the *first part* of the problem is solved, i.e., *after we have a system which consists of certain simple fundamental notions and certain simple statements (the so-called axioms), and which is in accord with the simplest facts of our perception.* These axioms may be subdivided, of course, according to taste, into separate parts which are independent of one another. Otherwise we have great freedom in choosing them. The one condition which the system of axioms must satisfy is imposed by the *second part* of our problem: *It must be possible to deduce the entire contents of geometry logically from these fundamental notions and axioms,* without making any further appeal to perception.

The whole course of these lectures suggests a definite characteristic way of treating this question. As a matter of principle, we have always availed ourselves of the aids of analysis, and in particular of the methods of analytic geometry. Hence we shall here again assume a knowledge of analysis, and we shall inquire *how we can go, in the shortest way, from a given system of axioms to the theorems of analytic geometry.* This simple formulation is, unfortunately, rarely employed, because geometricians often have a certain aversion to the use of analysis, and desire, insofar as possible, to get along without the use of numbers.

The program thus indicated in general can be carried through in different ways, depending upon *which* fundamental notions and axioms we decide to use. It is convenient, and not unusual, to start with the *fundamental notions of projective geometry,* namely, with *point, straight line, and plane,* which we have already emphasized as fundamental concepts (p. 57 et seq.). We should not try to set up *definitions* as to what sort of things these are,—one must know that from the start. The program demands rather a statement of only so many characteristic properties and mutual relations that we can derive from them, in the sense indicated above, the whole of geometry. I shall not enumerate completely the separate axioms that would suffice for this purpose, for that would carry us too far afield. I shall only characterize their contents sufficiently for you to get a clear idea of them.

At the head are the *theorems of connection,* which I enunciated earlier (p. 58) for projective geometry. We shall not demand, at the outset, as we did there, the existence, without exception, of a point of intersection of two lines in a plane or of a line of intersection of two planes. Instead, as befits the relations of metric and affine geometry, we shall restrict ourselves to the theorem that *two lines of a plane have one point, or none, in common, two planes have either a line or else not a single point in common.* We can then derive, by the adjunction of "improper" points, lines, and planes, the complete system of projective geometry.

Next come the *theorems of order,* which describe how different points in the plane and on the line can lie with respect to each other. Thus, of three points *a*, *b*, *c* on a line, there is always one, say *b*, which lies between the other two, *a* and *c*; and so on. These statements are also called *theorems of betweenness*. (See Fig. 103.)

Finally, as to properties of continuity, I shall emphasize here, for the present, only the fact that the straight line has no gaps in it. If we separate, in any way, the segment between two points *a* and *b* into two parts 1 and 2, so that (if *a* lies to the left of *b*) all the points of 1 lie to the left of all the points of 2, then there exists just one point *c* which brings about this separation, so that the points of 1 lie between *a* and *c*, those of 2 between *c* and *b*. This corresponds obviously to the introduction of irrational numbers by means of the Dedekind cut.[1]

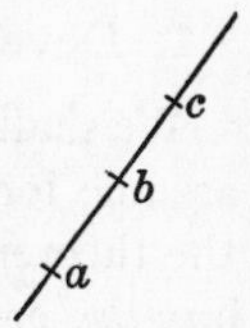

FIG. 103

From these axioms we can actually derive by logical deduction the whole of projective geometry of space. In particular, we could, of course, promptly introduce coordinates and treat projective geometry analytically.

If we desire to go over to *metric geometry*, we must take into consideration that in projective geometry we have also the notion of the *group of ∞^{15} collineations* or projective transformations of space. We know how to characterize, as a subgroup of this, the seven-parameter *principal group* of motions in space whose invariant theory constitutes metric geometry. This group consists of the collineations which leave unchanged a certain plane, namely, the *infinitely distant plane*, and in that plane a curve of the second degree, namely, the *imaginary spherical circle* (or the *absolute polar system* which represents it). However, we must go a step farther than this, if we wish to get exactly the theorems of elementary geometry. We must separate out from the principal group the six-parameter *subgroup of proper movements* (translations and rotations) which, unlike the similarity transformations, leave the distance between two points wholly unchanged. In this way, we shall have the metric geometry of congruences as our invariant theory. We can derive the motions from the principal group, for example, by setting up the requirement that the *"path curves" of a motion are closed* insofar as it leaves only one point fixed.

The plan thus sketched for building up geometry is theoretically perhaps the *simplest*, since it operates, at first, for projective geometry, exclusively with linear manifolds, and only later adjoins a quadratic manifold, the imaginary spherical circle, when this becomes necessary in order to get metric geometry. To carry this plan through is quite an abstract and tedious matter, however, and it would be appropriate only in a course of lectures devoted to projective geometry alone. It will suffice after this general exposition, to refer you to that presentation in the literature which is the most

---

[1] See Part I, p. 33 et seq.

readable, namely, to the translation, by H. Fleischer of the book by F. Enriques, entitled *Vorlesungen über projective Geometrie.*[1]

For general purposes of instruction, I prefer another method of developing
the subject of geometry, to which I now turn. For simplicity's sake I confine myself to *geometry of the plane.*

1. Development of Plane Geometry with Emphasis upon Motions

We shall take as fundamental notions *point* and *straight line,* and we shall
assume for them axioms of *connection, order, and continuity.* Here again,
the theorems of connection contain only the facts of perception *that through
any two points there always passes one and only one line,* while two lines can
have either *one point or none in common.* Concerning the *order* of the points
on a line we shall retain the conditions already indicated above. A careful
formulation of the additional axioms of order and of the axioms of continuity
will be considered during the course of the investigation.

With this foundation, we shall now avoid the roundabout use of projectivities, and we shall introduce immediately the *group of* ∞^3 *motions in the
plane,* in order, through it, to reach our goal, the system of plane analytic
geometry. First of all, we must formulate abstractly, in a series of axioms,
the properties of these motions which we shall assume and use, with respect
to our system of points and lines. We shall be guided here, of course, by the
vivid conception of motion which we have had in our experience with rigid
bodies. Accordingly, a motion must, in the first place, be a reversibly unique
transformation of the points of our space. In particular, it must coordinate
with every point a point lying in finite space. Moreover, it must carry a
straight line over into a straight line, without exception. It is convenient
to use again, in general, the word *collineation* for transformations of this
kind. To be sure, we do not yet know whether or not there are such collineations, since we are not now in possession
of projective geometry, as we were before.
Hence we must expressly postulate the existence,
at least, of these particular collineations, by
means of a *new axiom.* Accordingly, we assume
that there is a group of ∞^3 *collineations, which we
shall call motions,* and whose invariant theory
we shall look upon as the geometry of the plane.

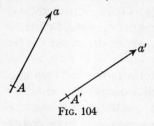

Fig. 104

We must explain more precisely what is meant here by "triply infinite."
Given any two points A and A' (see Fig. 104) and two rays a and a' drawn
from A and A', respectively. Then there will always be one and only one
motion which carries the point A into the point A' and the ray a into the

---

[1] Leipzig, 1903 [2nd German edition 1915]. The title of the original is *Lezioni di geo-
metria proiettiva,* Bologna, 1898; third edition, 1909.

ray a'. Figures which can be carried into each other by motion are called *congruent*.

However, we shall not yet make use of this entire group of motions, but only of a particular class of motions concerning which we shall set up some *special postulates*. In fact, there is just one motion which carries a point A into an arbitrary given point A' and the straight line from A to A' (together with this direction) into itself. We call such a motion a *translation*, or, more precisely, a *parallel translation*. *We shall assume now that each such translation carries into itself (with maintenance of its direction) the straight line which joins any two of its corresponding points B and B'*, and, what is essential, that *the ∞^{12} translations of the plane constitute a subgroup of the group of motions.*

If we perform repeatedly one and the same translation (see Fig. 105), the point A goes over into points A', A'', A''', $\cdots$ of that ray of the line AA' which points toward A'. We must assume, as *another postulate, that these points ultimately reach or include every point of this ray*. By repetition of the inverse transformation we obtain a series of points of the same character on the opposite ray. If we think of each translation as performed continuously, from the initial point to the endpoint, which is what we shall use

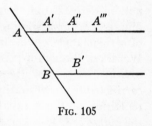

Fig. 105

later, we call the line in question the *path curve* of the point A under the translation. Every line is thus the path curve of infinitely many points, and for every translation there are ∞' path curves, namely, the straight lines which the translation carries over into themselves.

Now it should be noted that *two different path curves of the same translation cannot intersect*. Otherwise, the point of intersection obviously would result from the translation of two different points, namely, one from each of the two path curves, which is contrary to the character of a translation as a reversibly unique point transformation. We say that all the path curves of one and the same translation are *parallel* to one another. We have thus derived this notion from a property of our motions. At the same time, it is clear that through a given point A there is *certainly a parallel to a line a*, namely, the path curve of A under a translation along a.

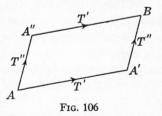

Fig. 106

Finally, we must set up a *last axiom* for these translations, *namely, that any two translations T', T'' are interchangeable*, i.e., that the same point B will result when we subject a definite point A first to the translation T' and then to T'', as when we perform first T'' and then T' (see Fig. 106). Symbolically we may write $T' \cdot T'' = T'' \cdot T'$.

I shall have something to say later regarding the method by which we arrive at such axioms. For the present, let me emphasize that our initial theorems are merely the expression of that which is familiar to everyone, from the beginning of geometric drawing. Indeed,

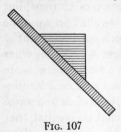

the first thing that one does is to move a rigid body, ruler or compasses or other instrument from one part of the drawing plane to another, in order to transfer magnitudes. In particular, we perform the operation of translation very often by sliding a triangle, say, along a straight edge (see Fig. 107). Here experience shows again and again that all the points of the triangle describe parallel lines. Our assumptions, which we shall not analyze logically any further, are thus not in the least artificial.

FIG. 107

We shall now see how far we can get in analytic geometry with these first notions derived from translations. We cannot talk about rectangular coordinates, of course, since we have nothing yet upon which to base a definition of a right angle. We can, however, introduce *general parallel coordinates*. We draw, through a point O, any two straight lines, which we call *the x axis and the y axis*. (See Fig. 108.) We consider the translation T which carries 0 into an arbitrarily chosen *point 1* on the x axis, and we suppose that repetition of the translation T yields the *points* $2, 3, 4, \cdots$ on the x axis. If we perform, in the same way, the *inverse operation* T^{-1}, so defined as to carry 1 into 0, the point 0 will go successively into the *points* $-1, -2, -3, \cdots$ of the x axis. We assign to the points thus obtained the positive and negative *integers* $0, 1, 2, \cdots, -1, -2, \cdots$ *as "abscissas"* x. To be sure, they will not exhaust all the points on the

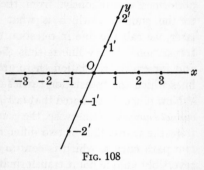

FIG. 108

x axis, but they will, according to one of our postulates, lie so that every other point will be included between some pair of them.

In similar manner, we start from any translation T' along the y axis, and, by performing it repeatedly forwards and backwards, we obtain the points $1', 2', 3', \cdots, -1', -2', -3', \cdots$, to which we assign positive and negative *integral y coordinates*. However, we should note here that we cannot set the x and y segments, thus determined, into reciprocal relation with each other, since we have not yet introduced the motion (rotation) which would carry the x axis into the y axis.

We can now consider the *points on the x axis with non-integral abscissas*, if we keep fixed the arbitrarily determined unit. We shall discuss first the *rational points*. In order to make the matter clear by an example, we shall seek a translation S along the x axis, which, if repeated once, would produce the unit translation T. We shall denote as the point $1/2$ that point into which S carries O, while repeated application of S will yield points with abscissas $3/2, 5/2, \cdots$. In order to establish the existence of such a translation S and of these points, we shall first show that the line from $1/2$ to the point $1'$ on the y axis must be parallel to the line $1\ 2'$ (which corresponds to the known construction for bisecting a segment). In-

deed, if we consider the translation S (see Fig. 109) of 0 to $1/2$ as made up of the translation T' of 0 to $1'$, followed by the translation S' of $1'$ to $1/2$, then the once repeated translation S, which, by def-inition, is identical with T, can be replaced, in view of the interchangeableness of two translations, by the once repeated translation T' followed by the once repeated translation S'. But since the first carries 0 to $2'$, this amounts to saying that two

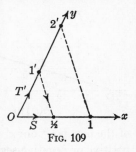

Fig. 109

applications of S' carries $2'$ to 1. Then $2'1$ is a path curve of the translation S' and, as such, is parallel to $1'\frac{1}{2}$, a path curve of the same translation.

By what precedes, we are already in possession of the points $2'$ and 1, and consequently of the translation S'. Thus the unique constructibility, from given elements, of the point $1/2$, as the intersection of the x axis with the path curve from $1'$ in the translation S', would be assured if we only knew that this path curve really cut the x axis. Of course, no one would doubt this, intuitively, but in the framework of our axiomatic deduction we need here a special axiom, the so-called *"betweenness axiom" for the plane*. This axiom states that if a line enters a triangle through a side, it must leave it through *another* side,—a trivial fact of our space perception which requires emphasis as such, because it is logically independent of the other axioms. Completely analogous considerations show, obviously, the exist-ence of *a point for every rational abscissa* x. We can easily infer from our postulates that there are such "rational points" inside of every segment, however small it may be.

In order, now, really to reach all the points which we actually consider in geometry, we must take into account irrational abscissas. For this pur-pose we need a new, likewise very obvious axiom, one that is merely a *precise statement* of the *requirements of continuity* mentioned above. *There are in-finitely many other points on the x axis (translations of the axis into itself) which have to the rational points the same relations of order and continuity which the irrational numbers have to the rational.* This axiom is the more plausible, in that, conversely, the introduction of irrational numbers came about historically from a consideration of geometric continuity.[1] We have, finally, *all the points of the x axis brought into reversibly unique correspondence*

---

[1] See the discussion in Part I, p. 31 et seq.

with all the positive and negative real numbers x. An analogous relation can of course be set up for the points of the y axis.

Let me remind you that the method thus sketched for constructing a scale on a line is a thoroughly natural one. When we make a scale, we do it by sliding a rigid body that has the arbitrary length of the unit (say the dis-

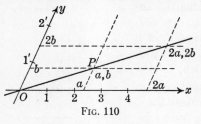

FIG. 110

tance between the points of the compasses) along a straight edge, and by subdividing the segments thus obtained.

Each translation of the plane along the x axis can now be characterized by a simple equation, which, for every point x of the x axis, gives the abscissa of the new position: $x' = x + a$. In other words, the rational or irrational, positive or negative segment a is added to x. Similarly, a translation along the y axis is described by the equation $y' = y + b$. If we perform both these translations successively, in either order, O goes over into a definite point P, since the translations are interchangeable. We say that P has the *abscissa a* and the *ordinate b*. Conversely, to any point P one can assign uniquely two numbers a and b. We need only translate O to P and determine the abscissa and ordinate of the intersections of the new positions of the axes with their original positions. *There is thus established a one to one correspondence between the aggregate of the points in the plane and the aggregate of number pairs (a, b), i.e., we have a complete determination of coordinates in the plane.*

It remains for us to consider how the *equation of the line* looks. Let us study first the line from O to P (a, b). Obviously, it must contain all the points which arise through iteration of the translation which takes O to P, i.e., the points $x = \lambda a, y = \lambda b$, where λ is an integer. Moreover, we see that the points determined by these equations for rational values of λ, and finally for irrational values of λ, also lie on this line, but that then all the points on the line are exhausted. Eliminating λ, we obtain the equation of the line in the form $x : y = a : b$, or $bx - ay = 0$. It follows that every equation of the form $\alpha x + \beta y = 0$ represents a line through O, provided that α and β do not vanish simultaneously. Now any line can be derived from a selected line through O by translation. It follows then, finally, *that all straight lines are given by all equations of first order,*

$$\alpha x + \beta y + \gamma = 0,$$

which, for this reason, are called *linear equations.*

From the fact that the straight line has a linear equation, it follows that a large part of the theorems of geometry can be derived without difficulty by methods of analytic geometry. I cannot go into details here, and I add merely that we can deduce in this way the *whole of affine geometry* and hence also the *whole of projective geometry*. We can get this far simply on the basis of the special postulates concerning the subgroup of ∞^2 translations. I shall lay stress upon only one more fact, which we shall use later. We proved earlier, by means of the theorems of projective geometry, the *theorem of Möbius*, that every *collineation* is a *projective* transformation, i.e., a transformation which is given by a linear fractional or a linear integral substitution of coordinates. Now, according to our first assumptions, all motions were collineations, *under which there corresponds to every finite point likewise a finite point*. On the other hand, however, we possess now the whole of projective geometry, so that, from our standpoint, the theorem of Möbius is also valid. Thus *every motion will be represented necessarily by a linear integral transformation of the parallel coordinates x and y*, which were *introduced* above (see p. 169).

Thus far we can talk only of the distance between two points on the x or on the y axis, if we wish now to press farther into the *metric notions of geometry*, and, in particular, to know about the *angle* between two lines and the *distance* between two arbitrary points, we must turn our attention to the *entire group of motions*.

We shall consider, in particular, the motions which leave a point, say the origin O, unchanged. These are the so-called *rotations* about this point. According to the general postulate concerning the determination of a motion, *there is just one rotation* which carries a ray a through O into an arbitrary ray a' through O (see Fig. 111). These rotations are, in a sense, *dual* to the translations,

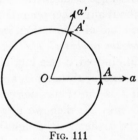

FIG. 111

since they leave a point unchanged, whereas translations carry a line into itself. Just as with the translations, we shall think of the rotations as carried out continuously from the initial position on, and we shall talk again of the *path curve* which each point describes.

There is, however, one essential difference between rotations and translations, which we must expressly formulate here as a postulate. *The rays a', a'', $\cdots$, which are derived from a by repetition of one and the same rotation about O ultimately coincide with or include every ray through O* (whereas a translation only yields the points of a single ray). In particular, therefore, the continuous rotation of the ray a must ultimately return it to its initial position, whereby each point of a returns to its original position. *The path curves are thus closed lines* which meet each ray through O in just one point A, so that all segments OA are congruent to each other (i.e., can be carried over into one another by a motion). They are what are commonly called *circles with center O*.

By means of these rotations, we shall now establish a *scale* in the pencil of rays about O, much as we constructed a scale on the line by means of translations. In this also we must make suitable *assumptions* as to *continuity*. I do not need to carry this out in detail and I give only the result, that we

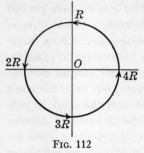

FIG. 112

associate with every rotation a real number, the *angle of this rotation*, and every real number appears as an angle of rotation. The periodicity of the rotation appears, of course, as a new concept, and it would be natural to select, as a unit, the complete rotation which carries a ray into itself. As a matter of tradition, however, we select *as unit a quarter of a rotation*, which, when repeated four times, gives a full rotation and whose angle is called *a right angle R*. Each rotation is

thus measured by its angle $\omega \cdot R$, where ω may be any real number, but may be restricted, on account of periodicity, to the values from 0 to 4 (see Fig. 112).

In the same way, we can define the angle scale in the pencil of rays about any other point O_1. But, with the aid of translation, we can *transfer the angle scale of O immediately to O_1*. Indeed, if (see Fig. 113) the rays a_1 and a_1' through O_1 are given, and if T is the translation which carries O into O_1, then we designate by a and a' the rays through O into which

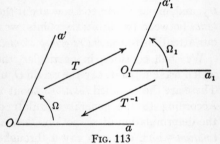

FIG. 113

the rays a_1 and a_1' go under the reciprocal translation T^{-1}. If, now, Ω is the rotation about O which carries a into a', then the rotation Ω_1, of a_1 into a_1' about O_1, is given by the succession of T^{-1}, Ω, and T, or, in symbols,

$$\Omega_1 = T^{-1}\Omega T.$$

This follows from the fact that the right side represents also a motion which carries O_1a_1 into O_1a_1', and such a motion is uniquely determined. We assign now to Ω_1 the same angle $\omega \cdot R$ which Ω has by the above definition. If we have a second rotation, Ω', in the pencil O, there will correspond to it, in the pencil O_1, the rotation

$$\Omega_1' = T^{-1}\Omega'T,$$

and the combination of Ω_1 and Ω_1' is

$$\Omega_1\Omega_1' = T^{-1}\Omega T T^{-1}\Omega'T = T^{-1}(\Omega\Omega')T,$$

which corresponds to the composition of Ω and Ω'. It follows that our transfer actually gives the same scale at O_1 that would arise through repetition of the original procedure.

There is a theorem in *Euclid*, which is omitted from most of our elementary textbooks, *that all right angles are congruent.* Of course every boy will look upon this theorem as self-evident, and I think that it should be ignored in the schools, since the pupils do not appreciate what it means. However, its content is identical with the result of the preceding discussion, namely, that equal angles, which are defined by rotations at different points, can be brought into coincidence by motions, i.e., that they are congruent.

Now that we have given a general definition of angle, we shall define the *distance between two arbitrary points.* Thus far we have been able to compare distances only on one and the same line by means of translation. If a distance r is laid off on the x axis, say, from O, we can transfer it (see Fig. 114) by rotation about O, to any line a' through O. Then we can transfer to a' the scale of length on the x axis and then also, by translation, to any line parallel to a', and thus to any line whatever. *We can, then, actually measure the distance between any two points by joining them by a line and transferring*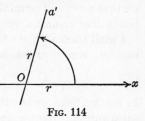

FIG. 114

to it, in the way indicated, the scale on the x axis. In particular, we shall think of the scale initially chosen for the y axis as having been derived thus from the one on the x axis.

Using the new notion of rotation, we shall now complete our apparatus for *analytic geometry.* In doing this, we shall use, as we now may, the special *rectangular coordinates x and y,* instead of general parallel coordinates.

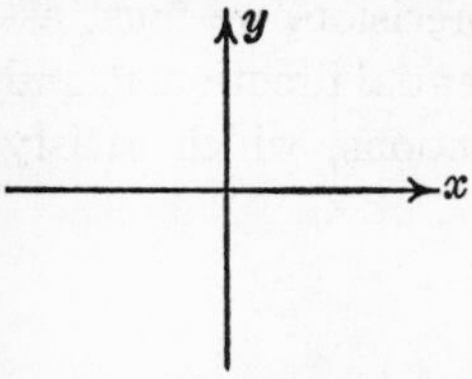

We know already (p. 167) that every motion is given by a linear substitution in x and y:

$$x' = (a_1x + b_1y + c_1) : N,$$
$$y' = (a_2x + b_2y + c_2) : N.$$

FIG. 115

Since this carries each finite point into another finite point, the denominator N must be constant and may be set equal to 1. If we consider in particular a rotation about O, then $c_1 = c_2 = 0$, and we have

(1) $$x' = a_1x + b_1y, \qquad y' = a_2x + b_2y.$$

For the special rotation through a *right angle*, we can state at once the form of the equations. Since we have rectangular coordinates, the x axis is carried into the y axis, and the y axis is carried into the negative x axis, so that we have

(2) $$x' = -y, \qquad y' = x.$$

The question as to the determination of the formulas of rotation is now reduced to the following purely analytic problem. *We seek a simply infinite group of substitutions of the form* (1) *which shall include the substitution* (2) *and such that, if ω is a real parameter, every substitution of the group, speaking generally, arises from* (2) *by ω-tuple iteration.* For a rational fractional value of ω, say p/q, this expression means, of course, that the substitution repeated q times gives the substitution (1) iterated p times, while an irrational value of ω is to be approximated by rational values, according to our assumptions regarding continuity. It must be understood clearly that we may presuppose no geometric knowledge whatever, especially concerning the formulas of rotation of a rectangular coordinate system; however, we may and we shall use all of our knowledge of analysis without any scruples. The structure which we thus erect will certainly not be immediately usable for school instruction, but it does assume a very elegant and simple form.

I shall start with the remark that the rotation (2), by the use of *complex numbers*, can be expressed by the one formula

$$(2')\qquad\qquad x' + iy' = i(x + iy).$$

From this form we see that the result of two successive applications of the substitution is represented by the relation $x' + iy' = i^2(x + iy)$. This is an equation of the same form, where the factor i^2 has taken the place of the factor i. Similarly an ω-tuple iteration, in the foregoing sense, produces the factor i^ω for each real ω. We have, therefore, as the *analytic representation of the rotation of the plane about O through the angle* ω · R, the formula

$$(3)\qquad\qquad x' + iy' = i^\omega(x + iy).$$

In order to carry out this line of thought with precision, we must assume from analysis a complete knowledge of the exponential function e^z, and also a complete knowledge of the trigonometric functions, which satisfy Euler's formula

$$e^{iz} = \cos z + i \sin z.$$

In writing down this relation we do not need to have, at present, even a suspicion of its geometric significance.

We know also the number π, by means of the formula $e^{i\pi} = -1$, and we may write

$$i = e^{\frac{i\pi}{2}}.$$

By i^ω we understand here the value uniquely defined by the formula

$$i^\omega = e^{\omega\frac{i\pi}{2}} = \cos\frac{\omega\pi}{2} + i \sin\frac{\omega\pi}{2}.$$

If we substitute this value in (3), and separate the real and the imaginary parts, we have

$$(4) \quad \begin{cases} x' = \cos \dfrac{\omega\pi}{2} \cdot x - \sin \dfrac{\omega\pi}{2} \cdot y \\[2ex] y' = \sin \dfrac{\omega\pi}{2} \cdot x + \cos \dfrac{\omega\pi}{2} \cdot y, \end{cases}$$

which is, in elementary analytic symbols, the desired representation of the rotation group.

With this result, it is natural *to choose, as the unit, not the right angle, but the angle $\pi/2$*. We shall call this the natural angle scale, as we speak of the natural logarithm, to indicate that these notions are based upon the nature of things, although their full appreciation requires deeper insight. In this natural scale we write simply ω instead of $\omega\pi/2$, and we have, as formulas of rotation, instead of (4), the well-known equations

$$(5) \quad \begin{cases} x' = \cos \omega \cdot x - \sin \omega \cdot y, \\ y' = \sin \omega \cdot x + \cos \omega \cdot y. \end{cases}$$

We must now examine these formulas to see what geometric truths they contain. These will turn out to be the elementary theorems which are usually employed in setting up the formulas (5).

1. Let us start with a consideration of the point on the x axis, at a distance r from the origin: $x = r$, $y = 0$. If we turn it through the angle ω, the formulas (5) give as coordinates of its new position

$$(6) \qquad x = r \cos \omega, \qquad y = r \sin \omega,$$

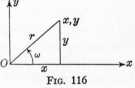

FIG. 116

where, for brevity, the accents have been omitted from the new coordinates. If, to fix ideas, we take $\omega < \pi/2$ and consider the right triangle (see Fig. 116) formed by the radius vector r, the abscissa x, and the ordinate y of the point (x, y), then the formulas (6) exhibit the connection between the sides and the angle ω. From the relation $\cos^2 \omega + \sin^2 \omega = 1$, which follows from the analytic definition of these functions, we find at once from (6)

$$(6a) \qquad\qquad x^2 + y^2 = r^2.$$

This is the *Pythagorean theorem*, which we thus obtain *as a result of our assumptions concerning motions in the plane*. Moreover, we can write (6) in the form

$$\cos \omega = \frac{x}{r}, \qquad \sin \omega = \frac{y}{r} \cdot$$

We obtain thus the elementary trigonometric significance of our angle functions, which is the exact form in which they are usually defined: The cosine and the sine are the ratios of the adjacent side and the opposite side, respectively, to the hypotenuse.

2. It is now easy to state the *general analytic expressions for the fundamental notions distance and angle*, if we bring the given elements, points or lines, through translation and rotation, into the special position just considered. For *the distance between two points* (x_1, y_1) *and* (x_2, y_2), we have

$$r = \sqrt{(x_1 - x_2)^2 + (y_1 - y_2)^2}.$$

To obtain this result, it is merely necessary to carry the point (2) to the origin by a translation, whereupon, by the translation formulas (p. 166), the differences $x_1 - x_2$, $y_1 - y_2$ become the new coordinates of the point (1), and (6a) gives at once our expression for r. In the same way, we obtain from (6b) for the *angle* ω *between two lines* whose equations are $\alpha_1 x + \beta_1 y + \delta_1 = 0$, $\alpha_2 x + \beta_2 y + \delta_2 = 0$, the formula

$$\cos \omega = \frac{\alpha_1 \alpha_2 + \beta_1 \beta_2}{\sqrt{\alpha_1^2 + \beta_1^2}\, \sqrt{\alpha_2^2 + \beta_2^2}}, \qquad \sin \omega = \frac{\alpha_1 \beta_2 - \alpha_2 \beta_1}{\sqrt{\alpha_1^2 + \beta_1^2}\, \sqrt{\alpha_2^2 + \beta_2^2}}.$$

I hardly need to give the details of the proof.

3. Finally we have still to discuss the *notion of area*, of which we have not made the slightest use, thus far, in our development of geometry. Nevertheless, this notion is present in the naive space consciousness of every person, even if in more or less inexact form. Every peasant knows what it means to say that a piece of land has an area of so many acres. Although we have succeeded, then, in laying completely the foundations of geometry—and we have actually done just that—without using this fundamental notion, it behooves us to add it now as a supplement to the system, i.e., to express it in terms of coordinates.

We must begin with a simple *geometric discussion*, such as the one given in Euclid or the one given in the elementary presentations. If we have a rec-

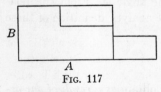

Fig. 117

tangle with sides A and B, we define its *area* to be the *product* AB. If we combine two rectangles, or any two figures of known area, we define the area of the resulting figure as the *sum* of the two areas. If we remove from a rectangle, or from another figure, a smaller piece lying entirely within it, the remainder has for area the *difference* of the given areas. (See Fig. 117.)

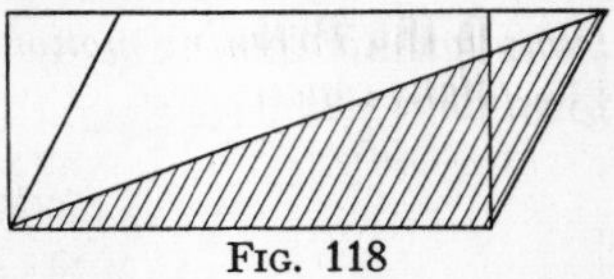

With these conventions, we can proceed at once to the *area of a parallelogram*. This figure

Fig. 118

arises from a rectangle of equal base and height by taking away a triangle and adding a congruent one. (See Fig. 118.) Hence its area is equal to that of the rectangle, i.e., to the *product of base and altitude*. A diagonal divides the parallelogram into two congruent triangles, each of which has for area, therefore, half that of the parallelogram: *The area of a triangle is half the product of base and altitude.*

If we apply this to a triangle with sides r_1, r_2, and include angle ω, the altitude upon r_1 is $r_2 \sin \omega$; hence the area is

$$\Delta = \frac{r_1 r_2 \sin \omega}{2}.$$

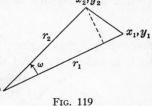

FIG. 119

If we place one vertex of this triangle (see Fig. 119) at the origin and call the coordinates of the other two vertices (x_1, y_1) and (x_2, y_2), then this formula, with the aid of the above expressions for distance and for angle, can be written in the form

$$\Delta = \frac{x_1 y_2 - x_2 y_1}{2}.$$

It is easy to show that rotation of the coordinate system leaves this expression Δ unchanged, so that it really supplies a "geometric concept." In order to have invariance under translation, and so under all motions, however, we must transform the third vertex, i.e., we must set up the formula for the area of a triangle with vertices at three arbitrary points (x_1, y_1), (x_2, y_2), (x_3, y_3). We obtain in this way the formula

$$\Delta = \tfrac{1}{2} \begin{vmatrix} x_1 & y_1 & 1 \\ x_2 & y_2 & 1 \\ x_3 & y_3 & 1 \end{vmatrix},$$

which is, indeed, the formula with which we began these lectures (see p. 3). It is easy to show that, if triangles are combined or subdivided, their areas, defined as above, are added or subtracted. The proof, as we saw earlier, depends upon simple determinant relations.

The addition of the idea of area to our system of analytic geometry is thus completed, and we have, at the same time, gained something which is not contained in the naive conception: Area has become a magnitude affected with a *sign*. I discussed (see p. 3 et seq.) at the beginning of these lectures the great advantage thus gained with respect to the free operation with the formulas and their universal validity, in contrast with the naive notion of area as an absolute magnitude.

4. Another example of a concept which occurs with more or less precision in the naive perception of space, which we must add as a supplement to our system of geometry, is the *notion of an (arbitrary) curve*. Every person believes that he knows what a curve is until he has learned so much mathe-

matics that the countless possible abnormalities confuse him. Good orientation in this field can be found in the *encyclopedia report* by v. Mangoldt entitled *Die Begriffe "Linie" und "Fläche"* (III, Ab 2). We shall not bother here with details but we shall state simply that, for us, a curve is the totality of points whose coordinates are continuous functions ϕ and χ of a parameter t, which are differentiable as many times as may be necessary:

$$x = \phi(t), \qquad y = \chi(t).$$

Proceeding in this manner, we can develop immediately, in the frame of our analytic geometry, all of the notions and theorems which are comprised

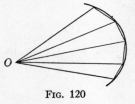

FIG. 120

usually under the name *infinitesimal geometry*, the notions of *length of arc, area* of curved *surfaces, curvature, evolute,* etc. The fundamental idea is always that we think of the curve as the limit of an inscribed rectilinear polygon (see Fig. 120). If the coordinates of two neighboring points are (x, y) and $(x + dx, y + dy)$, then it follows at once from the pythagorean formula that the *length of arc is:*

$$\int \sqrt{dx^2 + dy^2},$$

and it follows also, in the same way, from the formula for the area of a triangle with vertex at O, that the *area of the sector* between the curve and two radius vectors is given by the formula (see p. 10):

$$\tfrac{1}{2} \int (x\, dy - y\, dx).$$

With this I leave our first development of geometry, which was characterized by our placing in the foreground the existence and structure of the three parameter group of motions and then introducing coordinates, in order thereafter to make our inferences entirely within the field of arithmetic. There is a second method of developing geometry, one which is, in a sense, opposed to this. It leads likewise directly to metric geometry and it has always played an important role. We shall now turn our attention to it.

2. Another Development of Metric Geometry—the Role of the Parallel Axiom

The contrast with the first development consists in this, that now the *concept of motion is consistently avoided*, or, at most, brought in as an afterthought. The fact that this arrangement was preferred in ancient times, as it frequently still is, was due, in part, to philosophical considerations, which I should at least mention. It was feared that motion would bring into geometry an element foreign to it, namely, the notion of time. When an attempt was made to justify a preference for motion by the marked obviousness of the idea of the concept of a rigid body, the objection was raised that this idea in itself had no precise comprehensible meaning. On the contrary, it was held that this idea could have meaning for us only if we already possessed the notion of distance. The empiricist can reply, of course, that the abstract idea of distance can actually be inferred only from the presence of "sufficiently" rigid bodies. However, let me now indicate briefly the principal thoughts of this second development of geometry.

1. We begin, just as before, with the introduction of *points* and *lines*, and with the *theorems* concerning their *connection, order*, and *continuity*.

2. By the side of these—and this is new here—we assume the new fundamental notions, on one hand, of the *distance between two points* (segment) and, on the other hand, the *angle between two lines;* and we set up axioms concerning them which state, in substance, that *segments and angles can be measured by numbers in the customary manner.*

3. Here the *first congruence theorem* appears as the following characteristic axiom, which really replaces the axioms of the group of motions: *If two triangles have two sides and the included angle respectively equal, they are congruent*, i.e., they are equal in all their parts. In our earlier system, this was a provable theorem, for we can find a

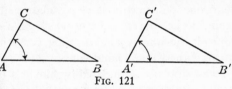

Fig. 121

motion which (see Fig. 121) brings the side $A'B'$ into coincidence with AB. Then $A'C'$ necessarily falls along AC, because of this assumption, and the triangles coincide throughout. But if we do not include motions among the fundamental notions, i.e., if we may not use them, there is no possibility of proving this theorem, and we must of necessity postulate it as a new axiom.

4. For the rest, the procedure is precisely opposite to that in our first development, as you know. Elementary instruction in geometry does this consistently, adhering essentially to the plan of Euclid, of whom I shall have something to say later. It is customary first to prove the pythagorean theorem, and then to introduce the trigonometric functions cosine and sine, from their meaning in the theory of triangles. From this beginning, the same analytic apparatus is finally derived that we have stated.

5. In this process it becomes necessary to set up another axiom which is very important, concerning the *theory of parallels*. In our first development, parallelism was one of the first fundamental notions, which appeared immediately upon consideration of translations. Lines were called parallel if they were path curves of the same translation. Here it is entirely different.

Parallelism is not among the fundamental notions considered thus far, and we must now discuss it. Indeed, if we have a line g (see Fig. 122) and a point O outside it, we join O with a point P of g and let P move out along g through

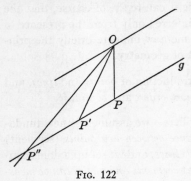

FIG. 122

the positions P', P'', $\cdots$. In other words, we consider the succession of points P, P', P'', $\cdots$, or the succession of lines OP, OP', OP'', $\cdots$, whereby there is no thought of motion in the earlier sense. The ray OP, under these circumstances, will reach a limiting position when P moves off to infinity, and we *call this limiting line a parallel to g through O*. It does not appear at all necessary that OP should approach the *same* limiting position when P goes to infinity in both directions, so that the *abstract possibility* arises of the existence of two *different parallels to g through O*.

In our present development, therefore, it is a *new axiom* if, according to our common perception, we postulate that the two limiting positions should coincide, i.e., that *there is only one parallel through a given point to a given line*. Such is the famous *parallel axiom*, concerning which there has been so much dispute these many hundreds of years. It is also called *Euclid's axiom*, since it was expressly formulated by him as a postulate.

I should like to tell you *something of the history of this axiom*. Through many years men used their best efforts in the attempt to *prove* the axiom, i.e., to show that it was a consequence of the other axioms, but always in vain. Of course, these attempts have not all been abandoned, even today. For although science advance never so far, there will always be people who think that they know better and who ignore the assured results of exact investigation. The fact is that mathematics has long since advanced, beyond these futile attempts, to fruitful new investigations and to positive results. As early as during the eighteenth century, there was raised the following *characterstic question, suggestive of new possibilities:* Is it not possible to set up a logically consistent system of geometry, free from contradictions, in which the parallel axiom is set aside, and in which the existence of *two* different limiting lines in the sense discussed above, i.e., of two different parallels to g through O, is admitted?

At the beginning of the nineteenth century, this question could be answered affirmatively. It was Gauss who first discovered the existence of *a "non-euclidean" geometry*, which is the name that he gave to such a geometric system. It appears from his posthumous papers that he certainly knew this in 1816. To be sure, the notes in which he discussed these things were found only much later and were not printed until 1900 in volume 8 of his collected works.[1] Gauss himself had published nothing about this great discovery, beyond a few occasional remarks. The jurist Schweikart, about 1818, independently of Gauss, constructed a non-euclidean geometry which he called astral geometry, but he likewise did not publish his results. They became known first through a letter to Gauss which was found in the latter's papers. The first publications on non-euclidean geometry came from the Russian, N. J. Lobatschefsky (1828), and the Hungarian, J. Bolyai de Bolya, the younger (1832),[2] both of whom had got these results independently of each other and were in possession of proofs by 1826 and 1823, respectively. In the course of the century, these things have come into the general possession of mathematicians through numerous articles, so that today, indeed, every person of general culture has heard of the existence of a non-euclidean geometry, even though a clear understanding of it can be attained only by an expert.

In the early part of the second half of the nineteenth century Riemann gave an essentially new direction to these problems. His work appeared in 1854 in his habilitation address entitled *Über die Hypothesen welche der Geometrie zugrunde liegen*.[3] Riemann remarked that at the bottom of all the preceding investigations there was the *assumption that the straight line was of infinite length*, which was certainly very natural and obvious. He asked what would happen if we should give up this assumption, that is, if we should allow the straight line to return into itself, as does the great circle on the sphere. We are confronted here with the *difference between the infinity and the unboundedness of space*, which can best be seen, perhaps, in two-dimensional space. The surface of the sphere and the ordinary plane are both unbounded, but only the second is infinite, whereas the first is of finite extent. Riemann assumes, in fact, that *space is only unbounded and not infinite*. Then the straight line on which the points lie will be a closed curve similar to a circle. If now we let a point P move, as before, in a definite direction, farther and farther on a line g, it will ultimately return to its original position. The ray OP of our former discussion will not have a limiting position and *there will be no parallel to g through O*. Thus there appears with Riemann a *second kind of non-euclidean* geometry, in contrast with the non-euclidean geometry of Gauss, Bolyai, and Lobatschefsky.

This seems at first paradoxical, but the mathematician notices here, at once, a *relation to the ordinary theory of quadratic equations*, which points

[1] Leipzig, 1900. The part in question was edited by P. Stäckel.

[2] Translated into German in *Urkunden zur Geschichte der nichteuklidischen Geometrie* by Engel and Stäckel: Part I (Lobatschefsky) by Engel (Leipzig, 1898). [Part 2 (W. and J. Bolyai) by Stäckel, Leipzig, 1913.] See also *Urkundensammlung zur Vorgeschichte der nichteuklidischen Geometrie* by Stäckel and Engel, Leipzig, 1895.

[3] Published in vol. 13 of Abhandlungen der Gesellschaft der Wissenschaften zu Göttingen = *Gesammelte mathematische Werke*, 2nd ed., p. 272 et seq. (Leipzig, 1892). [Publishing firm Springer, Berlin, 3rd edition by H. Weyl, 1923.]

the way to an understanding of the matter. Indeed, a quadratic equation has either two different real roots, or none at all (both being imaginary), or finally, as a transition case, one real root counted twice. This is entirely analogous to the two different real parallels of Gauss, to the absence of real parallels in Riemann, and finally to the transition case of one parallel counted in two ways, as the same limiting position, in euclidean geometry.

Before I enter more carefully upon the discussion of non-euclidean geometry, I shall touch, at least briefly, upon its great *significance from the philosophical side*, by virtue of which it has always aroused tremendous interest with the philosophers, but has also often been flatly rejected.

Above all, this new field throws light upon the *character of geometric axioms looked at from the standpoint of pure logic.* Indeed, from the existence of non-euclidean geometry, we can conclude at once that the euclidean axiom is not a consequence of the preceding fundamental notions and theorems, nor are we under any other logical compulsion to accept it. For if we retain all the other axioms but replace this one by a contrary assumption, we are not led to a contradiction, but we obtain, rather, non-euclidean geometry, as a logical structure which is just as correct as is euclidean geometry. *Details of our space perception, such as those described in the parallel axiom, are thus certainly not a purely logical necessity.*

The question arises, now, whether or not, perhaps by means of *sense perception*, we can decide as to the correctness of the parallel axiom; upon this also non-euclidean geometry throws a clear light. *In fact, it is certainly not true that immediate sense perception teaches us the existence of just one parallel.* For, our appreciation of space is decidedly *not absolutely exact.* As in every other region of sense perception, so here, we can no longer recognize as distinct, magnitudes (segments, angles, etc.) whose difference lies below a certain limit, the so-called *threshold of perception.* Thus if we draw, in particular, through the point O, two lines very close to one another (see Fig. 123), certainly we can no longer distinguish between them if we make the angle between them small enough, say 1″, or, if one will, .001″, or even still smaller. Thus it would be difficult to decide, by immediate sense perception, whether there is really just one parallel to g through O, or two which are separated from each other by such a small angle. We sense this still more distinctly if we think of O as very far away from g, say as far away as Sirius, or a million times that far. With such distances, sense perception loses completely the keenness which we

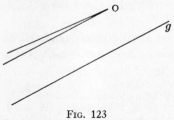

Fig. 123

otherwise expect of it, and we should certainly no longer be able to determine visually whether the limiting position of the rotating ray provided one or two parallels to the given line g.

Now this situation actually fits into the non-euclidean geometry of the first kind just as well as it does into euclidean geometry. As we shall soon see, when we look into the mathematical formulas, there is an arbitrary constant involved. By a suitable choice of this constant, we can make the angle between the two parallels to g arbitrarily small if the point O is moderately distant from g, and this angle becomes appreciably large only when O is sufficiently remote from g. *In view of the fact that our space perception is adapted only to a limited part of space, and then only with a limited degree of accuracy, it can obviously be satisfied by a non-euclidean geometry of the first kind as closely as we please.*

But a similar thing is true also for Riemannian non-euclidean geometry. It is only necessary to realize that the infinite length of the straight line cannot be an inference from our sense perception. We can follow any straight line only in a finite part of space; consequently it cannot contradict our space experience if we say that the line has a length that is enormously great but still finite, perhaps a million or more times the distance to Sirius. Imagination can conjure up arbitrarily large numbers which exceed every possibility of immediate perception. *In accord with these considerations, we can represent the situation in any limited part of space with any desired degree of accuracy by means of a Riemannian non-euclidean geometry, for such a geometry also has an arbitrary constant.*

The logical and intuitive facts here touched upon, as they present themselves from the standpoint of mathematics, run counter in high degree to that conception of space which many philosophers connect with the name Kant, and according to which all theorems of mathematics must have absolute validity. This explains why non-euclidean geometry, since its introduction into philosophical circles, has attracted so much attention and aroused so much opposition.

If we turn now to a *proper mathematical treatment of non-euclidean geometry*, we shall do best to choose the *path through projective geometry*. That is the derivation which I gave in 1871 in volume 4 of the *Mathematische Annalen.*[1]

We think of projective geometry as developed from the fundamental notions point, line, plane, and their axioms of connection, order, and continuity, independently of all measurement, as I indicated briefly in the beginning of the discussion of the foundations of geometry (p. 160 et seq.). In particular, we introduce point coordinates x, y, z, or homogeneous coordinates $\xi : \eta : \zeta : \tau$, and also plane coordinates $\alpha : \beta : \gamma : \delta$, so that the mutual incidence of point and plane is given by the bilinear equation

$$\alpha\xi + \beta\eta + \gamma\zeta + \delta\tau = 0.$$

[1] *Über die sogenannte nichteuklidische Geometrie*, p. 573 et seq. = [F. Klein, *Gesammelte mathematische Abhandlungen*, vol. 1, p. 254 et seq.].

Upon this foundation we have already set up *ordinary euclidean geometry*, by means of the theory of invariants and Cayley's principle, by adjoining the special quadratic form written in plane coordinates

$$\Phi_0 = \alpha^2 + \beta^2 + \gamma^2,$$

which, set equal to zero, represents the imaginary spherical circle. The angle between the two planes

$$\omega = \text{arc cos } \frac{\alpha_1\alpha_2 + \beta_1\beta_2 + \gamma_1\gamma_2}{\sqrt{\alpha_1^2 + \beta_1^2 + \gamma_1^2}\sqrt{\alpha_2^2 + \beta_2^2 + \gamma_2^2}},$$

and the distance between two points

$$r = \frac{\sqrt{(\xi_1\tau_2 - \xi_2\tau_1)^2 + (\eta_1\tau_2 - \eta_2\tau_1)^2 + (\zeta_1\tau_2 - \zeta_2\tau_1)^2}}{\tau_1\tau_2}$$

were then, as we showed (p. 156 et seq.), simple simultaneous invariants of the given figure (the two planes or the two points) and the form Φ_0.

We are going to try to set up *non-euclidian geometry* in the same way. Instead of the imaginary spherical circle $\alpha^2 + \beta^2 + \gamma^2 = 0$, we take *another quadratic form* which is "near" the preceding one, namely:

$$\Phi = \alpha^2 + \beta^2 + \gamma^2 - \epsilon \cdot \delta^2.$$

Here ϵ is a parameter which can be chosen arbitrarily small, and for $\epsilon = 0$, we have $\Phi = \Phi_0$. Our form is so chosen that for *positive* ϵ we get non-euclidean geometry of the first kind; for negative ϵ, Riemannian non-euclidean geometry; while for $\epsilon = 0$, we get the preceding formulas for ordinary euclidean geometry. It is essential in the setting up of this form Φ that its *determinant*

$$\Delta = \begin{vmatrix} 1 & 0 & 0 & 0 \\ 0 & 1 & 0 & 0 \\ 0 & 0 & 1 & 0 \\ 0 & 0 & 0 & -\epsilon \end{vmatrix} = -\epsilon$$

is, in general, different from zero. The determinant vanishes only in the special case $\epsilon = 0$, i.e., when $\Phi = 0$ represents the imaginary spherical circle. Our assumption then amounts to this, *that we replace the quadratic form whose determinant vanishes by a quadratic form whose determinant is positive or negative (but arbitrarily small in absolute value)*.

We shall obtain the definitions of a system of measurement for our non-euclidean geometry by constructing, from the general form Φ and from the figure consisting either of two planes or of two points, invariants entirely analogous to those which represent the euclidean magnitudes for the special form $\Phi_0 = \alpha^2 + \beta^2 + \gamma^2$. This is nothing else than the notion of Cayley,[1]

---

[1] In the *Sixth Memoir upon Quantities*, already cited (p. 145).

developed in 1859, "*that one can define a system of measurement just as well with respect to any quadratic surface (e.g., the surface $\Phi = 0$) as with respect to the imaginary spherical circle.* In view of the limited space to which this digression is confined, it will be expedient to set down the analytic formulas in advance. In this way the situation can be most quickly outlined with precision, and every shadow of mystery avoided. Of course, this presentation can lead to a full understanding of the material only if it is afterwards worked through carefully from the geometric side, as you will find it done in my article, already mentioned, in volume 4 of the *Mathematische Annalen*.

If we first consider two planes, it seems natural to set up the expression for the "*measure of the angle between them with respect to the surface $\Phi = 0$*" by generalizing the preceding expression for the angle. Just as there, we construct, from the values of the form Φ and of its polar form, the formula

$$\omega = \text{arc cos} \frac{\alpha_1\alpha_2 + \beta_1\beta_2 + \gamma_1\gamma_2 - \epsilon\delta_1\delta_2}{\sqrt{\alpha_1^2 + \beta_1^2 + \gamma_1^2 - \epsilon\delta_1^2}\sqrt{\alpha_2^2 + \beta_2^2 + \gamma_2^2 - \epsilon\delta_2^2}}.$$

In this way we obtain an expression which is obviously invariant, which for $\epsilon = 0$ actually goes over into the formula for angle of euclidean geometry.

It is not so immediately clear how one can transform the *expression for the distance between two points* for our system of measurement. In fact, the difficulty in the change lies in the fact that we now have a form whose determinant does not vanish, instead of the form Φ_0, whose determinant vanishes, which characterized euclidean measurement. However, we can discover how to set up the expression for distance if we *proceed exactly dualistically to the definition of the angle just given*. In this way, we are certain to get an invariant. We set up first, then, the equation of the surface $\Phi = 0$ in point coordinates. We get its left side $f(\xi, \eta, \zeta, \tau)$, as you know, by bordering with point coordinates the determinant Δ of Φ:

$$f = \begin{vmatrix} 1 & 0 & 0 & 0 & \xi \\ 0 & 1 & 0 & 0 & \eta \\ 0 & 0 & 1 & 0 & \zeta \\ 0 & 0 & 0 & -\epsilon & \tau \\ \xi & \eta & \zeta & \tau & 0 \end{vmatrix} = \epsilon(\xi^2 + \eta^2 + \zeta^2) - \tau^2.$$

We now transfer the expression for ω by writing the quotient of the polar form of f divided by the product of the square roots of the values of f formed for the points 1 and 2, and then taking the arc cosine:

$$r = k \text{ arc cos} \frac{\epsilon(\xi_1\xi_2 + \eta_1\eta_2 + \zeta_1\zeta_2) - \tau_1\tau_2}{\sqrt{\epsilon(\xi_1^2 + \eta_1^2 + \zeta_1^2) - \tau_1^2}\sqrt{\epsilon(\xi_2^2 + \eta_2^2 + \zeta_2^2) - \tau_2^2}}.$$

The factor k which we have inserted permits us to make an arbitrary segment equal to unity, as we are in the habit of doing. Moreover, this will become necessary when we go over to euclidean geometry. We must think of k *as real when ϵ is negative and as pure imaginary when ϵ is positive*, in order that r shall be real for all real points or at least for a certain sub-region of all real points (when $\epsilon > 0$), which then make the real substratum of non-euclidean geometry.

We have now reached a general definition of distance. It remains, only, to show *that, for $\epsilon = 0$, it leads to the customary expression of euclidean geometry.* This is not so easy here as it was before for the angle ω, for if one sets $\epsilon = 0$ outright, the quotient is 1, and r/k is equal to zero, to within an undetermined additive multiple of 2π. In spite of this somewhat paradoxical result, we can nevertheless obtain finally the euclidean expression by means of a certain device. To this end, it is convenient to transform the defining equation for r by means of the equation arc cos α = arc sin$\sqrt{1 - \alpha^2}$. Reducing to a common denominator, we find that the value of r is

$$k \cdot \text{arc sin} \sqrt{\frac{\{\epsilon(\xi_1^2+\eta_1^2+\zeta_1^2)-\tau_1^2\}\{\epsilon(\xi_2^2+\eta_2^2+\zeta_2^2)-\tau_2^2\}-\{\epsilon(\xi_1\xi_2+\eta_1\eta_2+\zeta_1\zeta_2)-\tau_1\tau_2\}^2}{\{\epsilon(\xi_1^2+\eta_1^2+\zeta_1^2)-\tau_1^2\}\{\epsilon(\xi_2^2+\eta_2^2+\zeta_2^2)-\tau_2^2\}}}.$$

We can now easily transform the numerator. Indeed, using a known determinant relation, the value of f (i.e., the determinant Δ of the form Φ, once bordered) for the point 1, multiplied by the same determinant for the point 2, minus the polar form taken for points 1 and 2, can be shown to be equal to the product of the determinant Δ itself by the determinant Δ bordered twice with the coordinates of 1 and 2, that is, equal to the product

$$\begin{vmatrix} 1 & 0 & 0 & 0 \\ 0 & 1 & 0 & 0 \\ 0 & 0 & 1 & 0 \\ 0 & 0 & 0 & -\epsilon \end{vmatrix} \cdot \begin{vmatrix} 1 & 0 & 0 & 0 & \xi_1 & \xi_2 \\ 0 & 1 & 0 & 0 & \eta_1 & \eta_2 \\ 0 & 0 & 1 & 0 & \zeta_1 & \zeta_2 \\ 0 & 0 & 0 & -\epsilon & \tau_1 & \tau_2 \\ \xi_1 & \eta_1 & \zeta_1 & \tau_1 & 0 & 0 \\ \xi_2 & \eta_2 & \zeta_2 & \tau_2 & 0 & 0 \end{vmatrix}.$$

Performing this multiplication, we find

$$-\epsilon \cdot \{(\xi_1\tau_2 - \xi_2\tau_1)^2 + (\eta_1\tau_2 - \eta_2\tau_1)^2 + (\zeta_1\tau_2 - \zeta_2\tau_1)^2$$
$$-\epsilon(\eta_1\zeta_2 - \eta_2\zeta_1)^2 - \epsilon(\zeta_1\xi_2 - \zeta_2\xi_1)^2 - \epsilon(\xi_1\eta_2 - \xi_2\eta_1)^2\}.$$

Anyone who is not skillful in calculating with determinants can show by direct transformation that this expression is identical with the numerator in the preceding expression for r. If we insert this expression in the formula for r and put $\epsilon = 0$, we get, of course, just as in the first form,

$$\frac{r}{k} = \text{arc sin } 0 = 0,$$

because of the factor $\sqrt{-\epsilon}$. But if we do not allow ϵ to become zero, but only to become very small, the arc sine is, as a first approximation, equal to the sine. We can neglect, in the numerator, the three squares, each multiplied by ϵ, and, in the denominator, that term in each factor which is multiplied by ϵ. There remains, as a first approximation,

$$r = k \cdot \sqrt{-\epsilon} \frac{\sqrt{(\xi_1\tau_2 - \xi_2\tau_1)^2 + (\eta_1\tau_2 - \eta_2\tau_1)^2 + (\zeta_1\tau_2 - \zeta_2\tau_1)^2}}{\tau_1 \cdot \tau_2}.$$

We come now to the device mentioned above. *During the passage to the limit, lim $\epsilon = 0$, we do not assign to k a fixed value, but we let it become infinite in such a way that* $\lim(k \cdot \sqrt{-\epsilon}) = 1$. For this purpose we must, of course, let k run through pure imaginary or through real values according as ϵ approaches zero through positive or through negative values. But it is evident *that the expression for distance in euclidean geometry (p.* 180) *actually does emerge from this passage to the limit.*

If we think our way into the geometric significance of the form f, as well as the significance of the expressions which have been only analytically put down here, it turns out *that we actually have, for $\epsilon > 0$, non-euclidean geometry of the first kind, for $\epsilon < 0$, that of the second kind, and for $\epsilon = 0$, of course, euclidean geometry.* To be sure, I cannot give the whole argument here. For that I must refer you to my article in volume 4 of the *Mathematische Annalen.*[1] At that time I proposed for these three gometries the names *hyperbolic, elliptic,* and *parabolic,* since the existence of two real, two imaginary, or two coincident parallels corresponds precisely to the behavior of the asymptotes of these three conics, respectively. You will find these names frequently in the literature.

I should like to show in greater detail, by an example, what form the theory of parallels takes from the expression for distance. For this purpose I choose *hyperbolic geometry* in the *plane.* We must then set the third coordinate equal to zero. Our quadratic form becomes $\Phi = \alpha^2 + \beta^2 - \epsilon\delta^2$ which, equated

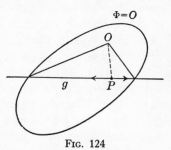

FIG. 124

to zero, represents a *real* conic which we can think of as an ellipse, since $\epsilon > 0$. The distance formula takes the form

$$r = k \text{ arc cos } \frac{\epsilon(\xi_1\xi_2 + \eta_1\eta_2) - \tau_1\tau_2}{\sqrt{\epsilon(\xi_1^2 + \eta_1^2) - \tau_1^2}\sqrt{\epsilon(\xi_2^2 + \eta_2^2) - \tau_2^2}},$$

where k is pure imaginary. It yields, as it is easy to see, real values for points which lie inside the real conic, where we mean by inside points the totality of the points in a plane from which no real tangents to the conic can be drawn. *Hence the field of operations of the real hyperbolic geometry*

---

[1] Attention is again drawn to *Einführung in die nichteuklidische Geometrie* by F. Klein (edited by W. Rosenbaum), which is about to appear as a revision of the earlier mimeographed volume of Klein's lectures on non-euclidean geometry.

consists exclusively of these interior points and of the lines which lie in this interior. The points on the conic (see Fig. 124) itself represent the *infinite* region. For, the formula yields the value ∞ for the distance of each point 1 from a point 2 on the conic [for which $\epsilon(\xi_2^2 + \eta_2^2) - \tau_2^2 = 0)$]. Thus there are, in this sense, two *infinitely distant points* in hyperbolic geometry on every straight line, namely its intersections with the conic $\Phi = 0$, but there is only *one* on each ray a. If we have a line g, and a point O not lying on it, then the parallels through O, in the sense of our earlier definition (p. 176), as the limiting positions of the lines joining O with a point which moves along g to infinity, are the lines joining O with the intersections of g with the conic. *There are, in fact, two parallels, essentially different from each other,* each of which belongs to one of the two directions on g.

Let me make one more brief remark, which concerns a *comparison with our first development of euclidean geometry.* We started there with the *group of motions.* That was the totality of collineations which left the relations of measure unchanged. But there are likewise such collineations in non-euclidean geometry. A general homogeneous equation of the second degree has ten terms and therefore nine essential constants. In the most general space collineation there are fifteen arbitrary parameters, so that there is a *six-fold infinity of collineations which transform a given quadratic form, e.g., our Φ form, into itself.* Indeed, this is the condition that the relations of measure which we have introduced should remain unchanged. *Hence there is also in each non-euclidean geometry a six-fold infinite group of "motions" which leave ω and r unchanged.* For geometry in the *plane* the number of parameters would reduce, as before, to three.

We can, therefore, develop each non-euclidean geometry also by starting from the *existence of a group of motions.* It remains only to point out how it came about that our earlier development led us exclusively to *euclidean* geometry. The reason was, of course, that we selected from among the motions the special two-parameter (in space it would be a three-parameter) *subgroup of so-called parallel translations,* which had only straight lines as path curves. *There are no such subgroups in any non-euclidean geometry, and since we postulated their existence at the beginning, we excluded non-euclidean geometry once and for all and retained only euclidean geometry.*

Let me conclude this special discussion of non-euclidean geometry with a few general advisory *statements,* as I may call them.

1. Whereas I reported earlier that, from the side of philosophy, non-euclidean geometry had frequently not been fully understood, I must emphasize that it is today quite generally recognized in the *science of mathematics.* In fact, for many purposes, e.g., in the modern theory of functions and in the theory of groups, it is used as a very convenient means for making clear visually relations that are arithmetically complicated.

2. *Every teacher certainly should know something of non-euclidean geometry.*
Thus, it forms one of the few parts of mathematics which, at least in scattered catch-words, is talked about in wide circles, so that any teacher may
be asked about it at any moment. In physics there are, of course, far more
such things which are on every tongue and about which, therefore, every
teacher should be informed. Indeed, almost every discovery in physics belongs in this category. Imagine a teacher of physics who is unable to say
anything about Röntgen rays, or about radium. A teacher of mathematics
who could give no answer to questions about non-euclidean geometry would
not make a much better impression.

3. On the other hand, I should like to advise emphatically against bringing non-euclidean geometry into *regular school instruction* (i.e., beyond
occasional suggestions, upon inquiry by interested pupils), as enthusiasts
are always recommending. Let us be satisfied if the preceding advice is
followed and if the pupils learn really to understand *euclidean* geometry.
After all, it is in order for the teacher to know a little more than the average
pupil.

I should like to consider briefly the *further development of modern science*
which has been occasioned by non-euclidean geometry. A good starting
point was made from one of its results, namely, that the euclidean parallel
axiom was logically independent of the other axioms of geometry (see p. 176).
This *stimulated the study of the other geometric axioms as to their mutual logical
dependence or independence.* From this arose the *modern theory of geometric
axioms,* which in its procedure follows closely the path which the older investigation had disclosed. In it, we determine what parts of geometry can
be set up without using certain axioms, and whether or not, by assuming
the opposite of a given axiom, we can also secure a system free from contradictions, that is, a so-called "*pseudo-geometry.*"

As the most important work belonging here, I should mention Hilbert's
Grundlagen der Geometrie.[1] Its *chief aim* as compared with earlier investigations, is to *establish, in the manner indicated, the significance of the axioms
of continuity.* To accomplish this, it is of course necessary, above all, to
arrange the system of geometric axioms so that the *theorems on continuity*
come at the end, whereas for us they have thus far stood at the beginning.
Thus we were unable, in our development of non-euclidean geometry, to
make use of the first arrangement of the axioms (p. 162 et seq.), which put
the notion of parallels at the head. To the contrary, we were obliged to
create a system of axioms in which the greater part of the discussion said
nothing about parallels, and in which the parallel axiom was added at the
end. Setting aside the essential departure thus indicated, Hilbert's system

---

[1] 5th edition, Leipzig and Berlin, 1922.

of axioms accords, in the main, with our second development of elementary geometry (p. 174 et seq.).

In this sense, Hilbert inquired *in how far geometry can be developed without using the axioms of continuity. He includes in the treatment also the " pseudo-geometries," in which all the other geometric axioms are valid, excepting only the axioms of continuity.* Such geometries consist essentially of those facts which are concerned with the one-to-one correspondence between the points of a line and the ordinary real numbers (their abscissas). (See p. 161 and p. 164.) Of course, I cannot give the details of the line of thought of Hilbert's investigations or the interesting results which he obtained concerning the logical connection between certain geometric theorems and axioms. With these few explanatory remarks, I leave it to you to read all this in Hilbert's own writings. Let me recall, however, that his *non-archimedean geometry*, which we discussed in the first volume of these lectures [1] belongs here. This is, indeed, such a pseudo-geometry in which that axiom of continuity which was formerly named after Archimedes, but which now often bears the name of Eudoxus, is no longer satisfied, i.e., in which the abscissas of two different points may differ by an "actually infinitely small quantity," of which no finite multiple is equal to an ordinary finite real number.

I do not wish to conclude these brief remarks on the modern theory of axioms without saying a few words on the important question concerning the *true nature of geometric axioms and theorems.* Of course, this takes me out of the strict field of mathematics into that of philosophy and the theory of knowledge. I have already emphasized one thing about which most people today are in reasonable agreement. That is that we are concerned here with the *leading concepts and statements which one must of necessity put into the front rank of geometry in order to be able to deduce mathematical proofs from them by pure logic.* This agreement does not answer the question as to the *real source of these leading concepts and statements.* There is the old point of view that they are the *intuitive possession of every person*, and that they are of such obvious simplicity that no one could question them. This view, however, was shaken, in large measure, by the discovery of non-euclidean geometry; for here it is clearly shown (see p. 177 et seq.) that space perception and logic by no means lead compellingly to the euclidean parallel axiom. To the contrary, we saw that, with an assumption which contradicts the parallel axiom, we come to a logically closed geometric system which represents actual perceptual relations with any desired degree of approximation. However, it may well be claimed that this parallel axiom is the assumption which permits the *simplest* representation of space relations. Thus it is true in general that *fundamental concepts and axioms are not immediately facts of perception, but are appropriately selected idealizations*

---

[1] See Part I, p. 218 et seq.

of these facts. The precise notion of a point, for example, does not exist in our immediate sense perception, but is only a fictitious limit which, with our mental pictures of a small bit of shrinking space, we can approach without ever reaching.

In contrast with this, one finds frequently now, on the part of persons who are interested only in the logical side of things and not in the side of perception or of the general theory of knowledge, the opinion that *the axioms are only arbitrary statements which we set up at pleasure and the fundamental concepts, likewise, are only arbitrary symbols for things with which we wish to operate.* The truth about such a view is, of course, that *within pure logic* there is no room for these statements and concepts, and that they must therefore be supplied or suggested from other sources—precisely through the influence of perception. Many authors express themselves much more one-sidedly, however, so that in recent years, in the modern theory of axioms, we have frequently found ourselves led in the direction of that philosophy which has long been called *nominalism.* Here interest in things themselves and their properties is entirely lost. What is discussed is the way things are named, and the logical scheme according to which one operates with the names. For example, it is said that we *call* the aggregate of three coordinates a point, "without thinking of any particular object," and we agree "arbitrarily" upon certain statements which shall hold for these points. In such a discussion, we may set up axioms arbitrarily, and without limit, provided only that the laws of logic are satisfied and, above all, that no contradictions appear in the completed structure of statements. For one, I cannot share this point of view. I regard it, rather, as the death of all science. *The axioms of geometry are—according to my way of thinking— not arbitrary, but sensible, statements, which are, in general, induced by space perception and are determined as to their precise content by expediency.*

As a counterpart to the philosophical digressions to which we have repeatedly been led in the foregoing pages, I should like to give some *account of the history of geometry,* in particular of the development of views concerning its foundations. In contrast with similar considerations which we repeatedly gave last winter in the fields of algebra, arithmetic, and analysis, we notice, at the outset, a great difference. These other disciplines, in their modern form, really have a history of only a few centuries. They had their start when men began to calculate with decimal fractions and letters, in round numbers about the year 1500. *Geometry, however, as an independent discipline has a history reaching far back into Greek antiquity.* Indeed, it had even then reached such a high stage of development that for a long period, reaching almost to the present time, men looked upon Greek geometry as a model of a completed science. At the same time, the famous *Elements* (στοιχεῖα) *of Euclid,* by far the most significant systematic textbook to survive, was looked upon as the whole of Greek mathematics. There is, indeed, hardly another book which, for so long, maintained such a place in its field of science. Even today, every mathematician must come to terms with Euclid. To him, therefore, we shall devote the last section of the present chapter.

3. Euclid's Elements

Let me first put before you the edition of this work prepared by J. L. Heiberg [1] of Copenhagen, which is the best from a philological standpoint. In it, the Latin translation of the original Greek text is added, which is also very helpful for those who have not studied Greek. Indeed, Euclid's Greek differs widely, especially in the technical terms, from the Greek taught in the schools. As literature to serve as an introduction to Euclid, I should recommend Zeuthen's *Geschichte der Mathematik im Altertum und Mittelalter* [2] and Max Simon's *Euklid und die 6 planimetrischen Bücher*.[3] You will find your way into the subject if you read first Simon, then Zeuthen's more general discussion, and then the text of Heiberg, but the latter should be read by all means carefully and with a critical mistrust of each translation.

Very little is known of Euclid personally. We know only that he lived *in Alexandria about* 300 B.C. However, we are informed about the *general scientific activity* that existed in Alexandria. After the founding of Alexander's world empire, there arose gradually the need for collecting and bringing into a unified scientific system, everything that the past centuries had created, so that there developed in Alexandria a system of instruction which corresponded closely to certain phases of our university teaching of today. But the *collection and arrangement of the material at hand took precedence over the free onward drive of scientific investigation*, so that a certain tendency to pedantry manifested itself in this whole activity.

Before we go over to a detailed consideration of the *Elements*, let me make some general remarks about *the place in history and the scientific importance of Euclid, or rather of Euclid's Elements*. Although a complete picture of Euclid would require the consideration of his numerous lesser writings, I am nevertheless justified in discussing here only the one great work; for this alone has achieved the remarkable commanding position which, from our standpoint, urgently demands discussion.

As a justification for this commentary, I offer the remark that the underlying reason for the erroneous appraisal of Euclid's *Elements* is a *mistaken belief as to the Greek spirit*, which was widespread for a long time, and which indeed still persists. It was believed that Greek culture confined itself to relatively few fields, but that it wrought in these fields with such complete

---

[1] *Euclid's Opera Omnia*, Books I–V, *Elementa*, Leipzig, 1883–1888.

[2] Copenhagen, 1896.

[3] Leipzig, 1901 = *Abhandlungen zur Geschichte der mathematischen Wissenschaften*, XI. [See also the annotations of T. L. Heath in his English translation of the Heiberg text: *The Thirteen Books of Euclid's Elements*, 3 vols., Cambridge, 1908.]

mastery that its achievements must remain a model for all time supreme and unattainable. The fact is, however, that modern philological science has long since shown this view to be untenable. It has taught us, rather, that the Greeks, as no other people, busied themselves, with the greatest possible versatility, in *all* fields of human culture. Just as their accomplishments in every field were certainly admirable, for their era, so certainly they failed in many things to get beyond what we now consider the very beginnings. In no field can it be said that they attained the all-time summit of human achievement.

As to *mathematics*, in particular, this overestimate—or should I say underestimate?—of Hellenism found expression in the dogma that the Greeks had given very substantial attention to geometry and had set up there a system that could not be surpassed. This belief had led, in particular, to an outright *cult of Euclid's Elements*, in which it was claimed that such a system had been completely realized. In opposition to this old and outworn belief, I make the assertion that although *the Greeks worked fruitfully, not only in geometry, but also in the most varied fields of mathematics, nevertheless we today have gone beyond them everywhere and certainly also in geometry.*

I shall consider this assertion in detail and shall try to justify it. In writing his *Elements*, Euclid wished by no means to compile a cyclopedia of the accumulated geometric knowledge of his time; otherwise he would not have disregarded entire portions of geometry which were certainly known in his day. I need mention only the *theory of conics and of higher curves* which the Greeks had already begun to treat extensively,[1] although we owe its full development to Apollonius (about 200 B.C.). Moreover, the *Elements* were to be merely an *introduction* to the study of geometry, and therefore to mathematics itself. Hence it seems they were intended for a particular purpose. They were to treat mathematics in the way considered necessary, in the sense of the platonic school, as a *preparation for philosophical studies in general*. With this in mind, we see why emphasis was placed upon working out the logical connections and upon setting forth geometry as a closed system, while all practical applications were laid aside. In favor of this system, however, Euclid certainly passed over an entire part of the theoretical knowledge of his time which was not far enough developed to fit into his needs.

We can best obtain a correct impression of the *limited character of the material of Euclid's Elements*, compared with the range of Greek mathematics as a whole, if we use for comparison the individuality and the achievement of the *most eminent of Greek mathematicians, Archimedes*, who lived shortly after Euclid, in Syracuse, about 250 B.C. I shall mention only a few especially interesting and distinguishing facts.

---

[1] Euclid had himself written a work on conics, which has not survived.

1. In marked contrast to the controlling spirit in Euclid's *Elements*, Archimedes shows a strongly developed *sense for numerical calculation*. Indeed, one of his greatest feats, to mention only one definite example, was the calculation of the number π by approximating to the circle with regular polygons. Among other results, he derived the approximation $22/7$ for π. Euclid shows no trace of interest for such numerical values. Instead, we find in Euclid the fact that two circles are to each other as the squares of their radii, or that two circumferences are to each other as the radii themselves; but the calculation of the proportionality factor, this number π, is not even attempted.

2. Characteristic of Archimedes was his far-reaching *interest in applications*. It is well known that he discovered the fundamental principle of hydrostatics, and that he took an active part in the defense of Syracuse, by constructing effective machines. How little thought Euclid gave to applications, on the contrary, appears clearly from the fact that he does not once mention even the simplest drawing instruments—the ruler and compasses. He merely postulates, in the abstract, that one can draw a line through two points, or a circle about a point, without devoting a single word to *how* one does it. Here Euclid is doubtless under the influence of the notion which prevailed in certain ancient schools of philosophy, that practical application of a science was something inferior, artisan-like. Unfortunately this view persists in many places today, and there are still always university teachers who cannot be too scornful of any concern with applications, as being ignoble. The arrogance of such views should be vigorously combatted. We should value equally highly every admirable performance, whether in the theoretical or in the practical field, and we should allow each individual to concern himself with those things to which he feels most strongly inclined. In this way, any person will show himself the more versatile, the more talents he possesses. The most eminent mathematicians, as Archimedes, Newton, Gauss, have always uniformly included both theory and applications.

3. Finally, another difference attracts particular attention. Archimedes was a *great investigator and pioneer*, who, in every one of his works, made advances in knowledge. Euclid's *Elements*, however, are concerned merely with the *collection and systematization* of knowledge already at hand. That is the reason for the difference in the *form of presentation*, to which I drew your attention last semester when I was talking more generally.[1] In this connection, there is an especially characteristic manuscript [2] of Archimedes

---

[1] See Part I, p. 80.

[2] See Heiberg und Zeuthen, *Eine neue Schrift des Archimedes*, Leipzig, 1907. Bibliotheca Mathematica, 3rd series, vol. 7, p. 321 et seq. [See also the edition of Archimedes by T. L. Heath, which was translated into German by F. Klein (Berlin, 1914); the handwriting is reproduced there, p. 413 et seq.]

which was discovered in 1906 (mentioned in Part I), in which he confides to a scientific friend his most recent investigations on the volumes of space figures. His presentation resembles closely our present method of instruction. He proceeds *genetically,* first indicating the train of thought, and by no means using the rigid arrangement of hypothesis, proof, conclusion which characterizes the euclidean *Elements.* Moreover, it was known before this new discovery, that the Greeks had, besides this crystallized "euclidean" presentation of a systematized discipline, also a free genetic form, which was used, not only by the investigator, but also by the teacher in his instruction. Presumably Euclid also employed this method in his other works as well as in his teaching. Indeed, there was in Alexandria at that time an analog of our present-day mimeographed volumes of lectures, called *hypomnemata,* i.e., loose-leaf reproductions of oral presentations.

This will suffice as a comparison of the *Elements* with the whole range of Greek mathematics. As a conclusion of this discussion, I shall show, by means of a few simple examples, how far *modern mathematics* has advanced beyond that of the Greeks. One of the important differences is that the Greeks possessed *no independent* arithmetic or *analysis,* neither decimal fractions, which lighten numerical calculation, nor general use of letters in reckoning. Both of these, as I showed in my lectures last winter, are inventions of early modern times, during the renaissance. As a substitute, the Greeks had only a *calculus in geometric form,* in which operations were performed constructively with segments or other geometric magnitudes, instead of with numbers, a process much more cumbersome than is our arithmetic. Coupled with this also is the fact that the Greeks did not have *negative and imaginary numbers,* which are really what give facility to our arithmetic and analysis. Consequently they lacked the generality of method which permits the inclusion in a formula of all possible cases. A tedious distinguishing of cases played a great role with them. This lack is often very noticeable in geometry, whereas today, by employing analytic aids, as we have actually done in these lectures, we can easily achieve complete generality, and we can avoid all distinction of cases. These few indications will suffice here. You will be able, from your own knowledge, to give many other instances of the advance of modern mathematics as compared with that of the Greeks.

After this general commentary on Euclid's *Elements,* we can turn to a special discussion. Let me begin with a *brief survey of the "thirteen books,"* i.e., chapters, of which they consist.[1]

Books 1–6 are devoted to *planimetry.* The *first four books contain general considerations about fundamental geometric forms,* such as segment, angle, area, etc., and the *theory of simple geometric figures* (triangles, parallelograms,

---

[1] One speaks also of Books 14 and 15 of the *Elements* (vol. 5 of Heiberg's edition); but these two books are not by Euclid. The first comes rather from Hypsikles; the second is ascribed to Damaskios.

circles, regular polygons, etc.), in the manner in which they are usually
given today. In this connection, there is given (Book 2) an *elementary arithmetic and algebra of geometric magnitudes* in which—to give but one example—
the product $a \cdot b$ of two segments a, b is represented as a rectangle. If we
wish to add two such products $a \cdot b$ and $c \cdot d$, which we can carry out at
once arithmetically, it is necessary, in order to represent the product as a
single rectangle again, to transform the two rectangles $a \cdot b$ and $c \cdot d$ into
rectangles with equal bases.

Book 5 goes much deeper, in that it introduces the *geometric equivalent of
the general positive real number*. This is the ratio a/b of any two segments
a, b, which Euclid calls logos (λόγοs). I referred to this last semester, in my
general discussion of irrational numbers.[1] The essential keynote of this
development is the *definition of the equality of two ratios a/b and a/d*. This
definition must be perfectly general, and must hold, therefore, when a/b is, in
our sense, irrational, i.e., when the segments a and b are (as Euclid says)
asymmetroi, i.e., without a common measure, or, as it was translated later,
incommensurable. Euclid proceeds as follows: He takes any two integers
m and n and compares, as to size, the two segments $m \cdot a$ and $n \cdot b$ on the
one hand, and $m \cdot c$ and $n \cdot d$, on the other. There must obtain one of the
three relations

$$m \cdot a \gtreqless n \cdot b \qquad \text{or} \qquad m \cdot c \gtreqless n \cdot d.$$

*If, then, for arbitrary values of m, n, the same sign always holds in both cases,
we say that $a/b = c/d$*. This corresponds completely, in fact, to the famous
cut process by means of which *Dedekind* introduces irrational numbers.

Euclid now proceeds with the consideration as to how one can reckon
with these ratios, and he develops his well-known *theory of proportion*, i.e.,
a geometric theory of all possible algebraic transformations of equations of
the type $a/b = c/d$. Euclid uses for a proportion the word *analogia* by
which he means that the *logos* of the two pairs of magnitudes is the same.
You see how far the word has drifted away today from its original meaning.
There are places in mathematics, however, where the word retains its old
meaning. We still speak in trigonometry of *Napier's analogies*, because these
have to do with certain proportions. To be sure, few persons seem to know
the real meaning of this name.

The *theory of proportion* is a characteristic example of the persistence with
which the euclidean tradition maintains itself in mathematical instruction.
Even today, this theory is taught in many—perhaps, indeed, in most—of
the schools, as a *special chapter of geometry*, although it is included completely,
in substance, in our modern arithmetic, and has therefore been taught twice
before this,—once during the study of the proportion, and again in the beginnings of reckoning with letters. Why the same thing should appear a

---

[1] See Part I, p. 31 et seq.

third time, and in especially mysterious geometric clothing, is truly hard to understand. The tendency to do so must be quite incomprehensible to the students. Of course, the only reason is that men still cling to the old euclidean plan, although, indeed, the sensible purpose which Euclid had in the theory of proportion—to create a substitute for the arithmetic which he lacked—is for us utterly useless.

This criticism of the present-day treatment of the theory of proportion does not refer, of course, to the *scientific importance of the fifth book of Euclid*. That is, of course, great, because there was given here, for the first time—speaking in modern terms—*the rigorous basis for calculation with irrational numbers*, based upon precise definitions. We observe clearly here that Euclid's *Elements* were, and are, by no means a school textbook, as has been so often erroneously assumed. The *Elements* presuppose, rather, a mature reader capable of scientific thinking.

I must mention the tradition that this fifth book was not written by Euclid himself, but by *Eudoxus of Knidos* (circa 350 B.C.). In fact, the *Elements* are looked upon, not as a unified work, written in one piece, but as having been put together out of different older parts.

However this may be, in any case, all of the information as to the authors is clouded with the greatest uncertainty, since there is absolutely nothing extant, in the nature of historical notes, by Euclid or by any of his contemporaries. The above tradition goes back to Proclus Diadochus, a commentator on Euclid who lived about 450 A.D., that is, more than 700 years after Euclid. Even though, for various reasons, the assertion of Proclus may have a certain essential probability, still we should be as little inclined to admit it as absolutely reliable evidence as we should be to accept a theory promulgated today as to the authority of a work compiled around 1200 A.D.

Proceeding with the contents of the *Elements*, we find in Book 6 the *theory of similar figures*, where the principal aid used is the doctrine of proportion.

In Books 7, 8, and 9, the *theory of integers* is treated, *partly in geometric form*. We find here, for proportions with integers, i.e., *for reckoning with rational fractions*, a theory which is entirely independent of the developments of Book 5. Although rational fractions are merely a special kind of real numbers, no reference of any sort is made to the more general theory. It is therefore difficult to believe that the two presentations are by the same author. Of the contents of these books, I should like to mention only two things, both of which are now used in the theory of numbers. One of these is the *euclidean algorithm* for finding the *greatest common divisor* of two integers a and b, which Euclid represents by segments. In modern terms, it consists in dividing a by b, then b by the remainder, and so on according to the scheme

$$a = m \cdot b + r_1, \qquad b = m_1 \cdot r_1 + r_2, \qquad r_1 = m_2 \cdot r_2 + r_3, \qquad \ldots \ldots$$

Finally, after a finite number of steps, the division will be exact. The last remainder is the divisor sought. Secondly, one finds in Euclid the well-known simple proof of the *existence of infinitely many prime numbers*, which I gave in my lectures last winter.[1]

In Book 10, which is especially tedious and hard to understand on account of the geometric form of expression, there is a *geometric classification of irrationalities that are expressible as square roots*, such as were to be used later in geometric constructions.

Not until in Book 11 do we find the beginnings of *stereometry*. You observe that Euclid is no "fusionist." He sets stereometry as far apart from planimetry as possible, whereas we consider it desirable today, in the sense of our oft-mentioned "striving toward fusion," to develop space perception as a whole as early as possible, and consequently to accustom the pupil from the beginning to three-dimensional figures, rather than to restrict artificially his first instruction to the plane.

In Book 12 there appear again *general considerations about irrational magnitudes*, which were necessary for *finding the volume of a pyramid* and of other bodies. Here we find a veiled application of the notion of a limit, in the so-called "proof by exhaustion," by means of which proportions between irrational numbers are rigorously deduced. This method is used first in proving the planimetric theorem that two circles are to each other as the squares

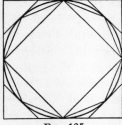

FIG. 125

of their radii, and it is by means of this example that I shall explain briefly the underlying conception of the method. Any circle can be increasingly approximated by an inscribed *n*-gon and also by a circumscribed *n*-gon of an increasing number of sides. It can, in a sense, be *exhausted*, in that the areas of the polygons differ arbitrarily little from the area of the circle. If, then, the proportion did not obtain, one could easily bring about a contradiction of the fact that every inscribed polygon is smaller than the circle, and that every circumscribed is larger than the circle. (See Fig. 125.)

Finally, Book 13 contains the *theory of the regular bodies*, and using the material collected in Book 10, culminates in the proof that one can construct all these bodies, i.e., the lengths of their sides, with ruler and compasses. This final result corresponds to the interest which the Greek philosophers always showed in the regular bodies.

Having given this general survey of the contents, let us turn our attention, in some detail, to those chapters of Euclid which treat of the *foundations of geometry*. The ideal purpose which Euclid had in mind was obviously the *logical derivation of all geometric theorems from a set of premises completely*

---

[1] See Part I, p. 40 et seq.

laid down in advance. The historic significance of the *Elements* rests mainly, without doubt, on the creation (or transmission) of this ideal. But Euclid did not, by any means, really reach his high goal. Indeed, modern science has gained deeper knowledge, in precisely the fundamental notions of geometry, and has found obscurities in Euclid. Nevertheless, tradition is so strong that Euclid's presentation is widely thought of today, especially in England, as the unexcelled pattern for the foundation of geometry. Men mistake the historical importance of the work for absolute and permanent importance. It is only natural, in view of this over-valuation of Euclid's *Elements*, that I should, in the following discussion, lay emphasis upon the negative side, upon those points in which Euclid's presentation no longer meets our requirements.

A special difficulty arises, in every such criticism of Euclid in the *uncertainty of the text.* Much of it is attested by Proclus, who is our oldest source. The oldest manuscripts which we possess are from the ninth century A.D., i.e., they are 1200 years younger than Euclid! Furthermore, these various manuscripts differ greatly, and often precisely in the fundamental parts on which so much depends. Then, too, there is the tradition of Latin and Arabian translators and commentators, in whose works there are many important divergences, due to the efforts to clarify the text. The production of a trustworthy text of the elements is thus an exceedingly complicated philological problem, upon which an amazing amount of acumen has been expended. We must be satisfied with the fact that what is gained by such philological work is, at best, the *most probable text,* but that it *cannot be the true original text.* It by no means follows that what we infer from many different statements, as the most probable course of events, agrees in *all* points with actuality. It is generally admitted that Heiberg's text stands at the summit of modern philological science, and we non-philologists cannot do better than to base our arguments upon it, although we must not forget that it is by no means necessarily identical with the original text. Hence, if we find shortcomings and contradictions in this text, we must always be in doubt as to whether they should be ascribed to Euclid, or whether they slipped in during transmission.

And now, coming to the point, let us first inquire how, in Book 1, the *foundations of geometry are laid.* Euclid places at the head three groups of propositions which he calls ὅροι (*definitiones*), αἰτήματα (*postulata*), and κοιναὶ ἔννοιαι (*communes animi conceptiones*) which we may render in German perhaps by *Erklärungen, Forderungen, und Grundsätze.*[1] For the last group we usually employ, with Proclus, the word *axioms,* which nowadays has extended its meaning to include that of the postulates.

In order to get at the contents of the *definitions,* let us recall how we

---

[1] In non-technical English, we may call these *explanations, agreements,* and *fundamental statements;* in technical terms, *definitions, postulates,* and *axioms.*—THE TRANSLATORS.

started earlier with our development of geometry. We said that we could not define certain things, such as point, line, plane, but that we must look upon them as fundamental concepts familiar to everybody, and that we should state precisely only such of their properties as we wished to use. With that understanding, we were able to construct geometry, up to the point of producing the system of coordinates (x, y, z) of analytic geometry. Only after that did we consider the general notion of a curve, by thinking of x, y, and z as continuous functions of a parameter t. At that time, I indicated that this would include bizarre degenerations, such as curves which completely cover a surface, etc.

Euclid did not have this spirit of cautiousness, or of strategic retreat. He begins with the "definition" of all sorts of geometric concepts, such as *point, line, straight line, surface, plane, angle, circle*, etc. The first "definition" runs: *A point is that which has no part.* We are hardly able to recognize this as a proper definition, since a point is by no means determined by this property alone. Again, we read: *A line is length without breadth.* Here, indeed, even the correctness of the statement is doubtful, if one recognizes the general notion of curve, mentioned above, of which Euclid, of course, knew nothing. Then, thirdly, *a straight line is "defined" as a line which lies evenly with respect to its points.* The meaning of this statement is wholly obscure; all sorts of meaning can be attached to it. It might mean that the line has the same direction everywhere, in which case direction must be admitted as a fundamental notion familiar to everyone. We might also interpret it by saying that a straight line, if realized as a rigid rod, always coincides

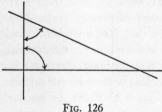

with itself under certain motions in space, namely, under rotation around itself as an axis or under translation along it. This view of Euclid's "definition" would, to be sure, presuppose the notion of motion; whether Euclid intended that is a disputed question to which we shall return. In any event, it has not been possible to find an unam-

FIG. 126

biguous interpretation for Euclid's definition of the straight line, and likewise for many of his other definitions which I cannot consider here in detail.

We come now to the postulates, of which five are given in the Heiberg edition. The first three of these require that *it shall be possible:*

(a) *To draw a straight line from one point to another;*

(b) *to prolong indefinitely a limited straight line;*

(c) *to draw a circle with a given center so as to pass through a given point;*

I shall withhold the fourth, temporarily, and pass on to the fifth, the so-called *parallel postulate:*

(d) *If two straight lines make with a third line, and on the same side of it, interior angles whose sum is less than a straight angle, the two lines cut each other, if they are sufficiently prolonged toward that side.* (See Fig. 126.)

These postulates state the possibility of certain constructions, or the existence of certain geometric figures, of which Euclid makes use later. But there are a considerable number of similar existence-postulates in geometry which he also uses and which cannot be deduced logically from those that he does state. I shall mention, as one example, the theorem that two circles intersect if each passes through the center of the other (see Fig. 127). It would be easy to state many other similar theorems. Hence we must say that the *euclidean system of postulates is certainly deficient.*

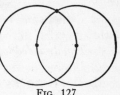

Fig. 127

Let us now consider the *fourth postulate:*

(e) *All right angles are equal.*

There has been much dispute as to what this postulate means, and why it appears where it does. Involved with this is the question as to whether or not Euclid uses the concept of motion. If we consistently put at the beginning the notion of the movement of figures as rigid bodies, as we did in our first development of geometry, then this postulate follows as a necessary logical consequence (see p. 169), and it would therefore be superfluous here, even if Euclid otherwise had this point of view. In all these fundamental theorems of Euclid, however, there is nowhere any explicit mention of motion, so that many interpreters assume that this fourth postulate is to serve precisely to *introduce the idea of motion*, though all would admit, to be sure, that the idea would still be in incomplete form.

On the other hand, most of the commentators on Euclid think that one of the essential tendencies of Euclid was precisely to keep the concept of motion out of geometry, as a matter of principle, in accordance with certain philosophical considerations (see p. 174). But then the *abstract concept of congruence* should be at the head—as in our second development—and then this fourth postulate would have to serve as the *basis for the theory of congruence.* The question arises here, to be sure, why analogous statements are not also made concerning the congruence of segments. But we shall soon see what grave difficulties result from each of these points of view, in the further developments in Euclid.

Let me remark that neither of the two interpretations adequately explains why this theorem is found among the *postulates* whose general tendency is characterized above. This has called forth an interesting explanation from Zeuthen, which is not wholly convincing. He argues that the postulate would state that the prolongation of a line through a point, which by postulate (b) is certainly possible, is *unique.* The details are to be found in Zeuthen's *Geschichte der Mathematik im Altertum und Mittelalter.*[1] Finally,

---

[1] *Loc. cit.*, p. 123 et seq.

there is always this loophole, the assumption that *the text here has been altered*. Indeed, this conclusion has been reached repeatedly and it cannot, in fact, be silenced.

I turn now to the *axioms*, of which there are again five in the Heiberg edition:

(a) *Things equal to the same thing are equal to each other; if $a = b$, $b = c$, then $a = c$.*

(b) *Equals added to equals give equals; if $a = b$, $c = d$, then $a + c = b + d$.*

(c) *If $a = b$, $c = d$, then $a - c = b - d$.*

(d) *Two coincident things are equal.*

(e) *The whole is greater than a part; $a > a - b$.*

Four of the theorems just stated are logical in nature, and, as introduced here, they are obviously intended to state that the general relations which they express hold, in particular, also for all the geometric magnitudes which occur (segments, angles, areas, etc.). The fourth statement, then, declares that the deciding criterion as to equality or inequality is, ultimately, *congruence* or *coincidence*—whereby, to be sure, it is again not clear whether or not the idea of motion is assumed.

Concerning the *difference between axioms and postulates*, Simon has advanced the idea that the former have to do with the *simplest facts of logic*, while the latter deal with those of *space perception*. This would be very fitting and illuminating if it were only certain that the order in the Heiberg text corresponded to that in the original. In the various manuscripts, however, there are actually essential divergences, both as to order and as to content of the postulates and axioms, which by no means fit into this scheme; e.g., the *parallel postulate* is often entered as the eleventh axiom.

Now we shall examine more closely the *beginnings of the euclidean structure of geometry* which is built upon these definitions, postulates, and axioms, namely, the first four paragraphs which immediately follow the axioms. In this we shall be able, at the same time, to make some interesting observations concerning Euclid's conception of the foundations, in particular his attitude toward the idea of motion.

The purpose of the first three paragraphs is to solve the problem of *laying off a given segment AB upon another segment CF, beginning at C*. Practically,

FIG. 128

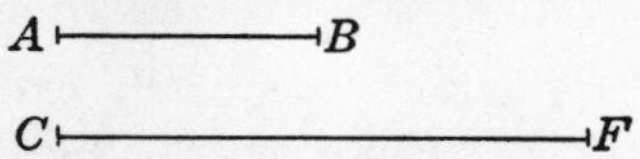

anyone would, of course, do this by direct transference, using a compass or a strip of paper, i.e., by displacing a rigid body in the plane. Euclid does it otherwise with his theoretical method. In his postulates, he has assumed no construction which corresponds to this free movement of the compass. His postulate (c) (see p. 196) permits the drawing of a circle about a point only when a point of the periphery is already given. Now he may make use only of the possibilities afforded by the postulates, and he must therefore break up this apparently simple construction into a number of more complicated, but very clever, steps:

1. *Upon a given segment AB to erect an equilateral triangle.* Postulate (c) permits us to draw a circle about A with radius AB, and one about B with radius BA. That these circles will have a point of intersection C is, as mentioned above, assumed without any explanation. Then follows a rigorous formal logical proof, with use of the appropriate axioms, that ABC is actually equilateral.

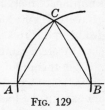

Fig. 129

2. *To lay off from a given point C a segment equal to a given segment AB* (see Fig. 130). By (1), erect

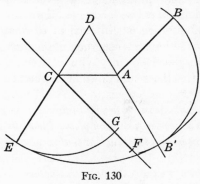

Fig. 130

upon AC an equilateral triangle ACD. Prolong DA beyond A (Postulate b), and strike a circle about A with radius AB (Postulate c), so as to get the intersection B' with DA. (The reason for the existence of this intersection is, to be sure, again not explained.) Now draw a circle about D, with a radius DB', and obtain its intersection E with the extension of DC; then $CE = AB$. The proof, which is obvious, is then given in detail.

3. *Given two segments AB, CF, such that CF > AB; to lay off from C upon CF a segment equal to AB.* By (2), draw from C any segment $CE = AB$ and describe about C a circle, with a radius CE, meeting CF in G; then CG is the desired segment.

With this, the given problem is solved. Euclid now states, as No. 4, the *first congruence*

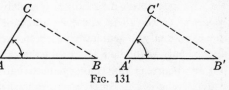

Fig. 131

theorem: If two triangles ABC and $A'B'C'$ have, in each, two sides and their included angle respectively equal ($AB = A'B'$, $AC = A'C'$, $A = A'$), the triangles are equal in all their parts. In proving this theorem, Euclid is guilty, in view of the preceding construction, of a noteworthy *inconsistency*, which supplies the reason for my reproducing this entire proof. He thinks of the triangle $A'B'C'$ laid upon ABC so that the sides $A'B'$ and $A'C'$ fall respectively upon AB and AC, and angle A' upon A. Now we have learned, indeed, in what precedes, how to lay off a *segment* upon another, but not a word has been said as to the laying off of an *angle*, and still less about what would happen, in this process of transfer, *to the third side B'C'*, not even whether or not it would, indeed, remain a *straight line*. Intuitively this is, of course, quite clear; but Euclid's entire purpose is the *logical* completeness of the deduction. Nevertheless he concludes here, without further explanation, that $B'C'$ must also go over into a straight line, which must then, of course, coincide with BC. However, this is nothing else than the assumption of motions which do not change the form and the measurements of geometric figures—just as we explicitly did do in our first development of geometry. If this is done, it is then obvious, of course, that the first congruence theorem can be proved (see p. 175).

Thus this proof of Euclid's would seem to show that he was a supporter of the idea of motion. The question then remains as to why nothing is said about it in the foundations. Above all, his skillful proof of Exercises 2 and 3 would then be without purpose, since that proof could be given in a word by use of the concept of motion. On the other hand, however, if we look upon No. 4 as a later interpolation, the question is still open as to what Euclid's attitude may have been toward the first congruence theorem. Hence there remains an *essential gap* in his development. Without the concept of motion, it is impossible to prove this theorem and we must place it, as we did in our second development, among the axioms (p. 175). We can only say, in concluding this discussion, *that so many essential difficulties present themselves, precisely in the first theorems of the first book of the Elements, that there can be no talk about the attainment of an ideal, such as that mentioned above.*

But all these gaps and obscurities do not weigh so heavily as *another objection* which must be made to Euclid's presentation of the foundations if one measures him by his own ideal and at the same time considers our present knowledge. If we resort to the familiar language of analysis, Euclid, with his geometric magnitudes (segment, angle, surface, etc.), *never uses a sign*—he treats all of these as absolute magnitudes. He carries on, in a sense, an analytic geometry in which the coordinates and other magnitudes appear only with their absolute values. The result of this is that he cannot obtain theorems that have general validity, but must always drag along

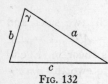

FIG. 132

different cases according as, in a concrete instance, the parts lie thus or so. To mention a simple example, the so-called extended pythagorean theorem, expressed in the modern formula $c^2 = a^2 + b^2 - 2ab \cos \gamma$, holds generally for triangles with acute or obtuse angles (see Fig. 132) since $\cos \gamma$ takes on both positive and negative values. But Euclid knows only the absolute value $|\cos \gamma|$ and he must therefore distinguish the two cases in two different formulas:

$$c^2 = a^2 + b^2 - 2ab \,|\cos \gamma| \qquad \text{and} \qquad c^2 = a^2 + b^2 + 2ab \,|\cos \gamma|;$$

of course these case distinctions become more complicated and less perspicuous the farther one goes.

This lack of which we are talking can of course be formulated for pure geometry. A difference in sign in the analytic presentation corresponds, in pure geometry, to a difference in order, of the type as to whether a point C lies between the points A and B, or outside the segment AB. It is possible to carry out a completely logical construction of geometry, only if we expressly formulate the fundamental facts in this relation of position, the so-called "*axioms of betweenness*," as we did, with emphasis, in our first, as well as in our second, development of geometry. If we omit this, as Euclid does, we cannot reach the ideal of a pure logical control of geometry. We must continually recur to the figure and we must discuss these relations of position. *Our objection, then, against Euclid is, in brief, that he has no axioms of betweenness.*

This view that one must actually formulate certain assumptions concerning the concept "between," in other words, that we must endow the elementary magnitudes with signs, according to certain conventions, is relatively new. At the beginning of these lectures (p. 16), when we discussed this topic, I reported that the first consistent use of the rules of sign is to be found in Möbius' barycentric calculus, in 1827. In this connection there is an interesting letter from Gauss to W. Bolyai, dated March 6, 1832, but first published in 1900 in volume 8 of Gauss' works,[1] in which we find: "For complete achievement, we must first base such words as 'between' upon clear concepts, a thing which is quite feasible but which I have nowhere seen done."

The first careful geometric formulation of these "axioms of betweenness" was given by M. Pasch in 1882 in his *Vorlesungen über neuere Geometrie.*[2] Here there appeared for the first time the characteristic theorem, which we used, by the way, in our first development of geometry (p. 165): *If a straight line meets one side of a triangle, it also meets one of the other two sides.* (See Fig. 133.)

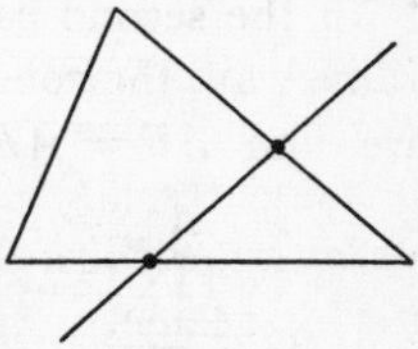

Fig. 133

The significance of these axioms of betweenness must not be underestimated. They are just as important as any of the other axioms, if we wish to develop geometry as a really logical science, which, *after* the axioms are selected, no longer needs to have recourse to intuition and to figures for the deduction of its conclusions. Such recourse is, however, stimulating, and will of course always remain a necessary aid in research. Euclid, who did not have these axioms, always had to consider different cases with the aid of figures. Since he placed so little importance upon correct geometric drawing, there is real danger that a pupil of Euclid may, because of a falsely drawn figure, come to a *false* conclusion. It is in this way that the numerous so-called *geometric sophisms* arise. These are formally correct proofs of false

---

[1] Page 222.   [2] Leipzig, 1882 (2nd edition, 1912).

theorems, which rest on figures which are wrongly drawn, i.e., which contradict the axioms of betweenness. As an example, I shall give one such sophism, which is certainly known to some of you, the *"proof" that every triangle is isosceles.*

Draw the bisector of the angle A, and the perpendicular to the side BC

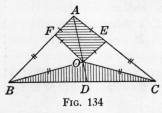

Fig. 134

at its middle point D. If these two lines were parallel, the angle bisector would be also the altitude, and the triangle would obviously be isosceles. We assume then that these two lines meet, and we distinguish two cases, according as the meeting point O lies inside or outside the triangle. In each case, draw OE and OF perpendicular to AC and AB, respectively, and join O to B and to C.

In the first case (see Fig. 134), the horizontally hatched triangles AOE and AOF are congruent, because the side AO is common, and the angles at A are equal, as are also the right angles. Hence $AF = AE$. Similarly the vertically hatched triangles OCD and OBD are congruent, since OD is common, $DB = DC$, and the right angles are equal, so that $OB = OC$. Now, because, from the first congruence, $OE = OF$, we can infer the congruence of the unhatched triangles OEC and OFB. Hence we have $FB = EC$, and, adding this to the former equation, we get actually $AB = AC$.

In the second case, where O lies outside (see Fig. 135) we show, in the same way, the congruence of the three pairs of corresponding triangles, and we find $AF = AE$, $FB = EC$. By subtraction it follows, again, that

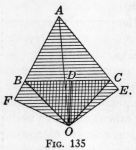

Fig. 135

$AB = AC$, as the figure shows. Hence it is proved that in every case the triangle is isosceles.

The only thing in this proof that is false is the figure. In the first place, O *can never fall inside the triangle;* and, in the second place, the positions can

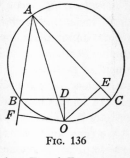

Fig. 136

never be as they are drawn in Fig. 135. Of the two feet E and F, *one must lie inside, the other outside* the side on which it lies, as shown in Fig. 136. Actually, then, we have

$$AB = AF - BF, \qquad AC = AE + CE = AF + BF,$$

and we can by no means infer the equality of the two sides.

This clears up this sophism completely, and we can dispose in a similar way of the many other known sham proofs. The argument is always based upon inaccurate figures, with perverted order of points and lines.

Having criticized some of the essential shortcomings in Euclid's development I should like to point out one of its greatest *refinements*, one which his enthusiastic supporters usually overlook, as they do his errors. I remarked earlier that in the fifth book the *ratio* (logos) of any two geometric magnitudes *a* and *b* is so considered that it gives the equivalent of the general concept of numbers. Now Euclid stipulates here expressly that he will consider the ratio of two geometric magnitudes of the same sort *a and b only under a certain condition: if, namely, two integers m and n can be found such that ma > b and a < nb*. His words are: *Magnitudes have a ratio if their multiples can exceed one another*. This requirement is called nowadays *Archimedes' axiom*, a name which is thoroughly at variance with history, since Euclid had it before Archimedes, and it is probable that Eudoxus knew it. Today the designation *axiom of Eudoxus* is gaining currency.

This archimedean axiom plays a great role as one of the most important continuity postulates in modern investigations in the foundations of geometry, as well as in the foundations of arithmetic. We have accordingly mentioned it repeatedly in these lectures. You will notice, in particular, that the postulate which we used in our first development of geometry, whereby the points arising from *A*, through iteration of a translation, ultimately include every point of a ray (p. 163), is identical in substance with the archimedean axiom. But we also discussed this axiom in detail in the first part of this present work.[1] We then called a quantity *a* which, after multiplication by any finite number *n*, remained always smaller than *b*, *actually infinitely small with respect to b*, or conversely, *b actually infinitely large with respect to a*. Thus what Euclid does, by his prescription, is to exclude systems of geometric magnitudes which contain actually infinitely small or infinitely large elements. In fact, it is necessary to exclude such systems, if we wish to develop the doctrine of proportion, which, as we have emphasized, is nothing else than another form of the modern theory of irrational number. Thus Euclid (or, indeed, Eudoxus before him) does here—and that is the remarkable part of it—fundamentally exactly what one does in the modern investigations of the concept of number, and he does it with exactly the same tools.

We shall appreciate best the significance of the axiom under discussion if we examine a *concrete system of geometric magnitudes which does not satisfy it*, and which is also particularly interesting because it was already known and much discussed in ancient and in medieval times. I refer to the so-called *horn-shaped angles*, that is, *angles between curves*, thought of in a certain general way. When we speak today of angles, we think always of angles between straight lines; and by the angle between two curves, in particular, we understand the angle between their *tangents* (Fig. 137). The angle between a curve, say a circle, and its own tangent is then always

---

[1] See Part I, p. 218.

zero. In this way, all angles form an ordinary "archimedean" system of magnitudes, to which we can apply the euclidean theory of ratio, which, in other words, is measured in terms of simple real numbers.

In contrast to this, we understand by the *horn-shaped angle between two curves* (see Fig. 138) the *portion of the plane enclosed* by the curves them-

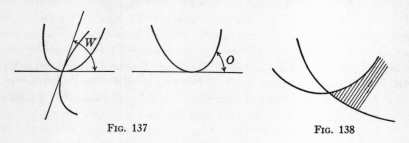

FIG. 137   FIG. 138

selves, in the neighborhood of their intersection (or point of contact), and we shall now see how this definition gives rise to the concept of a *non-archimedean magnitude*, i.e., *to a concept which does not satisfy that axiom*. We shall confine ourselves, here, to angles *one of whose arms is a fixed line* (the *x* axis), whose vertex is the origin *O*, and whose other arm is a circle (in case of need also a straight line) which cuts or touches the *x* axis in *O* (Fig. 139). It will then be natural to call that one of two horn-shaped angles the smaller *whose free arm ultimately remains below the free arm of the other, when we approach O*, i.e., the one which ultimately bounds the narrower portion of the plane. The angle of a *tangent* circle will thus always be smaller than that of an *intersecting* circle or of a straight line. Of two tangent circles,

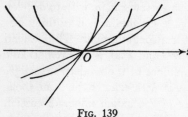

FIG. 139

the one with the *larger* radius will make the *smaller* angle, since it passes below the other. It is clear that these agreements determine, for any two of our horn-shaped angles, which of them is the smaller and which the larger, so that the totality of horn-shaped angles is *simply ordered*, as one says today in point set theory, precisely as is the case with the totality of ordinary real numbers.

In order to appreciate the difference between these two aggregates, we must agree upon something more precise concerning the *measuring of horn-shaped angles*. Let us, first of all, measure the angle of a straight line through *O* in *ordinary angle units*. Then every angle *a*, made by a circle tangent to the *x* axis, will be smaller, by definition, than any angle bounded by two straight lines, however small it may be, provided only that it is but different from zero. Such a situation is impossible, however, in the ordinary number continuum, for a number a different from zero, and it characterizes our a as "actually infinitely small."

In order to follow this in connection with the archimedean axiom, we must define, for these curvilinear angles, *multiplication by an integer*. If we have a circle of radius R tangent at O, then it seems natural to ascribe to the tangent circle of radius R/n the n-fold angle. This actually accords with the preceding definition, insofar as the angles of tangent circles with radii R, $R/2$, $R/3$, $\cdots$, get larger and larger. Thus multiplication of the angle a of a tangent circle by an integer always yields another angle of a *tangent* circle, and every multiple na is necessarily smaller, by our definition, than, say, the angle b of a fixed intersecting straight line (see Fig. 140), however large we take n. Thus the *axiom of Archimedes is not satisfied;* and the angles of the tangent circles must be looked upon, accordingly, as actually infinitely small with respect to the angle of an intersecting straight line. As to *general addition* of two such angles, that will be done, in view of the definition already set up for multiplication by integers, by adding the reciprocal values of the radii, which will serve,

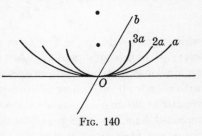

Fig. 140

after all, as the measures of the actually infinitely small angles.

If we have now an *arbitrary circle through O* (see Fig. 141), we can look upon its angle as the sum of the angle of its tangent with the x axis (measured in the ordinary sense), and of its own actually infinitely small angle with

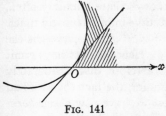

Fig. 141

that tangent, in the sense just defined. If we then apply addition and multiplication to these separate summands, we shall have set up a complete method for operating with horn-shaped angles. But in this field the axiom of Archimedes does not hold, and one may not, therefore, employ in it "logoi," or ordinary real numbers. Presumably this was known to Euclid (and Eudoxus), and he consciously excluded such systems of magnitudes by means of his axiom.

With modern methods we can *extend* the field of these horn-shaped angles, whereby the definitions become both broader and simpler—if we consider *all of the analytic curves through O*. Any such curve will be given by a power series $y_1 = \alpha_1 x + \beta_1 x^2 + \gamma_1 x^3 + \cdots$, $y_2 = \alpha_2 x + \beta_2 x^2 + \gamma_2 x^3 + \cdots$. We shall say that the angle of the curve 1 with the x axis is greater or less than that of 2 according as $\alpha_1 > \alpha_2$ or $\alpha_1 < \alpha_2$; if, however, $\alpha_1 = \alpha_2$, then relative size depends upon the inequalities $\beta_1 \gtrless \beta_2$; if $\beta_1 = \beta_2$, then the decision rests upon the inequalities $\gamma_1 \gtrless \gamma_2$, etc. It is clear that, in this way, *the angles of all analytic curves are brought into a definite simply ordered series*, in which circles are included in the order defined for them above.

To get the n-tuple of the angle of curve 1 with the x axis, we can simply take the angle of the curve $n \cdot y = n\alpha_1 x + n\beta_1 x^2 + \cdots$, obtained by multiplying the power series by n. Before, we had to employ a more complicated operation, in order not to go outside the field of circles; namely, we replaced the circle of radius R, whose series expansion is

$$y = \frac{x^2}{2R} + \frac{x^4}{8R^3} + \cdots$$

by one of radius R/n:

$$y = n\frac{x^2}{2R} + n^3 \frac{x^4}{8R^3} + \cdots,$$

which agrees only to the first term with n times the first expansion. However, with this new and simpler definition we also have again a non-archimedean system of magnitudes. A curve whose series expansion begins with $x^2 (\alpha_2 = 0)$ will, after multiplication by arbitrarily large n, still make a smaller angle than a curve with non-vanishing α_1. We have, in essence, only repeated here, in more perspicuous form, what we did in volume 1.[1] In the power series $y = \alpha x + \beta x^2 + \gamma x^3 + \cdots$, the successive powers x, x^2, x^3, $\cdots$, simply play, in this interpretation, the role of actually infinitely small magnitudes of different, ever-increasing order.

It is interesting that we can condense this succession of horn-shaped angles still more by adding *certain non-analytic curves*. However, in order to permit of comparison as to size, they must not oscillate infinitely often, or, more precisely, they may not cut an analytic curve infinitely many times. It will suffice if I give one example, the curve $y = e^{-1/x^2}$. This curve has the property that all its derivatives vanish at $x = 0$. Hence it does not permit there a development in power series. It is clear, therefore, that it ultimately passes below *every* analytic curve. Notwithstanding the fact that we had before a dense succession of horn-shaped angles, we have now a *new horn-shaped angle which, together with its finite multiples, is smaller than any angle made with the x axis by any analytic curve*.

With this we shall conclude these discussions and our entire study of Euclid. In closing, I shall summarize, in a few sentences, the *judgment concerning Euclid's Elements which we have reached in all these deliberations*.

1. The *great historical significance* of Euclid's *Elements* consists in the fact that through them there was passed on to later times the *ideal of a consistent logical development of geometry*.

---

[1] Part I, p. 218 et seq., where the magnitudes of different orders were called η, ζ, $\cdots$.

2. *As to its execution, much of it is very nicely done; much of the remainder, however, remains decidedly below our present scientific requirements.*

3. Numerous *details of an important nature*, especially at the beginning of the first book, remain *doubtful*, because of uncertainties in the text.

4. The entire development seems often *unnecessarily cumbersome*, because Euclid had *no arithmetic* ready at hand.

5. *One-sided emphasis on the logical processes* renders difficult both the understanding of the work as a whole, and its essential connections.

I should like to characterize farther our own attitude toward the development of geometry, by recalling two conceptions which have already been noticed at different points.

One of these has to do with the fact that we were able to develop geometry according to entirely different plans. We gave careful attention to two of these. The one method started with the notion of a group of motions, in particular the group of translations. The other began with the axioms of congruence and pushed parallelism to a much later place. This juxtaposition gives prominence to the freedom which we have in the axiomatic foundation of geometry. And I should like especially to emphasize again this fact, in the face of intolerant utterances which one often hears, and which are aimed at championing this or that pet concept of the author, as *absolutely* the simplest and, in fact, the *only* suitable one to use in the foundations of geometry. As a matter of fact, the source of all fundamental geometric concepts and axioms is our naive geometric perception. From it we choose the data which, in appropriate idealization, we lay at the base of the logical treatment. As to which choice should be made, however, there can be no *absolute* judgment. The freedom which exists here is subject to only one restriction, namely, the requirement that the system of axioms shall fulfill its purpose of guaranteeing a consistent development of geometry.

Another observation concerns our attitude to analytic geometry, and our criticism of certain traditions, from Euclid on, which have long since ceased to conform to the position of mathematical science, and which should, on that account, be given up in school instruction. In Euclid, geometry, by reason of its axioms, is the rigorous foundation of general arithmetic, including also the arithmetic of irrational numbers. Arithmetic remained in this position of bondage to geometry well on into the nineteenth century, but since then there has been a change. Today arithmetic, as a proper fundamental discipline, has reached a dominating place. This is a fact which ought to be reckoned with in the development of scientific geometry, i.e., geometry should make its start upon the basis of the results of arithmetic. The attitude to analytic geometry which we took in our development, and the fact that we have systematically made use of the resources of analysis in the treatment of geometry, merit approval in this sense.

With this we bring to a close our discussions of the theories of pure geometry, with the hope that they have given you the desired survey of the whole field, insofar as it has any relation to the needs of the schools.

INDEX OF NAMES

INDEX OF CONTENTS

CATALOG OF DOVER BOOKS

BOOKS EXPLAINING SCIENCE AND MATHEMATICS

THE COMMON SENSE OF THE EXACT SCIENCES, W. K. Clifford. Introduction by James Newman, edited by Karl Pearson. For 70 years this has been a guide to classical scientific and mathematical thought. Explains with unusual clarity basic concepts, such as extension of meaning of symbols, characteristics of surface boundaries, properties of plane figures, vectors, Cartesian method of determining position, etc. Long preface by Bertrand Russell. Bibliography of Clifford. Corrected, 130 diagrams redrawn. 249pp. 5⅜ x 8.
T61 Paperbound **$1.60**

SCIENCE THEORY AND MAN, Erwin Schrödinger. This is a complete and unabridged reissue of SCIENCE AND THE HUMAN TEMPERAMENT plus an additional essay: "What is an Elementary Particle?" Nobel Laureate Schrödinger discusses such topics as nature of scientific method, the nature of science, chance and determinism, science and society, conceptual models for physical entities, elementary particles and wave mechanics. Presentation is popular and may be followed by most people with little or no scientific training. "Fine practical preparation for a time when laws of nature, human institutions . . . are undergoing a critical examination without parallel," Waldemar Kaempffert, N. Y. TIMES. 192pp. 5⅜ x 8.
T428 Paperbound **$1.35**

PIONEERS OF SCIENCE, O. Lodge. Eminent scientist-expositor's authoritative, yet elementary survey of great scientific theories. Concentrating on individuals—Copernicus, Brahe, Kepler, Galileo, Descartes, Newton, Laplace, Herschel, Lord Kelvin, and other scientists—the author presents their discoveries in historical order adding biographical material on each man and full, specific explanations of their achievements. The clear and complete treatment of the post-Newtonian astronomers is a feature seldom found in other books on the subject. Index. 120 illustrations. xv + 404pp. 5⅜ x 8.
T716 Paperbound **$1.50**

THE EVOLUTION OF SCIENTIFIC THOUGHT FROM NEWTON TO EINSTEIN, A. d'Abro. Einstein's special and general theories of relativity, with their historical implications, are analyzed in non-technical terms. Excellent accounts of the contributions of Newton, Riemann, Weyl, Planck, Eddington, Maxwell, Lorentz and others are treated in terms of space and time, equations of electromagnetics, finiteness of the universe, methodology of science. 21 diagrams. 482pp. 5⅜ x 8.
T2 Paperound **$2.00**

THE RISE OF THE NEW PHYSICS, A. d'Abro. A half-million word exposition, formerly titled THE DECLINE OF MECHANISM, for readers not versed in higher mathematics. The only thorough explanation, in everyday language, of the central core of modern mathematical physical theory, treating both classical and modern theoretical physics, and presenting in terms almost anyone can understand the equivalent of 5 years of study of mathematical physics. Scientifically impeccable coverage of mathematical-physical thought from the Newtonian system up through the electronic theories of Dirac and Heisenberg and Fermi's statistics. Combines both history and exposition; provides a broad yet unified and detailed view, with constant comparison of classical and modern views on phenomena and theories. "A must for anyone doing serious study in the physical sciences," JOURNAL OF THE FRANKLIN INSTITUTE. "Extraordinary faculty . . . to explain ideas and theories of theoretical physics in the language of daily life," ISIS. First part of set covers philosophy of science, drawing upon the practice of Newton, Maxwell, Poincaré, Einstein, others, discussing modes of thought, experiment, interpretations of causality, etc. In the second part, 100 pages explain grammar and vocabulary of mathematics, with discussions of functions, groups, series, Fourier series, etc. The remainder is devoted to concrete, detailed coverage of both classical and quantum physics, explaining such topics as analytic mechanics, Hamilton's principle, wave theory of light, electromagnetic waves, groups of transformations, thermodynamics, phase rule, Brownian movement, kinetics, special relativity, Planck's original quantum theory, Bohr's atom, Zeeman effect, Broglie's wave mechanics, Heisenberg's uncertainty, Eigen-values, matrices, scores of other important topics. Discoveries and theories are covered for such men as Alembert, Born, Cantor, Debye, Euler, Foucault, Galois, Gauss, Hadamard, Kelvin, Kepler, Laplace, Maxwell, Pauli, Rayleigh, Volterra, Weyl, Young, more than 180 others. Indexed. 97 illustrations. ix + 982pp. 5⅜ x 8.
T3 Volume 1, Paperbound **$2.00**
T4 Volume 2, Paperbound **$2.00**

CONCERNING THE NATURE OF THINGS, Sir William Bragg. Christmas lectures delivered at the Royal Society by Nobel laureate. Why a spinning ball travels in a curved track; how uranium is transmuted to lead, etc. Partial contents: atoms, gases, liquids, crystals, metals, etc. No scientific background needed; wonderful for intelligent child. 32pp. of photos, 57 figures. xii + 232pp. 5⅜ x 8.
T31 Paperbound **$1.35**

THE UNIVERSE OF LIGHT, Sir William Bragg. No scientific training needed to read Nobel Prize winner's expansion of his Royal Institute Christmas Lectures. Insight into nature of light, methods and philosophy of science. Explains lenses, reflection, color, resonance, polarization, x-rays, the spectrum, Newton's work with prisms, Huygens' with polarization, Crookes' with cathode ray, etc. Leads into clear statement of 2 major historical theories of light, corpuscle and wave. Dozens of experiments you can do. 199 illus., including 2 full-page color plates. 293pp. 5⅜ x 8.
S538 Paperbound **$1.85**

PHYSICS, THE PIONEER SCIENCE, L. W. Taylor. First thorough text to place all important physical phenomena in cultural-historical framework; remains best work of its kind. Exposition of physical laws, theories developed chronologically, with great historical, illustrative experiments diagrammed, described, worked out mathematically. Excellent physics text for self-study as well as class work. Vol. 1: Heat, Sound: motion, acceleration, gravitation, conservation of energy, heat engines, rotation, heat, mechanical energy, etc. 211 illus. 407pp. 5⅜ x 8. Vol. 2: Light, Electricity: images, lenses, prisms, magnetism, Ohm's law, dynamos, telegraph, quantum theory, decline of mechanical view of nature, etc. Bibliography. 13 table appendix. Index. 551 illus. 2 color plates. 508pp. 5⅜ x 8.

Vol. 1 S565 Paperbound **$2.00**
Vol. 2 S566 Paperbound **$2.00**
The set **$4.00**

FROM EUCLID TO EDDINGTON: A STUDY OF THE CONCEPTIONS OF THE EXTERNAL WORLD, Sir Edmund Whittaker. A foremost British scientist traces the development of theories of natural philosophy from the western rediscovery of Euclid to Eddington, Einstein, Dirac, etc. The inadequacy of classical physics is contrasted with present day attempts to understand the physical world through relativity, non-Euclidean geometry, space curvature, wave mechanics, etc. 5 major divisions of examination: Space; Time and Movement; the Concepts of Classical Physics; the Concepts of Quantum Mechanics; the Eddington Universe. 212pp. 5⅜ x 8.
T491 Paperbound **$1.35**

THE STORY OF ATOMIC THEORY AND ATOMIC ENERGY, J. G. Feinberg. Wider range of facts on physical theory, cultural implications, than any other similar source. Completely non-technical. Begins with first atomic theory, 600 B.C., goes through A-bomb, developments to 1959. Avogadro, Rutherford, Bohr, Einstein, radioactive decay, binding energy, radiation danger, future benefits of nuclear power, dozens of other topics, told in lively, related, informal manner. Particular stress on European atomic research. "Deserves special mention . . . authoritative," Saturday Review. Formerly "The Atom Story." New chapter to 1959. Index. 34 illustrations. 251pp. 5⅜ x 8.
T625 Paperbound **$1.45**

THE STRANGE STORY OF THE QUANTUM, AN ACCOUNT FOR THE GENERAL READER OF THE GROWTH OF IDEAS UNDERLYING OUR PRESENT ATOMIC KNOWLEDGE, B. Hoffmann. Presents lucidly and expertly, with barest amount of mathematics, the problems and theories which led to modern quantum physics. Dr. Hoffmann begins with the closing years of the 19th century, when certain trifling discrepancies were noticed, and with illuminating analogies and examples takes you through the brilliant concepts of Planck, Einstein, Pauli, de Broglie, Bohr, Schroedinger, Heisenberg, Dirac, Sommerfeld, Feynman, etc. This edition includes a new, long postscript carrying the story through 1958. "Of the books attempting an account of the history and contents of our modern atomic physics which have come to my attention, this is the best," H. Margenau, Yale University, in "American Journal of Physics." 32 tables and line illustrations. Index. 275pp. 5⅜ x 8.
T518 Paperbound **$1.45**

SPACE AND TIME, Emile Borel. An entirely non-technical introduction to relativity, by world-renowned mathematician, Sorbonne Professor. (Notes on basic mathematics are included separately.) This book has never been surpassed for insight, and extraordinary clarity of thought, as it presents scores of examples, analogies, arguments, illustrations, which explain such topics as: difficulties due to motion; gravitation a force of inertia; geodesic lines; wave-length and difference of phase; x-rays and crystal structure; the special theory of relativity; and much more. Indexes. 4 appendixes. 15 figures. xvi + 243pp. 5⅜ x 8.
T592 Paperbound **$1.45**

THE RESTLESS UNIVERSE, Max Born. New enlarged version of this remarkably readable account by a Nobel laureate. Moving from sub-atomic particles to universe, the author explains in very simple terms the latest theories of wave mechanics. Partial contents: air and its relatives, electrons & ions, waves & particles, electronic structure of the atom, nuclear physics. Nearly 1000 illustrations, including 7 animated sequences. 325pp. 6 x 9.
T412 Paperbound **$2.00**

SOAP BUBBLES, THEIR COLOURS AND THE FORCES WHICH MOULD THEM, C. V. Boys. Only complete edition, half again as much material as any other. Includes Boys' hints on performing his experiments, sources of supply. Dozens of lucid experiments show complexities of liquid films, surface tension, etc. Best treatment ever written. Introduction. 83 illustrations. Color plate. 202pp. 5⅜ x 8.
T542 Paperbound **95¢**

SPINNING TOPS AND GYROSCOPIC MOTION, John Perry. Well-known classic of science still unsurpassed for lucid, accurate, delightful exposition. How quasi-rigidity is induced in flexible and fluid bodies by rapid motions; why gyrostat falls, top rises; nature and effect on climatic conditions of earth's precessional movement; effect of internal fluidity on rotating bodies, etc. Appendixes describe practical uses to which gyroscopes have been put in ships, compasses, monorail transportation. 62 figures. 128pp. 5⅜ x 8.
T416 Paperbound **$1.00**

MATTER & LIGHT, THE NEW PHYSICS, L. de Broglie. Non-technical papers by a Nobel laureate explain electromagnetic theory, relativity, matter, light and radiation, wave mechanics, quantum physics, philosophy of science. Einstein, Planck, Bohr, others explained so easily that no mathematical training is needed for all but 2 of the 21 chapters. Unabridged. Index. 300pp. 5⅜ x 8.
T35 Paperbound **$1.60**

A SURVEY OF PHYSICAL THEORY, Max Planck. One of the greatest scientists of all time, creator of the quantum revolution in physics, writes in non-technical terms of his own discoveries and those of other outstanding creators of modern physics. Planck wrote this book when science had just crossed the threshold of the new physics, and he communicates the excitement felt then as he discusses electromagnetic theories, statistical methods, evolution of the concept of light, a step-by-step description of how he developed his own momentous theory, and many more of the basic ideas behind modern physics. Formerly "A" Survey of Physics." Bibliography. Index. 128pp. 5⅜ x 8.   S650 Paperbound **$1.15**

THE NATURE OF LIGHT AND COLOUR IN THE OPEN AIR, M. Minnaert. Why is falling snow sometimes black? What causes mirages, the fata morgana, multiple suns and moons in the sky? How are shadows formed? Prof. Minnaert of the University of Utrecht answers these and similar questions in optics, light, colour, for non-specialists. Particularly valuable to nature, science students, painters, photographers. Translated by H. M. Kremer-Priest, K. Jay. 202 illustrations, including 42 photos. xvi + 362pp. 5⅜ x 8.   T196 Paperbound **$1.95**

THE STORY OF X-RAYS FROM RONTGEN TO ISOTOPES, A. R. Bleich. Non-technical history of x-rays, their scientific explanation, their applications in medicine, industry, research, and art, and their effect on the individual and his descendants. Includes amusing early reactions to Röntgen's discovery, cancer therapy, detections of art and stamp forgeries, potential risks to patient and operator, etc. Illustrations show x-rays of flower structure, the gall bladder, gears with hidden defects, etc. Original Dover publication. Glossary. Bibliography. Index. 55 photos and figures. xiv + 186pp. 5⅜ x 8.   T662 Paperbound **$1.35**

TEACH YOURSELF ELECTRICITY, C. W. Wilman. Electrical resistance, inductance, capacitance, magnets, chemical effects of current, alternating currents, generators and motors, transformers, rectifiers, much more. 230 questions, answers, worked examples. List of units. 115 illus. 194pp. 6⅞ x 4¼.   Clothbound **$2.00**

TEACH YOURSELF HEAT ENGINES, E. De Ville. Measurement of heat, development of steam and internal combustion engines, efficiency of an engine, compression-ignition engines, production of steam, the ideal engine, much more. 318 exercises, answers, worked examples. Tables. 76 illus. 220pp. 6⅞ x 4¼.   Clothbound **$2.00**

TEACH YOURSELF MECHANICS, P. Abbott. The lever, centre of gravity, parallelogram of force, friction, acceleration, Newton's laws of motion, machines, specific gravity, gas, liquid pressure, much more. 280 problems, solutions. Tables. 163 illus. 271pp. 6⅞ x 4¼.
                                                                                       Clothbound **$2.00**

GREAT IDEAS OF MODERN MATHEMATICS: THEIR NATURE AND USE, Jagjit Singh. Reader with only high school math will understand main mathematical ideas of modern physics, astronomy, genetics, psychology, evolution, etc., better than many who use them as tools, but comprehend little of their basic structure. Author uses his wide knowledge of non-mathematical fields in brilliant exposition of differential equations, matrices, group theory, logic, statistics, problems of mathematical foundations, imaginary numbers, vectors, etc. Original publication. 2 appendixes. 2 indexes. 65 illustr. 322pp. 5⅜ x 8.   S587 Paperbound **$1.55**

MATHEMATICS IN ACTION, O. G. Sutton. Everyone with a command of high school algebra will find this book one of the finest possible introductions to the application of mathematics to physical theory. Ballistics, numerical analysis, waves and wavelike phenomena, Fourier series, group concepts, fluid flow and aerodynamics, statistical measures, and meteorology are discussed with unusual clarity. Some calculus and differential equations theory is developed by the author for the reader's help in the more difficult sections. 88 figures. Index. viii + 236pp. 5⅜ x 8.   T440 Clothbound **$3.50**

FREE! All you do is ask for it!

THE FOURTH DIMENSION SIMPLY EXPLAINED, edited by H. P. Manning. 22 essays, originally Scientific American contest entries, that use a minimum of mathematics to explain aspects of 4-dimensional geometry: analogues to 3-dimensional space, 4-dimensional absurdities and curiosities (such as removing the contents of an egg without puncturing its shell), possible measurements and forms, etc. Introduction by the editor. Only book of its sort on a truly elementary level, excellent introduction to advanced works. 82 figures. 251pp. 5⅜ x 8.
                                                                                T711 Paperbound **$1.35**

FAMOUS BRIDGES OF THE WORLD, D. B. Steinman. An up-to-the-minute revised edition of a book that explains the fascinating drama of how the world's great bridges came to be built. The author, designer of the famed Mackinac bridge, discusses bridges from all periods and all parts of the world, explaining their various types of construction, and describing the problems their builders faced. Although primarily for youngsters, this cannot fail to interest readers of all ages. 48 illustrations in the text. 23 photographs. 99pp. 6⅛ x 9¼.
                                                                                T161 Paperbound **$1.00**

BRIDGES AND THEIR BUILDERS, David Steinman and Sara Ruth Watson. Engineers, historians, everyone who has ever been fascinated by great spans will find this book an endless source of information and interest. Dr. Steinman, recipient of the Louis Levy medal, was one of the great bridge architects and engineers of all time, and his analysis of the great bridges of history is both authoritative and easily followed. Greek and Roman bridges, medieval bridges, Oriental bridges, modern works such as the Brooklyn Bridge and the Golden Gate Bridge, and many others are described in terms of history, constructional principles, artistry, and function. All in all this book is the most comprehensive and accurate semipopular history of bridges in print in English. New, greatly revised, enlarged edition. 23 photographs, 26 line drawings. Index. xvii + 401pp. 5⅜ x 8.   T431 Paperbound **$2.00**

FADS AND FALLACIES IN THE NAME OF SCIENCE, Martin Gardner. Examines various cults, quack systems, frauds, delusions which at various times have masqueraded as science. Accounts of hollow-earth fanatics like Symmes; Velikovsky and wandering planets; Hoerbiger; Bellamy and the theory of multiple moons; Charles Fort; dowsing, pseudoscientific methods for finding water, ores, oil. Sections on naturopathy, iridiagnosis, zone therapy, food fads, etc. Analytical accounts of Wilhelm Reich and orgone sex energy; L. Ron Hubbard and Dianetics; A. Korzybski and General Semantics; many others. Brought up to date to include Bridey Murphy, others. Not just a collection of anecdotes, but a fair, reasoned appraisal of eccentric theory. Formerly titled IN THE NAME OF SCIENCE. Preface. Index. x + 384pp. 5⅜ x 8.   T394 Paperbound **$1.50**

See also: A PHILOSOPHICAL ESSAY ON PROBABILITIES, P. de Laplace; ON MATHEMATICS AND MATHEMATICIANS, R. E. Moritz; AN ELEMENTARY SURVEY OF CELESTIAL MECHANICS, Y. Ryabov; THE SKY AND ITS MYSTERIES, E. A. Beet; THE REALM OF THE NEBULAE, E. Hubble; OUT OF THE SKY, H. H. Nininger; SATELLITES AND SCIENTIFIC RESEARCH, D. King-Hele; HEREDITY AND YOUR LIFE, A. M. Winchester; INSECTS AND INSECT LIFE, S. W. Frost; PRINCIPLES OF STRATIGRAPHY, A. W. Grabau; TEACH YOURSELF SERIES.

HISTORY OF SCIENCE AND MATHEMATICS

DIALOGUES CONCERNING TWO NEW SCIENCES, Galileo Galilei. This classic of experimental science, mechanics, engineering, is as enjoyable as it is important. A great historical document giving insights into one of the world's most original thinkers, it is based on 30 years' experimentation. It offers a lively exposition of dynamics, elasticity, sound, ballistics, strength of materials, the scientific method. "Superior to everything else of mine," Galileo. Trans. by H. Crew, A. Salvio. 126 diagrams. Index. xxi + 288pp. 5⅜ x 8.
    S99 Paperbound **$1.65**

A DIDEROT PICTORIAL ENCYCLOPEDIA OF TRADES AND INDUSTRY, Manufacturing and the Technical Arts in Plates Selected from "L'Encyclopédie ou Dictionnaire Raisonné des Sciences, des Arts, et des Métiers" of Denis Diderot. Edited with text by C. Gillispie. This first modern selection of plates from the high point of 18th century French engraving is a storehouse of valuable technological information to the historian of arts and science. Over 2000 illustrations on 485 full page plates, most of them original size, show the trades and industries of a fascinating era in such great detail that the processes and shops might very well be reconstructed from them. The plates teem with life, with men, women, and children performing all of the thousands of operations necessary to the trades before and during the early stages of the industrial revolution. Plates are in sequence, and show general operations, closeups of difficult operations, and details of complex machinery. Such important and interesting trades and industries are illustrated as sowing, harvesting, beekeeping, cheesemaking, operating windmills, milling flour, charcoal burning, tobacco processing, indigo, fishing, arts of war, salt extraction, mining, smelting, casting iron, steel, extracting mercury, zinc, sulphur, copper, etc., slating, tinning, silverplating, gilding, making gunpowder, cannons, bells, shoeing horses, tanning, papermaking, printing, dyeing, and more than 40 other categories. Professor Gillispie, of Princeton, supplies a full commentary on all the plates, identifying operations, tools, processes, etc. This material, presented in a lively and lucid fashion, is of great interest to the reader interested in history of science and technology. Heavy library cloth. 920pp. 9 x 12.   T421 Two volume set **$18.50**

DE MAGNETE, William Gilbert. This classic work on magnetism founded a new science. Gilbert was the first to use the word "electricity", to recognize mass as distinct from weight, to discover the effect of heat on magnetic bodies; invent an electroscope, differentiate between static electricity and magnetism, conceive of the earth as a magnet. Written by the first great experimental scientist, this lively work is valuable not only as an historical landmark, but as the delightfully easy to follow record of a perpetually searching, ingenious mind. Translated by P. F. Mottelay. 25 page biographical memoir. 90 figures. lix + 368pp. 5⅜ x 8.   S470 Paperbound **$2.00**

CHARLES BABBAGE AND HIS CALCULATING ENGINES, edited by P. Morrison and E. Morrison. Babbage, leading 19th century pioneer in mathematical machines and herald of modern operational research, was the true father of Harvard's relay computer Mark I. His Difference Engine and Analytical Engine were the first machines in the field. This volume contains a valuable introduction on his life and work; major excerpts from his autobiography, revealing his eccentric and unusual personality; and extensive selections from "Babbage's Calculating Engines," a compilation of hard-to-find journal articles by Babbage, the Countess of Lovelace, L. F. Menabrea, and Dionysius Lardner. 8 illustrations, Appendix of miscellaneous papers. Index. Bibliography. xxxviii + 400pp. 5⅜ x 8.   T12 Paperbound **$2.00**

A HISTORY OF ASTRONOMY FROM THALES TO KEPLER, J. L. E. Dreyer. (Formerly A HISTORY OF PLANETARY SYSTEMS FROM THALES TO KEPLER.) This is the only work in English to give the complete history of man's cosmological views from prehistoric times to Kepler and Newton. Partial contents: Near Eastern astronomical systems, Early Greeks, Homocentric Spheres of Eudoxus, Epicycles, Ptolemaic system, medieval cosmology, Copernicus, Kepler, etc. Revised, foreword by W. H. Stahl. New bibliography. xvii + 430pp. 5⅜ x 8.
S79 Paperbound **$1.98**

A SHORT HISTORY OF ANATOMY AND PHYSIOLOGY FROM THE GREEKS TO HARVEY, Charles Singer. Corrected edition of THE EVOLUTION OF ANATOMY, classic work tracing evolution of anatomy and physiology from prescientific times through Greek & Roman periods, Dark Ages, Renaissance, to age of Harvey and beginning of modern concepts. Centered on individuals, movements, periods that definitely advanced anatomical knowledge: Plato, Diocles, Aristotle, Theophrastus, Herophilus, Erasistratus, the Alexandrians, Galen, Mondino, da Vinci, Linacre, Sylvius, others. Special section on Vesalius; Vesalian atlas of nudes, skeletons, muscle tabulae. Index of names, 20 plates. 270 extremely interesting illustrations of ancient, medieval, Renaissance, Oriental origin. xii + 209pp. 5⅜ x 8.   T389 Paperbound **$1.75**

FROM MAGIC TO SCIENCE, Charles Singer. A great historian examines aspects of medical science from the Roman Empire through the Renaissance. Includes perhaps the best discussion of early herbals, and a penetrating physiological interpretation of "The Visions of Hildegarde of Bingen." Also examined are Arabian and Galenic influences; the Sphere of Pythagoras; Paracelsus; the reawakening of science under Leonardo da Vinci, Vesalius; the Lorica of Gildas the Briton; etc. Frequent quotations with translations. New introduction by the author. New unabridged, corrected edition. 158 unusual illustrations from classical and medieval sources. Index. xxvii + 365pp. 5⅜ x 8.   T390 Paperbound **$2.00**

HISTORY OF MATHEMATICS, D. E. Smith. Most comprehensive non-technical history of math in English. Discusses lives and works of over a thousand major and minor figures, with footnotes supplying technical information outside the book's scheme, and indicating disputed matters. Vol I: A chronological examination, from primitive concepts through Egypt, Babylonia, Greece, the Orient, Rome, the Middle Ages, the Renaissance, and up to 1900. Vol 2: The development of ideas in specific fields and problems, up through elementary calculus. Two volumes, total of 510 illustrations, 1355pp. 5⅜ x 8. Set boxed in attractive container.   T429, 430 Paperbound, the set **$5.00**

A SHORT ACCOUNT OF THE HISTORY OF MATHEMATICS, W. W. R. Ball. Most readable non-technical history of mathematics treats lives, discoveries of every important figure from Egyptian, Phoenician mathematicians to late 19th century. Discusses schools of Ionia, Pythagoras, Athens, Cyzicus, Alexandria, Byzantium, systems of numeration; primitive arithmetic; Middle Ages, Renaissance, including Arabs, Bacon, Regiomontanus, Tartaglia, Cardan, Stevinus, Galileo, Kepler; modern mathematics of Descartes, Pascal, Wallis, Huygens, Newton, Leibnitz, d'Alembert, Euler, Lambert, Laplace, Legendre, Gauss, Hermite, Weierstrass, scores more. Index. 25 figures. 546pp. 5⅜ x 8.   S630 Paperbound **$2.00**

A SOURCE BOOK IN MATHEMATICS, D. E. Smith. Great discoveries in math, from Renaissance to end of 19th century, in English translation. Read announcements by Dedekind, Gauss, Delamain, Pascal, Fermat, Newton, Abel, Lobachevsky, Bolyai, Riemann, De Moivre, Legendre, Laplace, others of discoveries about imaginary numbers, number congruence, slide rule, equations, symbolism, cubic algebraic equations, non-Euclidean forms of geometry, calculus, function theory, quaternions, etc. Succinct selections from 125 different treatises, articles, most unavailable elsewhere in English. Each article preceded by biographical, historical introduction. Vol. I: Fields of Number, Algebra. Index. 32 illus. 338pp. 5⅜ x 8. Vol. II: Fields of Geometry, Probability, Calculus, Functions, Quaternions. 83 illus. 432pp. 5⅜ x 8.
Vol. 1: S552 Paperbound **$1.85**
Vol. 2: S553 Paperbound **$1.85**
2 vol. set, boxed **$3.50**

A HISTORY OF THE CALCULUS, AND ITS CONCEPTUAL DEVELOPMENT, Carl B. Boyer. Provides laymen and mathematicians a detailed history of the development of the calculus, from early beginning in antiquity to final elaboration as mathematical abstractions. Gives a sense of mathematics not as a technique, but as a habit of mind, in the progression of ideas of Zeno, Plato, Pythagoras, Eudoxus, Arabic and Scholastic mathematicians, Newton, Leibnitz, Taylor, Descartes, Euler, Lagrange, Cantor, Weierstrass, and others. This first comprehensive critical history of the calculus was originally titled "The Concepts of the Calculus." Foreword by R. Courant. Preface. 22 figures. 25-page bibliography. Index. v + 364pp. 5⅜ x 8.   S509 Paperbound **$2.00**

A CONCISE HISTORY OF MATHEMATICS, D. Struik. Lucid study of development of mathematical ideas, techniques from Ancient Near East, Greece, Islamic science, Middle Ages, Renaissance, modern times. Important mathematicians are described in detail. Treatment is not anecdotal, but analytical development of ideas. "Rich in content, thoughtful in interpretation," U.S. QUARTERLY BOOKLIST. Non-technical; no mathematical training needed. Index. 60 illustrations, including Egyptian papyri, Greek mss., portraits of 31 eminent mathematicians. Bibliography. 2nd edition. xix + 299pp. 5⅜ x 8.　　　　　　　　　　　T255 Paperbound $1.75

See also: **NON-EUCLIDEAN GEOMETRY, R. Bonola; THEORY OF DETERMINANTS IN HISTORICAL ORDER OF DEVELOPMENT, T. Muir; HISTORY OF THE THEORY OF ELASTICITY AND STRENGTH OF MATERIALS, I. Todhunter and K. Pearson; A SHORT HISTORY OF ASTRONOMY, A. Berry; CLASSICS OF SCIENCE.**

PHILOSOPHY OF SCIENCE AND MATHEMATICS

FOUNDATIONS OF SCIENCE: THE PHILOSOPHY OF THEORY AND EXPERIMENT, N. R. Campbell. A critique of the most fundamental concepts of science in general and physics in particular. Examines why certain propositions are accepted without question, demarcates science from philosophy, clarifies the understanding of the tools of science. Part One analyzes the presuppositions of scientific thought: existence of the material world, nature of scientific laws, multiplication of probabilities, etc.: Part Two covers the nature of experiment and the application of mathematics: conditions for measurement, relations between numerical laws and theories, laws of error, etc. An appendix covers problems arising from relativity, force, motion, space, and time. A classic in its field. Index. xiii + 565pp. 5⅝ x 8⅜.
　　　　　　　　　　　　　　　　　　　　　　　　　　　　S372 Paperbound $2.95

WHAT IS SCIENCE?, Norman Campbell. This excellent introduction explains scientific method, role of mathematics, types of scientific laws. Contents: 2 aspects of science, science & nature, laws of science, discovery of laws, explanation of laws, measurement & numerical laws, applications of science. 192pp. 5⅜ x 8.　　　　　　　　　　　S43 Paperbound $1.25

THE VALUE OF SCIENCE, Henri Poincaré. Many of the most mature ideas of the "last scientific universalist" covered with charm and vigor for both the beginning student and the advanced worker. Discusses the nature of scientific truth, whether order is innate in the universe or imposed upon it by man, logical thought versus intuition (relating to math, through the works of Weierstrass, Lie, Klein, Riemann), time and space (relativity, psychological time, simultaneity), Hertz's concept of force, interrelationship of mathematical physics to pure math, values within disciplines of Maxwell, Carnot, Mayer, Newton, Lorentz, etc. Index. iii + 147pp. 5⅜ x 8.　　　　　　　　　　　　　　　　S469 Paperbound $1.35

SCIENCE AND METHOD, Henri Poincaré. Procedure of scientific discovery, methodology, experiment, idea-germination—the intellectual processes by which discoveries come into being. Most significant and most interesting aspects of development, application of ideas. Chapters cover selection of facts, chance, mathematical reasoning, mathematics, and logic; Whitehead, Russell, Cantor; the new mechanics, etc. 288pp. 5⅜ x 8.　　　　S222 Paperbound $1.35

SCIENCE AND HYPOTHESIS, Henri Poincaré. Creative psychology in science. How such concepts as number, magnitude, space, force, classical mechanics were developed, and how the modern scientist uses them in his thought. Hypothesis in physics, theories of modern physics. Introduction by Sir James Larmor. "Few mathematicians have had the breadth of vision of Poincaré, and none is his superior in the gift of clear exposition," E. T. Bell. Index. 272pp. 5⅜ x 8.　　　　　　　　　　　　　　　　S221 Paperbound $1.35

PHILOSOPHY AND THE PHYSICISTS, L. S. Stebbing. The philosophical aspects of modern science examined in terms of a lively critical attack on the ideas of Jeans and Eddington. Discusses the task of science, causality, determinism, probability, consciousness, the relation of the world of physics to that of everyday experience. Probes the philosophical significance of the Planck-Bohr concept of discontinuous energy levels, the inferences to be drawn from Heisenberg's Uncertainty Principle, the implications of "becoming" involved in the 2nd law of thermodynamics, and other problems posed by the discarding of Laplacean determinism. 285pp. 5⅜ x 8.　　　　　　　　　　　　　　　　T480 Paperbound $1.65

EXPERIMENT AND THEORY IN PHYSICS, Max Born. A Nobel laureate examines the nature and value of the counterclaims of experiment and theory in physics. Synthetic versus analytical scientific advances are analyzed in the work of Einstein, Bohr, Heisenberg, Planck, Eddington, Milne, and others by a fellow participant. 44pp. 5⅜ x 8.　　　　S308 Paperbound 60¢

MATHEMATICAL PUZZLES

AMUSEMENTS IN MATHEMATICS, Henry Ernest Dudeney. The foremost British originator of mathematical puzzles is always intriguing, witty, and paradoxical in this classic, one of the largest collections of mathematical amusements. More than 430 puzzles, problems, and paradoxes. Mazes and games, problems on number manipulation, unicursal and other route problems, puzzles on measuring, weighing, packing, age, kinship, chessboards, joiners', crossing river, plane figure dissection, and many others. Solutions. More than 450 illustrations. vii + 258pp. 5⅜ x 8.   T473 Paperbound **$1.25**

THE CANTERBURY PUZZLES, Henry Ernest Dudeney. Chaucer's pilgrims set one another problems in story form. Also Adventures of the Puzzle Club, the Strange Escape of the King's Jester, the Monks of Riddlewell, the Squire's Christmas Puzzle Party, and others. All puzzles are original, based on dissecting plane figures, arithmetic, algebra, elementary calculus, and other branches of mathematics, and purely logical ingenuity. "The limit of ingenuity and intricacy . . ." The Observer. Over 110 puzzles. Full solutions. 150 illustrations. viii + 225pp. 5⅜ x 8.   T474 Paperbound **$1.25**

SYMBOLIC LOGIC and THE GAME OF LOGIC, Lewis Carroll. "Symbolic Logic" is not concerned with modern symbolic logic, but is instead a collection of over 380 problems posed with charm and imagination, using the syllogism, and a fascinating diagrammatic method of drawing conclusions. In "The Game of Logic," Carroll's whimsical imagination devises a logical game played with 2 diagrams and counters (included) to manipulate hundreds of tricky syllogisms. The final section, "Hit or Miss" is a lagniappe of 101 additional puzzles in the delightful Carroll manner. Until this reprint edition, both of these books were rarities costing up to $15 each. Symbolic Logic: Index, xxxi + 199pp. The Game of Logic: 96pp. Two vols. bound as one. 5⅜ x 8.   T492 Paperbound **$1.50**

INGENIOUS MATHEMATICAL PROBLEMS AND METHODS, L. A. Graham. 100 best problems from Graham "Dial," at least ¾ absolutely original in book form, submitted by applied mathematicians and math puzzle fans. Posed in practical terms, utilize number theory, statistics, compass geometry, networks, inversion, in proofs. Accent on heuristics (problem-solving technique) with various methods of solution discussed, compared, for each problem. First publication. Full solutions. 254pp. 5⅜ x 8.   T545 Paperbound **$1.45**

101 PUZZLES IN THOUGHT AND LOGIC, C. R. Wylie, Jr. Designed for readers who enjoy the challenge and stimulation of logical puzzles without specialized mathematical or scientific knowledge. These problems are entirely new, and range from relatively easy to brain-teasers that will afford hours of subtle entertainment. It contains detective puzzles, how to find the lying fisherman, how a blind man can identify color by logic, and many more. Easy-to-understand introduction to the logic of puzzle solving and general scientific method. 128pp. 5⅜ x 8.   T367 Paperbound **$1.00**

MAZES AND LABYRINTHS: A BOOK OF PUZZLES, W. Shepherd. Mazes, formerly associated with mystery and ritual, are still among the most intriguing of intellectual puzzles. This is a novel and different collection of 50 amusements that embody the principle of the maze: mazes in the classical tradition; 3-dimensional, ribbon, and Möbius-strip mazes; hidden messages; spatial arrangements; etc.—almost all built on amusing story situations. 84 illustrations. Essay on maze psychology. Solutions. xv + 122pp. 5⅜ x 8.   T731 Paperbound **$1.00**

MATHEMAGIC, MAGIC PUZZLES, AND GAMES WITH NUMBERS, Royal V. Heath. Over 60 new puzzles and stunts based on properties of numbers. Demonstrates easy techniques for multiplying large numbers mentally, identifying unknown numbers, determining date of any day in any year, dozens of similar useful, entertaining applications of mathematics. Entertainments like The Lost Digit, 3 Acrobats, Psychic Bridge, magic squares, triangles, cubes, circles, other material not easily found elsewhere. Edited by J. S. Meyer. 76 illustrations. 128pp. 5⅜ x 8   T110 Paperbound **$1.00**

MATHEMATICAL RECREATIONS, M. Kraitchik. Some 250 puzzles, problems, demonstrations of recreational mathematics for beginners & advanced mathematicians. Unusual historical problems from Greek, Medieval, Arabic, Hindu sources: modern problems based on "mathematics without numbers," geometry, topology, arithmetic, etc. Pastimes derived from figurative numbers, Mersenne numbers, Fermat numbers; fairy chess, latruncles, reversi, many topics. Full solutions. Excellent for insights into special fields of math. 181 illustrations. 330pp. 5⅜ x 8.   T163 Paperbound **$1.75**

PUZZLE QUIZ AND STUNT FUN, Jerome Meyer. 238 high-priority puzzles, stunts, and tricks—mathematical puzzles like The Clever Carpenter, Atom Bomb, Please Help Alice; mysteries and deductions like The Bridge of Sighs, Dog Logic, Secret Code; observation puzzlers like The American Flag, Playing Cards, Telephone Dial; more than 200 others involving magic squares, tongue twisters, puns, anagrams, word design. Answers included. Revised, enlarged edition of FUN-TO-DO. Over 100 illustrations. 238 puzzles, stunts, tricks. 256pp. 5⅜ x 8.   T337 Paperbound **$1.00**

THE BOOK OF MODERN PUZZLES, G. L. Kaufman. More than 150 word puzzles, logic puzzles. No warmed-over fare but all new material based on same appeals that make crosswords and deduction puzzles popular, but with different principles, techniques. Two-minute teasers, involved word-labyrinths, design and pattern puzzles, puzzles calling for logic and observation, puzzles testing ability to apply general knowledge to peculiar situations, many others. Answers to all problems. 116 illustrations. 192pp. 5⅜ x 8.   **T143 Paperbound $1.00**

NEW WORD PUZZLES, Gerald L. Kaufman. Contains 100 brand new challenging puzzles based on words and their combinations, never published before in any form. Most are new types invented by the author—for beginners or experts. Chess word puzzles, addle letter anagrams, double word squares, double horizontals, alphagram puzzles, dual acrostigrams, linkogram lapwords—plus 8 other brand new types, all with solutions included. 196 figures. 100 brand new puzzles. vi + 122pp. 5⅜ x 8.   **T344 Paperbound $1.00**

MATHEMATICAL RECREATIONS

MATHEMATICS, MAGIC AND MYSTERY, Martin Gardner. Card tricks, feats of mental mathematics, stage mind-reading, other "magic" explained as applications of probability, sets, theory of numbers, topology, various branches of mathematics. Creative examination of laws and their applications with scores of new tricks and insights. 115 sections discuss tricks wtih cards, dice, coins; geometrical vanishing tricks, dozens of others. No sleight of hand needed; mathematics guarantees success. 115 illustrations. xii + 174pp. 5⅜ x 8.
          T335 Paperbound $1.00

MATHEMATICAL EXCURSIONS, Helen A. Merrill. Fun, recreation, insights into elementary problem-solving. A mathematical expert guides you along by-paths not generally travelled in elementary math courses—how to divide by inspection, Russian peasant system of multiplication; memory systems for pi; building odd and even magic squares; dyadic systems; facts about 37; square roots by geometry; Tchebichev's machine; drawing five-sided figures; dozens more. Solutions to more difficult ones. 50 illustrations. 145pp. 5⅜ x 8.
          T350 Paperbound $1.00

CRYPTOGRAPHY, L. D. Smith. Excellent elementary introduction to enciphering, deciphering secret writing. Explains transposition, substitution ciphers; codes; solutions. Geometrical patterns, route transcription, columnar transposition, other methods. Mixed cipher systems; single-alphabet, polyalphabetical substitution; mechanical devices; Vigenere system, etc. Enciphering Japanese; explanation of Baconian Biliteral cipher; frequency tables. More than 150 problems provide practical application. Bibliography. Index. 164pp. 5⅜ x 8.
          T247 Paperbound $1.00

CRYPTANALYSIS, Helen F. Gaines. (Formerly ELEMENTARY CRYPTANALYSIS.) A standard elementary and intermediate text for serious students. It does not confine itself to old material, but contains much that is not generally known, except to experts. Concealment, Transposition, Substitution ciphers; Vigenere, Kasiski, Playfair, multafid, dozens of other techniques. Appendix with sequence charts, letter frequencies in English, 5 other languages, English word frequencies. Bibliography. 167 codes. New to this edition: solution to codes. vi + 230pp. 5⅜ x 8.   **T97 Paperbound $1.95**

MAGIC SQUARES AND CUBES, W. S. Andrews. Only book-length treatment in English, a thorough non-technical description and analysis. Here are nasik, overlapping, pandiagonal, serrated squares; magic circles, cubes, spheres, rhombuses. Try your hand at 4-dimensional magical figures! Much unusual folklore and tradition included. High school algebra is sufficient. 754 diagrams and illustrations. viii + 419pp. 5⅜ x 8.   **T658 Paperbound $1.85**

PAPER FOLDING FOR BEGINNERS, W. D. Murray and F. J. Rigney. A delightful introduction to the varied and entertaining Japanese art of origami (paper folding), with a full crystal-clear text that anticipates every difficulty; over 275 clearly labeled diagrams of all important stages in creation. You get results at each stage, since complex figures are logically developed from simpler ones. 43 different pieces are explained: place mats, drinking cups, bonbon boxes, sailboats, frogs, roosters, etc. 6 photographic plates. 279 diagrams. 95pp. 5⅝ x 8⅜.
          T713 Paperbound $1.00

CHESS, CHECKERS, GAMES, GO

A TREASURY OF CHESS LORE, edited by Fred Reinfeld. A delightful collection of anecdotes, short stories, aphorisms by and about the masters, poems, accounts of games and tournaments, photographs. Hundreds of humorous, pithy, satirical, wise, and historical episodes, comments, and word portraits. A fascinating "must" for chess players; revealing and perhaps seductive to those who wonder what their friends see in the game. 49 photographs (14 full page plates). 12 diagrams. xi + 306pp. 5⅜ x 8.   **T458 Paperbound $1.75**

THE ADVENTURE OF CHESS, Edward Lasker. A lively story of the history of chess, from its ancient beginnings in the Indian four-handed game of Chaturanga, through to the great players of our own day, as told by one of America's finest chess masters. He introduces such unusual sidelights and amusing oddities as Maelzel's chess playing automaton that beat Napoleon three times. One of the most valuable features of this work is the author's personal recollections of men he has played against and known—Nimzovich, Emanuel Lasker, Capablanca, Alekhine, etc. Lasker's discussion of chess-playing machines (revised for this edition) is particularly knowledgeable, since he is an electrical engineer by profession. 5 page chess primer. 11 illustrations; 53 diagrams. 296pp. 5⅜ x 8.

T510 Paperbound **$1.45**

FREE! All you do is ask for it!

HOW DO YOU PLAY CHESS?, Fred Reinfeld. A 40-page book of 86 lively questions and answers explaining all aspects of chess to beginners, by a noted writer on chess. Copies limited, no more than 1 to a customer.

THE PLEASURES OF CHESS, Assiac. Internationally-known British writer, influential chess columnist, writes wittily about wide variety of chess subjects: Andersen's "Immortal Game;" only game in which both opponents resigned at once; psychological tactics of Reshevsky, Lasker; varieties played by masters for relaxation, such as "losing chess;" sacrificial orgies; etc. These anecdotes, witty observations will give you fresh appreciation of game. 43 problems. 150 diagrams. 139pp. 5⅜ x 8.   T597 Paperbound **$1.25**

WIN AT CHESS, Fred Reinfeld. 300 practical chess situations enable you to sharpen your chess eye and test your skill against the masters. You start with simple examples and progress at your own pace to complex positions. This selected series of crucial moments in chess will stimulate your imagination and enable you to develop a stronger more versatile game. A simple grading system enables you to judge your progress through the course of the book. 300 diagrams. Notes and solutions to every situation. Formerly entitled CHESS QUIZ. vi + 120pp. 5⅜ x 8.   T438 Paperbound **$1.00**

THE ART OF CHESS, James Mason. An unabridged reprinting of the latest revised edition of the most famous general study of chess ever written. Also included, a complete supplement by Fred Reinfeld, "How Do You Play Chess?", invaluable to beginners for its lively question and answer method. Mason, an early 20th century master, teaches the beginning and intermediate player more than 90 openings, middle game, end game, how to see more moves ahead, to plan purposefully, attack, sacrifice, defend, exchange, and govern general strategy. Supplement. 448 diagrams. 1947 Reinfeld-Bernstein text. Bibliography. xvi + 340pp. 5⅜ x 8.   T463 Paperbound **$1.85**

THE PRINCIPLES OF CHESS, James Mason. This "great chess classic" (N. Y. Times) is a general study covering all aspects of the game: basic forces, resistance, obstruction, opposition, relative values, mating, typical end game situations, combinations, much more. The last section discusses openings, with 50 games illustrating modern master play of Rubinstein, Spielmann, Lasker, Capablanca, etc., selected and annotated by Fred Reinfeld. Will improve the game of any intermediate-skilled player. 1946 Reinfeld edition. 166 diagrams. 378pp. 5⅜ x 8.   T646 Paperbound **$1.85**

LASKER'S MANUAL OF CHESS, Dr. Emanuel Lasker. World Champion 28 years, perhaps greatest modern player, writes one of most thorough studies on all facets of chess. How to gain advantage, value of pieces, combinations, etc. Dozens of openings analyzed. Valuable illumination, elaboration of theories of Steinitz. For intermediate-skilled player, but may be read by beginner. Introduction. Indexes. 308 illus. 397pp. 5⅜ x 8.   T533 Paperbound **$1.00**

THE ART OF CHESS COMBINATION, E. Znosko-Borovsky. Proves that combinations, perhaps the most aesthetically satisfying, successful technique in chess, can be an integral part of your game, instead of a haphazard occurrence. Games of Capablanca, Rubinstein, Nimzovich, Bird, etc. grouped according to common features, perceptively analyzed to show that every combination begins in certain simple ideas. Will help you to plan many moves ahead. Technical terms almost completely avoided. "In the teaching of chess he may claim to have no superior," P. W. Sergeant. Introduction. Exercises. Solutions. Index. 223pp. 5⅜ x 8.

T583 Paperbound **$1.45**

CHESS STRATEGY, Edward Lasker. Classic study has taught 2 generations of players, including Grandmasters Fine, Keres. Emphasis is on general strategy, not memorization. How to formulate general strategy in terms of opponent's weaknesses, how to form "pawn skeleton," objects of attack, backward pawns, etc. 48 major tournament games analyzed. "The finest book I know of in the English language," J. R. Capablanca. Introduction. Index. 167 illus. 5⅜ x 8.   T528 Paperbound **$1.50**

REINFELD ON THE END GAME IN CHESS, Fred Reinfeld. Analyzes 62 end games by Alekhine, Flohr, Tarrasch, Morphy, Bogolyubov, Capablanca, Vidmar, Rubinstein, Lasker, Reshevsky, other masters. Only first-rate book with extensive coverage of error; of immense aid in pointing out errors you might have made. Centers around transitions from middle play to various types of end play. King & pawn endings, minor piece endings, queen endings, bad bishops, blockage, weak pawns, passed pawns, etc. Formerly titled PRACTICAL END-GAME PLAY. 62 figures. vi + 177pp. 5⅜ x 8. T417 Paperbound **$1.25**

HOW TO FORCE CHECKMATE, Fred Reinfeld. If you have trouble finishing off your opponent, this book is for you. It is a collection of lightning strokes and combinations from actual tournament play. Starting with one-move checkmates and working up to three-move mates, you develop the ability to look ahead, and gain new insights into combinations, complex or deceptive positions, and ways of estimating both your own and your opponent's strengths and weaknesses. 300 diagrams. Solutions to all positions. Formerly entitled CHALLENGE TO CHESS PLAYERS. 111pp. 5⅜ x 8. T439 Paperbound **$1.25**

CHESSBOARD MAGIC! A COLLECTION OF 160 BRILLIANT ENDINGS, compiled, annotated by Irving Chernev. Illustrate not only ingenuity of composition, method of solution, but inherent beauty of solution. Many, by foremost Russian chess authorities, have won first prize in Russian chess magazines; are unavailable in this country. "Marvelous . . . sheer magic," Emanuel Lasker. "An endless feast of delight," Reuben Fine. Introduction. 160 diagrams. Index. 184pp. 5⅜ x 8. T607 Paperbound **$1.00**

LEARN CHESS FROM THE MASTERS, Fred Reinfeld. Improve your chess, rate your improvement, by playing against Marshall, Znosko-Borovsky, Bronstein, Najdorf, others. Formerly titled CHESS BY YOURSELF, this book contains 10 games in which you move against masters, and grade your moves by an easy system. Games selected for interest, clarity, easy principles; illustrate common openings, both classical and modern. Ratings for 114 extra playing situations that might have arisen. Full annotations. 91 diagrams. viii + 144pp. 5⅜ x 8. T362 Paperbound **$1.00**

MORPHY'S GAMES OF CHESS, edited by Philip W. Sergeant. You can put boldness into your game by following the brilliant, forceful moves of the man who has been called the greatest chess player of all time. Here are 300 of Morphy's best games, carefully annotated to reveal Morphy's principles. 54 classics against masters like Anderssen, Harrwitz, Bird, Paulsen, and others. 52 games at odds; 54 blindfold games; plus over 100 others. Unabridged reissue of the latest revised edition. Bibliography. New introduction by Fred Reinfeld. Annotations and introduction by Sergeant. Index. 235 diagrams. x + 352pp. 5⅜ x 8. T386 Paperbound **$1.75**

MODERN IDEAS IN CHESS, R. Réti. Clearest and most readable explanation of major developments in chess styles. Concentrates on the games of the master most closely associated with each major advance of the last hundred years. Seven world champions (Anderssen, Morphy, Steinitz, Lasker, Capablanca, Alekhine, and Euwe) are analyzed by a modern master. 34 diagrams. 192pp. 5⅜ x 8. T638 Paperbound **$1.25**

THE BOOK OF THE NEW YORK INTERNATIONAL CHESS TOURNAMENT, 1924, annotated by A. Alekhine and edited by H. Helms. Long a rare collector's item, this is the book of one of the most brilliant tournaments of all time, during which Capablanca, Dr. Lasker, Alekhine, Reti, and others immeasurably enriched chess theory in a thrilling contest. All 110 games played, with Alekhine's unusually penetrating notes. 15 photographs. xi + 271pp. 5⅜ x 8. T752 Paperboard **$1.85**

KERES' BEST GAMES OF CHESS, selected, annotated by F. Reinfeld. 90 best games, 1931-1948, by one of boldest, most exciting players of modern chess. Games against Alekhine, Bogolyubov, Capablanca, Euwe, Fine, Reshevsky, other masters, show his treatments of openings such as Giuoco Piano, Alekhine Defense, Queen's Gambit Declined; attacks, sacrifices, alternative methods. Preface by Keres gives personal glimpses, evaluations of rivals. 110 diagrams. 272pp. 5⅜ x 8. T593 Paperbound **$1.35**

THE DEVELOPMENT OF A CHESS GENIUS: 100 INSTRUCTIVE GAMES OF ALEKHINE, by Fred Reinfeld. Games from vital formative years 1905-1914, most of them never before in book form, show a future great master being shaped by experience and challenge in matches against Bernstein, Bogolyubov, Capablanca, Marshall, Rubinstein, Tarrasch, others. Interesting as chess biography, instructive as a master's increasingly adept responses to problems of every player. Annotated by F. Reinfeld. "One of America's most significant contributions," Chess Life. Formerly "The Unknown Alekhine." Introduction. Indexes of players, openings. 204 illustrations. 242pp. 5⅜ x 8. T551 Paperbound **$1.35**

RESHEVSKY'S BEST GAMES OF CHESS, Samuel Reshevsky. One time 4-year old chess genius, 5-time winner U. S. Chess Championship, selects, annotates 110 of his best games, illustrating chess theories, favorite methods of play against Capablanca, Alekhine, Bogolyubov, Kashdan, Vidmar, Botvinnik, others. Clear, non-technical style. Personal impressions of opponents, autobiographical material, tournament match record. Formerly, "Reshevsky on Chess." 309 diagrams, 2 photos. 288pp. 5⅜ x 8. T606 Paperbound **$1.25**

HYPERMODERN CHESS as developed in the games of its greatest exponent, ARON NIMZOVICH, edited by Fred Reinfeld. An intensely original player and analyst, Nimzovich's extraordinary approaches startled and often angered the chess world. This volume, designed for the average player, shows in his victories over Alekhine, Lasker, Marshall, Rubinstein, Spielmann, and others, how his iconoclastic methods infused new life into the game. Use Nimzovich to invigorate your play and startle opponents. Introduction. Indices of players and openings. 180 diagrams. viii + 220pp. 5⅜ x 8. T448 Paperbound **$1.35**

ONE HUNDRED SELECTED GAMES, Mikhail Botvinnik. Author's own choice of his best games before becoming World Champion in 1948, beginning with first big tournament, the USSR Championship, 1927. Shows his great powers of analysis as he annotates these games, giving strategy, technique against Alekhine, Capablanca, Euwe, Keres, Reshevsky, Smyslov, Vidmar, many others. Discusses his career, methods of play, system of training, 6 studies of endgame positions. 221 diagrams. 272pp. 5⅜ x 8. T620 Paperbound **$1.50**

RUBINSTEIN'S CHESS MASTERPIECES, selected and annotated by H. Kmoch. Thoroughgoing mastery of opening, middle game; faultless technique in endgame, particularly rook and pawn endings; ability to switch from careful positional play to daring combinations; all distinguish the play of Rubinstein. 100 best games, against Janowski, Nimzowitch, Tarrasch, Vidmar, Capablanca, other greats, carefully annotated, will improve your game rapidly. Biographical introduction, B. F. Winkelman, 103 diagrams. 192pp. 5⅜ x 8. T617 Paperbound **$1.25**

TARRASCH'S BEST GAMES OF CHESS, selected & annotated by Fred Reinfeld. First definitive collection of games by Siegbert Tarrasch, winner of 7 international tournaments, and the leading theorist of classical chess. 183 games cover 50 years of play against Mason, Mieses, Paulsen, Teichmann, Pillsbury, Janowski, others. Reinfeld includes Tarrasch's own analyses of many of these games. A careful study and replaying of the games will give you a sound understanding of classical methods, and many hours of enjoyment. Introduction. Indexes. 183 diagrams. xxiv + 386pp. 5⅜ x 8. T644 Paperbound **$2.00**

MARSHALL'S BEST GAMES OF CHESS, F. J. Marshall. Grandmaster, U. S. champion for 27 years, tells story of career; presents magnificent collection of 140 of best games, annotated by himself. Games against Capablanca, Alekhine, Emanuel Lasker, Janowski, Rubinstein, Pillsbury, etc. Special section analyzes openings such as King's Gambit, Ruy Lopez, Alekhine's Defence, Giuoco Piano, others. A study of Marshall's brilliant "swindles," slashing attacks, extraordinary sacrifices, will rapidly improve your game. Formerly "My Fifty Years of Chess." Introduction. 19 diagrams. 13 photos. 250pp. 5⅜ x 8. T604 Paperbound **$1.35**

THE ENJOYMENT OF CHESS PROBLEMS, K. S. Howard. A classic treatise on this minor art by an internationally recognized authority that gives a basic knowledge of terms and themes for the everyday chess player as well as the problem fan: 7 chapters on the two-mover; 7 more on 3- and 4-move problems; a chapter on selfmates; and much more. "The most important one-volume contribution originating solely in the U.S.A.", Alain White. 200 diagrams. Index. Solutions. viii + 212pp. 5⅜ x 8. T742 Paperbound **$1.25**

HOW TO SOLVE CHESS PROBLEMS, K. S. Howard. Full of practical suggestions for the fan or the beginner—who need only know the moves of the chessmen. Contains preliminary section and 58 two-move, 46 three-move, and 8 four-move problems composed by 27 outstanding American problem creators in the last 30 years. Explanation of all terms and exhaustive index. "Just what is wanted for the student," Brian Warley. 112 problems, solutions. vi + 171pp. 5⅜ x 8. T748 Paperbound **$1.00**

CHESS AND CHECKERS: THE WAY TO MASTERSHIP, Edward Lasker. Complete, lucid instructions for the beginner—and valuable suggestions for the advanced player! For both games the great master and teacher presents fundamentals, elementary tactics, and steps toward becoming a superior player. He concentrates on general principles rather than a mass of rules, comprehension rather than brute memory. Historical introduction. 118 diagrams. xiv + 167pp. 5⅜ x 8. T657 Paperbound **$1.15**

WIN AT CHECKERS, M. Hopper. (Formerly CHECKERS). The former World's Unrestricted Checker Champion discusses the principles of the game, expert's shots and traps, problems for the beginner, standard openings, locating your best move, the end game, opening "blitzkrieg" moves, ways to draw when you are behind your opponent, etc. More than 100 detailed questions and answers anticipate your problems. Appendix. 75 problems with solutions and diagrams. Index. 79 figures. xi + 107pp. 5⅜ x 8. T363 Paperbound **$1.00**

GAMES ANCIENT AND ORIENTAL, AND HOW TO PLAY THEM, E. Falkener. A connoisseur's selection of exciting and different games: Oriental varieties of chess, with unusual pieces and moves (including Japanese shogi); the original pachisi; go; reconstructions of lost Roman and Egyptian games; and many more. Full rules and sample games. Now play at home the games that have entertained millions, not on a fad basis, but for millennia. 345 illustrations and figures. iv + 366pp. 5⅜ x 8. T739 Paperbound **$1.85**

GO AND GO-MOKU: THE ORIENTAL BOARD GAMES, Edward Lasker. Best introduction to Go and its easier sister-game, Go-Moku—games new to Western world, but ancient in China, Japan. Extensively revised work by famed chess master Lasker, Go-player for over 50 years, stresses theory rather than brute memory, presents step-by-step explanation of strategy, gives examples of world championship matches, in game which has replaced chess as favorite of many physicists, mathematicians. 72 diagrams. xix + 215 pp. 5⅜ x 8.

T613 Paperbound **$1.45**

FICTION

FLATLAND, E. A. Abbott. A science-fiction classic of life in a 2-dimensional world that is also a first-rate introduction to such aspects of modern science as relativity and hyperspace. Political, moral, satirical, and humorous overtones have made FLATLAND fascinating reading for thousands. 7th edition. New introduction by Banesh Hoffmann. 16 illustrations. 128pp. 5⅜ x 8.

T1 Paperbound **$1.00**

THE WONDERFUL WIZARD OF OZ, L. F. Baum. Only edition in print with all the original W. W. Denslow illustrations in full color—as much a part of "The Wizard" as Tenniel's drawings are of "Alice in Wonderland." "The Wizard" is still America's best-loved fairy tale, in which, as the author expresses it, "The wonderment and joy are retained and the heartaches and nightmares left out." Now today's young readers can enjoy every word and wonderful picture of the original book. New introduction by Martin Gardner. A Baum bibliography. 23 full-page color plates. viii + 268pp. 5⅜ x 8.

T691 Paperbound **$1.45**

THE MARVELOUS LAND OF OZ, L. F. Baum. This is the equally enchanting sequel to the "Wizard," continuing the adventures of the Scarecrow and the Tin Woodman. The hero this time is a little boy named Tip, and all the delightful Oz magic is still present. This is the book with the Animated Saw-horse, the Woggle-Bug, and Jack Pumpkinhead. All the original John R. Neill illustrations, 16 in full color. 287pp. 5⅜ x 8.

T692 Paperbound **$1.45**

FIVE GREAT DOG NOVELS, edited by Blanche Cirker. The complete original texts of five classic dog novels that have delighted and thrilled millions of children and adults throughout the world with stories of loyalty, adventure, and courage. Full texts of Jack London's "The Call of the Wild"; John Brown's "Rab and His Friends"; Alfred Ollivant's "Bob, Son of Battle"; Marshall Saunders' "Beautiful Joe"; and Ouida's "A Dog of Flanders." 21 illustrations from the original editions. 495pp. 5⅜ x 8.

T777 Paperbound **$1.50**

3 ADVENTURE NOVELS by H. Rider Haggard. Complete texts of "She," "King Solomon's Mines," "Allan Quatermain." Qualities of discovery; desire for immortality; search for primitive, for what is unadorned by civilization, have kept these novels of African adventure exciting, alive to readers from R. L. Stevenson to George Orwell. 636pp. 5⅜ x 8.

T584 Paperbound **$2.00**

The Space Novels of Jules Verne

TO THE SUN? and OFF ON A COMET!, Jules Verne. Complete texts of two of the most imaginative flights into fancy in world literature display the high adventure that have kept Verne's novels read for nearly a century. Only unabridged edition of the best translation, by Edward Roth. Large, easily readable type. 50 illustrations selected from first editions. 462pp. 5⅜ x 8.

T634 Paperbound **$1.75**

FROM THE EARTH TO THE MOON and ALL AROUND THE MOON, Jules Verne. Complete editions of two of Verne's most successful novels, in finest Edward Roth translations, now available after many years out of print. Verne's visions of submarines, airplanes, television, rockets, interplanetary travel; of scientific and not-so-scientific beliefs; of peculiarities of Americans; all delight and engross us today as much as when they first appeared. Large, easily readable type. 42 illus. from first French edition. 476pp. 5⅜ x 8.

T633 Paperbound **$1.75**

THE CASTING AWAY OF MRS. LECKS AND MRS. ALESHINE, F. R. Stockton. A charming light novel by Frank Stockton, one of America's finest humorists (and author of "The Lady, or the Tiger?"). This book has made millions of Americans laugh at the reflection of themselves in two middle-aged American women involved in some of the strangest adventures on record. You will laugh, too, as they endure shipwreck, desert island, and blizzard with maddening tranquility. Also contains complete text of "The Dusantes," sequel to "The Casting Away." 49 original illustrations by F. D. Steele. vii + 142pp. 5⅜ x 8.

T743 Paperbound **$1.00**

GESTA ROMANORUM, trans. by Charles Swan, ed. by Wynnard Hooper. 181 tales of Greeks, Romans, Britons, Biblical characters, comprise one of greatest medieval story collections, source plots for writers including Shakespeare, Chaucer, Gower, etc. Imaginative tales of wars, incest, thwarted love, magic, fantasy, allegory, humor, tell about kings, prostitutes, philosophers, fair damsels, knights, Noah, pirates, all walks and stations of life. Introduction. Notes. 500pp. 5⅜ x 8. T535 Paperbound $1.85

THREE PROPHETIC NOVELS BY H. G. WELLS, edited by E. F. Bleiler. Complete texts of "When the Sleeper Wakes" (1st book printing in 50 years), "A Story of the Days to Come," "The Time Machine" (1st complete printing in book form). Exciting adventures in the future are as enjoyable today as 50 years ago when first printed. Predict TV, movies, intercontinental airplanes, prefabricated houses, air-conditioned cities, etc. First important author to foresee problems of mind control, technological dictatorships. "Absolute best of imaginative fiction," N. Y. Times. Introduction. 335pp. 5⅜ x 8. T605 Paperbound $1.45

SEVEN SCIENCE FICTION NOVELS, H. G. Wells. Full unabridged texts of 7 science-fiction novels of the master. Ranging from biology, physics, chemistry, astronomy to sociology and other studies, Mr. Wells extrapolates whole worlds of strange and intriguing character. "One will have to go far to match this for entertainment, excitement, and sheer pleasure . . .," NEW YORK TIMES. Contents: The Time Machine, The Island of Dr. Moreau, First Men in the Moon, The Invisible Man, The War of the Worlds, The Food of the Gods, In the Days of the Comet. 1015pp. 5⅜ x 8. T264 Clothbound $3.95

28 SCIENCE FICTION STORIES OF H. G. WELLS. Two full unabridged novels, MEN LIKE GODS and STAR BEGOTTEN, plus 26 short stories by the master science-fiction writer of all time. Stories of space, time, invention, exploration, future adventure—an indispensable part of the library of everyone interested in science and adventure. PARTIAL CONTENTS: Men Like Gods, The Country of the Blind, In the Abyss, The Crystal Egg, The Man Who Could Work Miracles, A Story of the Days to Come, The Valley of Spiders, and 21 more! 928pp. 5⅜ x 8. T265 Clothbound $3.95

DAVID HARUM, E. N. Westcott. This novel of one of the most lovable, humorous characters in American literature is a prime example of regional humor. It continues to delight people who like their humor dry, their characters quaint, and their plots ingenuous. First book edition to contain complete novel plus chapter found after author's death. Illustrations from first illustrated edition. 192pp. 5⅜ x 8. T580 Paperbound $1.15

HUMOR

THE WIT AND HUMOR OF OSCAR WILDE, ed. by Alvin Redman. Wilde at his most brilliant, in 1000 epigrams exposing weaknesses and hypocrisies of "civilized" society. Divided into 49 categories—sin, wealth, women, America, etc.—to aid writers, speakers. Includes excerpts from his trials, books, plays, criticism. Formerly "The Epigrams of Oscar Wilde." Introduction by Vyvyan Holland, Wilde's only living son. Introductory essay by editor. 260pp. 5⅜ x 8. T602 Paperbound $1.00

A NONSENSE ANTHOLOGY, collected by Carolyn Wells. 245 of the best nonsense verses ever written, including nonsense puns, absurd arguments, mock epics and sagas, nonsense ballads, odes, "sick" verses, dog-Latin verses, French nonsense verses, songs. By Edward Lear, Lewis Carroll, Gelett Burgess, W. S. Gilbert, Hilaire Belloc, Peter Newell, Oliver Herford, etc., 83 writers in all plus over four score anonymous nonsense verses. A special section of Jimericks, plus famous nonsense such as Carroll's "Jabberwocky" and Lear's "The Jumblies" and much excellent verse virtually impossible to locate elsewhere. For 50 years considered the best anthology available. Index of first lines specially prepared for this edition. Introduction by Carolyn Wells. 3 indexes: Title, Author, First lines. xxxiii + 279pp. 5⅜ x 8. T499 Paperbound $1.25

THE BAD CHILD'S BOOK OF BEASTS, MORE BEASTS FOR WORSE CHILDREN, and A MORAL ALPHABET, H. Belloc. Hardly an anthology of humorous verse has appeared in the last 50 years without at least a couple of these famous nonsense verses. But one must see the entire volumes—with all the delightful original illustrations by Sir Basil Blackwood—to appreciate fully Belloc's charming and witty verses that play so subacidly on the platitudes of life and morals that beset his day—and ours. A great humor classic. Three books in one. Total of 157pp. 5⅜ x 8. T749 Paperbound $1.00

THE DEVIL'S DICTIONARY, Ambrose Bierce. Sardonic and irreverent barbs puncturing the pomposities and absurdities of American politics, business, religion, literature, and arts, by the country's greatest satirist in the classic tradition. Epigrammatic as Shaw, piercing as Swift, American as Mark Twain, Will Rogers, and Fred Allen. Bierce will always remain the favorite of a small coterie of enthusiasts, and of writers and speakers whom he supplies with "some of the most gorgeous witticisms of the English language." (H. L. Mencken) Over 1000 entries in alphabetical order. 144pp. 5⅜ x 8. T487 Paperbound $1.00

THE PURPLE COW AND OTHER NONSENSE, Gelett Burgess. The best of Burgess's early nonsense, selected from the first edition of the "Burgess Nonsense Book." Contains many of his most unusual and highly original pieces: 37 nonsense quatrains, the Poems of Patagonia, Alphabet of Famous Goops, and the other hilarious (and rare) adult nonsense that places him in the forefront of American humorists. All pieces are accompanied by the original Burgess illustrations. 123 illustrations. xiii + 113pp. 5⅜ x 8.
T772 Paperbound **$1.00**

THE HUMOROUS VERSE OF LEWIS CARROLL. Almost every poem Carroll ever wrote, the largest collection ever published, including much never published elsewhere: 150 parodies, burlesques, riddles, ballads, acrostics, etc., with 130 original illustrations by Tenniel, Carroll, and others. "Addicts will be grateful . . . there is nothing for the faithful to do but sit down and fall to the banquet," N. Y. Times. Index to first lines. xiv + 446pp. 5 x 8.
T654 Paperbound **$1.85**

DIVERSIONS AND DIGRESSIONS OF LEWIS CARROLL. A major new treasure for Carroll fans! Rare privately published humor, fantasy, puzzles, and games by Carroll at his whimsical best, with a new vein of frank satire. Includes many new mathematical amusements and recreations, among them the fragmentary Part III of "Curiosa Mathematica." Contains "The Rectory Umbrella," "The New Belfry," "The Vision of the Three T's," and much more. New 32-page supplement of rare photographs taken by Carroll. x + 375pp. 5⅜ x 8.
T732 Paperbound **$1.50**

THE COMPLETE NONSENSE OF EDWARD LEAR. This is the only complete edition of this master of gentle madness available at a popular price. A BOOK OF NONSENSE, NONSENSE SONGS, MORE NONSENSE SONGS AND STORIES in their entirety with all the old favorites that have delighted children and adults for years. The Dong With A Luminous Nose, The Jumblies, The Owl and the Pussycat, and hundreds of other bits of wonderful nonsense. 214 limericks, 3 sets of Nonsense Botany, 5 Nonsense Alphabets. 546 drawings by Lear himself, and much more. 320pp. 5⅜ x 8.
T167 Paperbound **$1.00**

PECK'S BAD BOY AND HIS PA, George W. Peck. The complete edition, containing both volumes, one of the most widely read of all American humor books. The endless ingenious pranks played by bad boy "Hennery" on his pa and the grocery man, the outraged pomposity of Pa, the perpetual ridiculing of middle class institutions, are as entertaining today as they were in 1883. No pale sophistications or subtleties, but rather humor vigorous, raw, earthy, imaginative, and, as folk humor often is, sadistic. This peculiarly fascinating book is also valuable to historians and students of American culture as a portrait of an age. 100 original illustrations by True Williams. Introduction by E. F. Bleiler. 347pp. 5⅜ x 8.
T497 Paperbound **$1.35**

FABLES IN SLANG & MORE FABLES IN SLANG, George Ade. 2 complete books of major American humorist in pungent colloquial tradition of Twain, Billings. 1st reprinting in over 30 years includes "The Two Mandolin Players and the Willing Performer," "The Base Ball Fan Who Took the Only Known Cure," "The Slim Girl Who Tried to Keep a Date that was Never Made," 42 other tales of eccentric, perverse, but always funny characters. "Touch of genius," H. L. Mencken. New introduction by E. F. Bleiler. 86 illus. 203pp. 5⅜ x 8.
T533 Paperbound **$1.00**

SINGULAR TRAVELS, CAMPAIGNS, AND ADVENTURES OF BARON MUNCHAUSEN, R. E. Raspe, with 90 illustrations by Gustave Doré. The first edition in over 150 years to reestablish the deeds of the Prince of Liars exactly as Raspe first recorded them in 1785—the genuine Baron Munchausen, one of the most popular personalities in English literature. Included also are the best of the many sequels, written by other hands. Introduction on Raspe by J. Carswell. Bibliography of early editions. xliv + 192pp. 5⅜ x 8. T698 Paperbound **$1.00**

HOW TO TELL THE BIRDS FROM THE FLOWERS, R. W. Wood. How not to confuse a carrot with a parrot, a grape with an ape, a puffin with nuffin. Delightful drawings, clever puns, absurd little poems point out farfetched resemblances in nature. The author was a leading physicist. Introduction by Margaret Wood White. 106 illus. 60pp. 5⅜ x 8.
T523 Paperbound **75¢**

MATHEMATICS, ELEMENTARY TO INTERMEDIATE

HOW TO CALCULATE QUICKLY, Henry Sticker. This handy volume offers a tried and true method for helping you in the basic mathematics of daily life—addition, subtraction, multiplication, division, fractions, etc. It is designed to awaken your "number sense" or the ability to see relationships between numbers as whole quantities. It is not a collection of tricks working only on special numbers, but a serious course of over 9,000 problems and their solutions, teaching special techniques not taught in schools: left-to-right multiplication, new fast ways of division, etc. 5 or 10 minutes daily use will double or triple your calculation speed. Excellent for the scientific worker who is at home in higher math, but is not satisfied with his speed and accuracy in lower mathematics. 256pp. 5 x 7¼. T295 Paperbound **$1.00**

TEACH YOURSELF books. For adult self-study, for refresher and supplementary study.

The most effective series of home study mathematics books on the market! With absolutely no outside help, they will teach you as much as any similar college or high-school course, or will helpfully supplement any such course. Each step leads directly to the next, each question is anticipated. Numerous lucid examples and carefully-wrought practice problems illustrate meanings. Not skimpy outlines, not surveys, not usual classroom texts, these 204- to 380-page books are packed with the finest instruction you'll find anywhere for adult self-study.

TEACH YOURSELF ALGEBRA, P. Abbott. Formulas, coordinates, factors, graphs of quadratic functions, quadratic equations, logarithms, ratio, irrational numbers, arithmetical, geometrical series, much more. 1241 problems, solutions. Tables. 52 illus. 307pp. 6⅞ x 4¼.
Clothbound $2.00

TEACH YOURSELF GEOMETRY, P. Abbott. Solids, lines, points, surfaces, angle measurement, triangles, theorem of Pythagoras, polygons, loci, the circle, tangents, symmetry, solid geometry, prisms, pyramids, solids of revolution, etc. 343 problems, solutions. 268 illus. 334pp. 6⅞ x 4¼.
Clothbound $2.00

TEACH YOURSELF TRIGONOMETRY, P. Abbott. Geometrical foundations, indices, logarithms, trigonometrical ratios, relations between sides, angles of triangle, circular measure, trig. ratios of angles of any magnitude, much more. Requires elementary algebra, geometry. 465 problems, solutions. Tables. 102 illus. 204pp. 6⅞ x 4¼.
Clothbound $2.00

TEACH YOURSELF THE CALCULUS, P. Abbott. Variations in functions, differentiation, solids of revolution, series, elementary differential equations, areas by integral calculus, much more. Requires algebra, trigonometry. 970 problems, solutions. Tables. 89 illus. 380pp. 6⅞ x 4¼.
Clothbound $2.00

TEACH YOURSELF THE SLIDE RULE, B. Snodgrass. Fractions, decimals, A-D scales, log-log scales, trigonometrical scales, indices, logarithms. Commercial, precision, electrical, dualistic, Brighton rules. 80 problems, solutions. 10 illus. 207pp. 6⅞ x 4¼.   Clothbound **$2.00**

See also: **TEACH YOURSELF ELECTRICITY, C. W. Wilman; TEACH YOURSELF HEAT ENGINES, E. De Ville; TEACH YOURSELF MECHANICS, P. Abbott.**

✳   ✳   ✳

HOW DO YOU USE A SLIDE RULE? by A. A. Merrill. Not a manual for mathematicians and engineers, but a lucid step-by-step explanation that presents the fundamental rules clearly enough to be understood by anyone who could benefit by the use of a slide rule in his work or business. This work concentrates on the 2 most important operations: multiplication and division. 10 easy lessons, each with a clear drawing, will save you countless hours in your banking, business, statistical, and other work. First publication. Index. 2 Appendixes. 10 illustrations. 78 problems, all with answers. vi + 36pp. 6⅛ x 9¼.   T62 Paperbound **60¢**

THEORY OF OPERATION OF THE SLIDE RULE, J. P. Ellis. Not a skimpy "instruction manual", but an exhaustive treatment that will save you uncounted hours throughout your career. Supplies full understanding of every scale on the Log Log Duplex Decitrig type of slide rule. Shows the most time-saving methods, and provides practice useful in the widest variety of actual engineering situations. Each operation introduced in terms of underlying logarithmic theory. Summary of prerequisite math. First publication. Index. 198 figures. Over 450 problems with answers. Bibliography. 12 Appendices. ix + 289pp. 5⅜ x 8.
S727 Paperbound $1.50

ARITHMETICAL EXCURSIONS: AN ENRICHMENT OF ELEMENTARY MATHEMATICS, H. Bowers and J. Bowers. For students who want unusual methods of arithmetic never taught in school; for adults who want to increase their number sense. Little known facts about the most simple numbers, arithmetical entertainments and puzzles, figurate numbers, number chains, mysteries and folklore of numbers, the "Hin-dog-abic" number system, etc. First publication. Index. 529 numbered problems and diversions, all with answers. Bibliography. 50 figures. xiv + 320pp. 5⅜ x 8.
T770 Paperbound $1.65

APPLIED MATHEMATICS FOR RADIO AND COMMUNICATIONS ENGINEERS, C. E. Smith. No extraneous material here!—only the theories, equations, and operations essential and immediately useful for radio work. Can be used as refresher, as handbook of applications and tables, or as full home-study course. Ranges from simplest arithmetic through calculus, series, and wave forms, hyperbolic trigonometry, simultaneous equations in mesh circuits, etc. Supplies applications right along with each math topic discussed. 22 useful tables of functions, formulas, logs, etc. Index. 166 exercises, 140 examples, all with answers. 95 diagrams. Bibliography. x + 336pp. 5⅜ x 8.
S141 Paperbound $1.75

FAMOUS PROBLEMS OF ELEMENTARY GEOMETRY, Felix Klein. Expanded version of the 1894 Easter lectures at Göttingen. 3 problems of classical geometry, in an excellent mathematical treatment by a famous mathematician: squaring the circle, trisecting angle, doubling cube. Considered with full modern implications: transcendental numbers, pi, etc. Notes by R. Archibald. 16 figures. xi + 92pp. 5⅜ x 8.   T348 Clothbound **$1.50**
                                                                                  T298 Paperbound **$1.00**

✳   ✳   ✳

ELEMENTARY MATHEMATICS FROM AN ADVANCED STANDPOINT, Felix Klein.

This classic text is an outgrowth of Klein's famous integration and survey course at Göttingen. Using one field of mathematics to interpret, adjust, illuminate another, it covers basic topics in each area, illustrating its discussion with extensive analysis. It is especially valuable in considering areas of modern mathematics. "Makes the reader feel the inspiration of . . . a great mathematician, inspiring teacher . . . with deep insight into the foundations and interrelations," BULLETIN, AMERICAN MATHEMATICAL SOCIETY.

Vol. 1. ARITHMETIC, ALGEBRA, ANALYSIS. Introducing the concept of function immediately, it enlivens abstract discussion with graphical and geometrically perceptual methods. Partial contents: natural numbers, extension of the notion of number, special properties, complex numbers. Real equations with real unknowns, complex quantities. Logarithmic, exponential functions, goniometric functions, infinitesimal calculus. Transcendence of e and pi, theory of assemblages. Index. 125 figures. ix + 274pp . 5⅜ x 8.   S150 Paperbound **$1.75**

Vol. 2. GEOMETRY. A comprehensive view which accompanies the space perception inherent in geometry with analytic formulas which facilitate precise formulation. Partial contents: Simplest geometric manifolds: line segment, Grassmann determinant principles, classification of configurations of space, derivative manifolds. Geometric transformations: affine transformations, projective, higher point transformations, theory of the imaginary. Systematic discussion of geometry and its foundations. Indexes. 141 illustrations. ix + 214pp. 5⅜ x 8.
                                                                                  S151 Paperbound **$1.75**

*   *   *

COORDINATE GEOMETRY, L. P. Eisenhart. Thorough, unified introduction. Unusual for advancing in dimension within each topic (treats together circle, sphere; polar coordinates, 3-dimensional coordinate systems; conic sections, quadric surfaces), affording exceptional insight into subject. Extensive use made of determinants, though no previous knowledge of them is assumed. Algebraic equations of 1st degree, 2 and 3 unknowns, carried further than usual in algebra courses. Over 500 exercises. Introduction. Appendix. Index. Bibliography. 43 illustrations. 310pp. 5⅜ x 8.   S600 Paperbound **$1.65**

MONOGRAPHS ON TOPICS OF MODERN MATHEMATICS, edited by J. W. A. Young. Advanced mathematics for persons who haven't gone beyond or have forgotten high school algebra. 9 monographs on foundation of geometry, modern pure geometry, non-Euclidean geometry, fundamental propositions of algebra, algebraic equations, functions, calculus, theory of numbers, etc. Each monograph gives proofs of important results, and descriptions of leading methods, to provide wide coverage. New introduction by Prof. M. Kline, N. Y. University. 100 diagrams. xvi + 416pp. 6⅛ x 9¼.   S289 Paperbound **$2.00**

MATHEMATICS, INTERMEDIATE TO ADVANCED

Geometry

THE FOUNDATIONS OF EUCLIDEAN GEOMETRY, H. G. Forder. The first rigorous account of Euclidean geometry, establishing propositions without recourse to empiricism, and without multiplying hypotheses. Corrects many traditional weaknesses of Euclidean proofs, and investigates the problems imposed on the axiom system by the discoveries of Bolya and Lobatchefsky. Some topics discussed are Classes and Relations; Axioms for Magnitudes; Congruence and Similarity; Algebra of Points; Hessenberg's Theorem; Continuity; Existence of Parallels; Reflections; Rotations; Isometries; etc. Invaluable for the light it throws on foundations of math. Lists: Axioms employed, Symbols, Constructions. 295pp. 5⅜ x 8.
                                                                                  S481 Paperbound **$2.00**

ADVANCED EUCLIDEAN GEOMETRY, R. A. Johnson. For years the standard textbook on advanced Euclidean geometry, requires only high school geometry and trigonometry. Explores in unusual detail and gives proofs of hundreds of relatively recent theorems and corollaries, many formerly available only in widely scattered journals. Covers tangent circles, the theorem of Miquel, symmedian point, pedal triangles and circles, the Brocard configuration, and much more. Formerly "Modern Geometry." Index. 107 diagrams. xiii + 319pp. 5⅜ x 8.
                                                                                  S669 Paperbound **$1.65**

NON-EUCLIDEAN GEOMETRY, Roberto Bonola. The standard coverage of non-Euclidean geometry. It examines from both a historical and mathematical point of view the geometries which have arisen from a study of Euclid's 5th postulate upon parallel lines. Also included are complete texts, translated, of Bolyai's THEORY OF ABSOLUTE SPACE, Lobachevsky's THEORY OF PARALLELS. 180 diagrams. 431pp. 5⅜ x 8.   S27 Paperbound **$1.95**

ELEMENTS OF NON-EUCLIDEAN GEOMETRY, D. M. Y. Sommerville. Unique in proceeding step-by-step, in the manner of traditional geometry. Enables the student with only a good knowledge of high school algebra and geometry to grasp elementary hyperbolic, elliptic, analytic non-Euclidean geometries; space curvature and its philosophical implications; theory of radical axes; homothetic centres and systems of circles; parataxy and parallelism; absolute measure; Gauss' proof of the defect area theorem; geodesic representation; much more, all with exceptional clarity. 126 problems at chapter endings provide progressive practice and familiarity. 133 figures. Index. xvi + 274pp. 5⅜ x 8.   S460 Paperbound **$1.50**

HIGHER GEOMETRY: AN INTRODUCTION TO ADVANCED METHODS IN ANALYTIC GEOMETRY, F. S. Woods. Exceptionally thorough study of concepts and methods of advanced algebraic geometry (as distinguished from differential geometry). Exhaustive treatment of 1-, 2-, 3-, and 4-dimensional coordinate systems, leading to n-dimensional geometry in an abstract sense. Covers projectivity, tetracyclical coordinates, contact transformation, pentaspherical coordinates, much more. Based on M.I.T. lectures, requires sound preparation in analytic geometry and some knowledge of determinants. Index. Over 350 exercises. References. 60 figures. x + 423pp. 5⅜ x 8.   S737 Paperbound **$2.00**

ELEMENTS OF PROJECTIVE GEOMETRY, L. Cremona. Outstanding complete treatment of projective geometry by one of the foremost 19th century geometers. Detailed proofs of all fundamental principles, stress placed on the constructive aspects. Covers homology, law of duality, anharmonic ratios, theorems of Pascal and Brianchon, foci, polar reciprocal figures, etc. Only ordinary geometry necessary to understand this honored classic. Index. Over 150 fully worked out examples and problems. 252 diagrams. xx + 302pp. 5⅜ x 8.   S668 Paperbound **$1.75**

A TREATISE ON THE DIFFERENTIAL GEOMETRY OF CURVES AND SURFACES, L. P. Eisenhart. Introductory treatise especially for the graduate student, for years a highly successful textbook. More detailed and concrete in approach than most more recent books. Covers space curves, osculating planes, moving axes, Gauss' method, the moving trihedral, geodesics, conformal representation, etc. Last section deals with deformation of surfaces, rectilinear congruences, cyclic systems, etc. Index. 683 problems. 30 diagrams. xii + 474pp. 5⅜ x 8.   S667 Paperbound **$2.75**

A TREATISE ON ALGEBRAIC PLANE CURVES, J. L. Coolidge. Unabridged reprinting of one of few full coverages in English, offering detailed introduction to theory of algebraic plane curves and their relations to geometry and analysis. Treats topological properties, Riemann-Roch theorem, all aspects of wide variety of curves including real, covariant, polar, containing series of a given sort, elliptic, polygonal, rational, the pencil, two parameter nets, etc. This volume will enable the reader to appreciate the symbolic notation of Aronhold and Clebsch. Bibliography. Index. 17 illustrations. xxiv + 513pp. 5⅜ x 8.   S543 Paperbound **$2.45**

AN INTRODUCTION TO THE GEOMETRY OF N DIMENSIONS, D. M. Y. Sommerville. An introduction presupposing no prior knowledge of the field, the only book in English devoted exclusively to higher dimensional geometry. Discusses fundamental ideas of incidence, parallelism, perpendicularity, angles between linear space; enumerative geometry; analytical geometry from projective and metric points of view; polytopes; elementary ideas in analysis situs; content of hyper-spacial figures. Bibliography. Index. 60 diagrams. 196pp. 5⅜ x 8.   S494 Paperbound **$1.50**

GEOMETRY OF FOUR DIMENSIONS, H. P. Manning. Unique in English as a clear, concise introduction. Treatment is synthetic, and mostly Euclidean, although in hyperplanes and hyperspheres at infinity, non-Euclidean geometry is used. Historical introduction. Foundations of 4-dimensional geometry. Perpendicularity, simple angles. Angles of planes, higher order. Symmetry, order, motion; hyperpyramids, hypercones, hyperspheres; figures with parallel elements; volume, hypervolume in space; regular polyhedroids. Glossary. 78 figures. ix + 348pp. 5⅜ x 8.   S182 Paperbound **$1.95**

ELEMENTARY CONCEPTS OF TOPOLOGY, P. Alexandroff. First English translation of the famous brief introduction to topology for the beginner or for the mathematician not undertaking extensive study. This unusually useful intuitive approach deals primarily with the concepts of complex, cycle, and homology, and is wholly consistent with current investigations. Ranges from basic concepts of set-theoretic topology to the concept of Betti groups. "Glowing example of harmony between intuition and thought," David Hilbert. Translated by A. E. Farley. Introduction by D. Hilbert. Index. 25 figures. 73pp. 5⅜ x 8.   S747 Paperbound **$1.00**

THE WORKS OF ARCHIMEDES, edited by T. L. Heath. All the known works of the great Greek mathematician are contained in this one volume, including the recently discovered Method of Archimedes. Contains: On Sphere & Cylinder, Measurement of a Circle, Spirals, Conoids, Spheroids, etc. This is the definitive edition of the greatest mathematical intellect of the ancient world. 186-page study by Heath discusses Archimedes and the history of Greek mathematics. Bibliography. 563pp. 5⅜ x 8.   S9 Paperbound **$2.00**

THE THIRTEEN BOOKS OF EUCLID'S ELEMENTS, edited by **Sir Thomas Heath.** Definitive edition of one of the very greatest classics of Western world. Complete English translation of Heiberg text, together with spurious Book XIV. Detailed 150-page introduction discussing aspects of Greek and Medieval mathematics. Euclid, texts, commentators, etc. Paralleling the text is an elaborate critical apparatus analyzing each definition, proposition, postulate, covering textual matters, mathematical analysis, commentators of all times, refutations, supports, extrapolations, etc. This is the FULL EUCLID. Unabridged reproduction of Cambridge U. 2nd edition. 3 volumes. Total of 995 figures, 1426pp. 5⅜ x 8.

S88,89,90, 3 volume set, paperbound **$6.00**

THE GEOMETRY OF RENE DESCARTES. With this book Descartes founded analytical geometry. Excellent Smith-Latham translation, plus original French text with Déscartes' own diagrams. Contains Problems the Construction of Which Requires Only Straight Lines and Circles; On the Nature of Curved Lines; On the Construction of Solid or Supersolid Problems. Notes. Diagrams. 258pp. 5⅜ x 8.
S68 Paperbound **$1.50**

See also: **FOUNDATIONS OF GEOMETRY,** B. Russell; **THE PHILOSOPHY OF SPACE AND TIME,** H. Reichenbach; **FAMOUS PROBLEMS OF ELEMENTARY GEOMETRY,** F. Klein; **MONOGRAPHS ON TOPICS OF MODERN MATHEMATICS,** ed. by J. W. Young.

Calculus and function theory, Fourier theory, real and complex functions, determinants

A COLLECTION OF MODERN MATHEMATICAL CLASSICS, edited by R. Bellman. 13 classic papers, complete in their original languages, by Hermite, Hardy and Littlewood, Tchebychef, Fejér, Fredholm, Fuchs, Hurwitz, Weyl, van der Pol, Birkhoff, Kellogg, von Neumann, and Hilbert. Each of these papers, collected here for the first time, triggered a burst of mathematical activity, providing useful new generalizations or stimulating fresh investigations. Topics discussed include classical analysis, periodic and almost periodic functions, analysis and number theory, integral equations, theory of approximation, non-linear differential equations, and functional analysis. Brief introductions and bibliographies to each paper. xii + 292pp. 6 x 9.
S730 Paperbound **$2.00**

MATHEMATICS OF MODERN ENGINEERING, E. G. Keller and R. E. Doherty. Written for the Advanced Course in Engineering of the General Electric Corporation, deals with the engineering use of determinants, tensors, the Heaviside operational calculus, dyadics, the calculus of variations, etc. Presents underlying principles fully, but purpose is to teach engineers to deal with modern engineering problems, and emphasis is on the perennial engineering attack of set-up and solve. Indexes. Over 185 figures and tables. Hundreds of exercises, problems, and worked-out examples. References. Two volume set. Total of xxxiii + 623pp. 5⅜ x 8.
S734 Vol I Paperbound **$1.65**
S735 Vol II Paperbound **$1.65**
The set **$3.30**

MATHEMATICAL METHODS FOR SCIENTISTS AND ENGINEERS, L. P. Smith. For scientists and engineers, as well as advanced math students. Full investigation of methods and practical description of conditions under which each should be used. Elements of real functions, differential and integral calculus, space geometry, theory of residues, vector and tensor analysis, series of Bessel functions, etc. Each method illustrated by completely-worked-out examples, mostly from scientific literature. 368 graded unsolved problems. 100 diagrams. x + 453pp. 5⅝ x 8⅜.
S220 Paperbound **$2.00**

THEORY OF FUNCTIONS AS APPLIED TO ENGINEERING PROBLEMS, edited by R. Rothe, F. Ollendorff, and K. Pohlhausen. A series of lectures given at the Berlin Institute of Technology that shows the specific applications of function theory in electrical and allied fields of engineering. Six lectures provide the elements of function theory in a simple and practical form, covering complex quantities and variables, integration in the complex plane, residue theorems, etc. Then 5 lectures show the exact uses of this powerful mathematical tool, with full discussions of problem methods. Index. Bibliography. 108 figures. x + 189pp. 5⅜ x 8.
S733 Paperbound **$1.35**

ADVANCED CALCULUS, E. B. Wilson. An unabridged reprinting of the work which continues to be recognized as one of the most comprehensive and useful texts in the field. It contains an immense amount of well-presented, fundamental material, including chapters on vector functions, ordinary differential equations, special functions, calculus of variations, etc., which are excellent introductions to these areas. For students with only one year of calculus, more than 1300 exercises cover both pure math and applications to engineering and physical problems. For engineers, physicists, etc., this work, with its 54 page introductory review, is the ideal reference and refresher. Index. ix + 566pp. 5⅜ x 8.
S504 Paperbound **$2.45**

CALCULUS OF VARIATIONS, A. R. Forsyth. Methods, solutions, rather than determination of weakest valid hypotheses. Over 150 examples completely worked-out show use of Euler, Legendre, Jacoby, Weierstrass tests for maxima, minima. Integrals with one original dependent variable; with derivatives of 2nd order; two dependent variables, one independent variable; double integrals involving 1 dependent variable, 2 first derivatives; double integrals involving partial derivatives of 2nd order; triple integrals; much more. 50 diagrams. 678pp. 5⅜ x 8⅜. S622 Paperbound **$2.95**

LECTURES ON THE CALCULUS OF VARIATIONS, O. Bolza. Analyzes in detail the fundamental concepts of the calculus of variations, as developed from Euler to Hilbert, with sharp formulations of the problems and rigorous demonstrations of their solutions. More than a score of solved examples; systematic references for each theorem. Covers the necessary and sufficient conditions; the contributions made by Euler, Du Bois Reymond, Hilbert, Weierstrass, Legendre, Jacobi, Erdmann, Kneser, and Gauss; and much more. Index. Bibliography. xi + 271pp. 5⅜ x 8. S218 Paperbound **$**

A TREATISE ON THE CALCULUS OF FINITE DIFFERENCES, G. Boole. A classic in the literature of the calculus. Thorough, clear discussion of basic principles, theorems, methods. Covers MacLaurin's and Herschel's theorems, mechanical quadrature, factorials, periodical constants, Bernoulli's numbers, difference-equations (linear, mixed, and partial), etc. Stresses analogies with differential calculus. 236 problems, answers to the numerical ones. viii + 336pp. 5⅜ x 8. S695 Paperbound **$1.85**

THE ANALYTICAL THEORY OF HEAT, Joseph Fourier. This book, which revolutionized mathematical physics, is listed in the Great Books program, and many other listings of great books. It has been used with profit by generations of mathematicians and physicists who are interested in either heat or in the application of the Fourier integral. Covers cause and reflection of rays of heat, radiant heating, heating of closed spaces, use of trigonometric series in the theory of heat, Fourier integral, etc. Translated by Alexander Freeman. 20 figures. xxii + 466pp. 5⅜ x 8. S93 Paperbound **$2.00**

AN INTRODUCTION TO FOURIER METHODS AND THE LAPLACE TRANSFORMATION, Philip Franklin. Concentrates upon essentials, enabling the reader with only a working knowledge of calculus to gain an understanding of Fourier methods in a broad sense, suitable for most applications. This work covers complex qualities with methods of computing elementary functions for complex values of the argument and finding approximations by the use of charts; Fourier series and integrals with half-range and complex Fourier series; harmonic analysis; Fourier and Laplace transformations, etc.; partial differential equations with applications to transmission of electricity; etc. The methods developed are related to physical problems of heat flow, vibrations, electrical transmission, electromagnetic radiation, etc. 828 problems with answers. Formerly entitled "Fourier Methods." Bibliography. Index. x + 289pp. 5⅜ x 8. S452 Paperbound **$1.75**

THE FOURIER INTEGRAL AND CERTAIN OF ITS APPLICATIONS, Norbert Wiener. The only book-length study of the Fourier integral as link between pure and applied math. An expansion of lectures given at Cambridge. Partial contents: Plancherel's theorem, general Tauberian theorem, special Tauberian theorems, generalized harmonic analysis. Bibliography. viii + 201pp. 5⅜ x 8. S272 Paperbound **$1.50**

INTRODUCTION TO THE THEORY OF FOURIER'S SERIES AND INTEGRALS, H. S. Carslaw. 3rd revised edition. This excellent introduction is an outgrowth of the author's courses at Cambridge. Historical introduction, rational and irrational numbers, infinite sequences and series, functions of a single variable, definite integral, Fourier series, Fourier integrals, and similar topics. Appendixes discuss practical harmonic analysis, periodogram analysis. Lebesgues theory. Indexes. 84 examples, bibliography. xiii + 368pp. 5⅜ x 8. S48 Paperbound **$2.00**

FOURIER'S SERIES AND SPHERICAL HARMONICS, W. E. Byerly. Continues to be recognized as one of most practical, useful expositions. Functions, series, and their differential equations are concretely explained in great detail; theory is applied constantly to practical problems, which are fully and lucidly worked out. Appendix includes 6 tables of surface zonal harmonics, hyperbolic functions, Bessel's functions. Bibliography. 190 problems, approximately half with answers. ix + 287pp. 5⅜ x 8. S536 Paperbound **$1.75**

ASYMPTOTIC EXPANSIONS, A. Erdélyi. The only modern work available in English, this is an unabridged reproduction of a monograph prepared for the Office of Naval Research. It discusses various procedures for asymptotic evaluation of integrals containing a large parameter and solutions of ordinary linear differential equations. Bibliography of 71 items. vi + 108pp. 5⅜ x 8. S318 Paperbound **$1.35**

LINEAR INTEGRAL EQUATIONS, W. V. Lovitt. Systematic survey of general theory, with some application to differential equations, calculus of variations, problems of math, physics. Partial contents: integral equation of 2nd kind by successive substitutions; Fredholm's equation as ratio of 2 integral series in lambda, applications of the Fredholm theory, Hilbert-Schmidt theory of symmetric kernels, application, etc. Neumann, Dirichlet, vibratory problems. Index. ix + 253pp. 5⅜ x 8. S175 Clothbound **$3.50**
S176 Paperbound **$1.60**

ELLIPTIC INTEGRALS, H. Hancock. Invaluable in work involving differential equations containing cubics or quartics under the root sign, where elementary calculus methods are inadequate. Practical solutions to problems that occur in mathematics, engineering, physics: differential equations requiring integration of Lamé's, Briot's, or Bouquet's equations; determination of arc of ellipse, hyperbola, lemniscate; solutions of problems in elastica; motion of a projectile under resistance varying as the cube of the velocity; pendulums; many others. Exposition is in accordance with Legendre-Jacobi theory and includes rigorous discussion of Legendre transformations. 20 figures. 5 place table. Index. 104pp. 5⅛ x 8.
S484 Paperbound **$1.25**

FIVE VOLUME "THEORY OF FUNCTIONS' SET BY KONRAD KNOPP

This five-volume set, prepared by Konrad Knopp, provides a complete and readily followed account of theory of functions. Proofs are given concisely, yet without sacrifice of completeness or rigor. These volumes are used as texts by such universities as M.I.T., University of Chicago, N. Y. City College, and many others. "Excellent introduction . . . remarkably readable, concise, clear, rigorous," JOURNAL OF THE AMERICAN STATISTICAL ASSOCIATION.

ELEMENTS OF THE THEORY OF FUNCTIONS, Konrad Knopp. This book provides the student with background for further volumes in this set, or texts on a similar level. Partial contents: foundations, system of complex numbers and the Gaussian plane of numbers, Riemann sphere of numbers, mapping by linear functions, normal forms, the logarithm, the cyclometric functions and binomial series. "Not only for the young student, but also for the student who knows all about what is in it," MATHEMATICAL JOURNAL. Bibliography. Index. 140pp. 5⅜ x 8.
S154 Paperbound **$1.35**

THEORY OF FUNCTIONS, PART I, Konrad Knopp. With volume II, this book provides coverage of basic concepts and theorems. Partial contents: numbers and points, functions of a complex variable, integral of a continuous function, Cauchy's integral theorem, Cauchy's integral formulae, series with variable terms, expansion of analytic functions in power series, analytic continuation and complete definition of analytic functions, entire transcendental functions, Laurent expansion, types of singularities. Bibliography. Index. vii + 146pp. 5⅜ x 8.
S156 Paperbound **$1.35**

THEORY OF FUNCTIONS, PART II, Konrad Knopp. Application and further development of general theory, special topics. Single valued functions, entire, Weierstrass, Meromorphic functions. Riemann surfaces. Algebraic functions. Analytical configuration, Riemann surface. Bibliography. Index. x + 150pp. 5⅜ x 8.
S157 Paperbound **$1.35**

PROBLEM BOOK IN THE THEORY OF FUNCTIONS, VOLUME 1, Konrad Knopp. Problems in elementary theory, for use with Knopp's THEORY OF FUNCTIONS, or any other text, arranged according to increasing difficulty. Fundamental concepts, sequences of numbers and infinite series, complex variable, integral theorems, development in series, conformal mapping. 182 problems. Answers. viii + 126pp. 5⅜ x 8.
S158 Paperbound **$1.35**

PROBLEM BOOK IN THE THEORY OF FUNCTIONS, VOLUME 2, Konrad Knopp. Advanced theory of functions, to be used either with Knopp's THEORY OF FUNCTIONS, or any other comparable text. Singularities, entire & meromorphic functions, periodic, analytic, continuation, multiple-valued functions, Riemann surfaces, conformal mapping. Includes a section of additional elementary problems. "The difficult task of selecting from the immense material of the modern theory of functions the problems just within the reach of the beginner is here masterfully accomplished," AM. MATH. SOC. Answers. 138pp. 5⅜ x 8. S159 Paperbound **$1.35**

* * *

LECTURES ON THE THEORY OF ELLIPTIC FUNCTIONS, H. Hancock. Reissue of the only book in English with so extensive a coverage, especially of Abel, Jacobi, Legendre, Weierstrasse, Hermite, Liouville, and Riemann. Unusual fullness of treatment, plus applications as well as theory, in discussing elliptic function (the universe of elliptic integrals originating in works of Abel and Jacobi), their existence, and ultimate meaning. Use is made of Riemann to provide the most general theory. 40 page table of formulas. 76 figures. xxiii + 498pp.
S483 Paperbound **$2.55**

THE THEORY AND FUNCTIONS OF A REAL VARIABLE AND THE THEORY OF FOURIER'S SERIES, E. W. Hobson. One of the best introductions to set theory and various aspects of functions and Fourier's series. Requires only a good background in calculus. Provides an exhaustive coverage of: metric and descriptive properties of sets of points; transfinite numbers and order types; functions of a real variable; the Riemann and Lebesgue integrals; sequences and series of numbers; power-series; functions representable by series sequences of continuous functions; trigonometrical series; representation of functions by Fourier's series; complete exposition (200pp.) on set theory; and much more. "The best possible guide," Nature. Vol. I: 88 detailed examples, 10 figures. Index. xv + 736pp. Vol. II: 117 detailed examples, 13 figures. Index. x + 780pp. 6⅛ x 9¼.
Vol. I: S387 Paperbound **$3.00**
Vol. II: S388 Paperbound **$3.00**

ALMOST PERIODIC FUNCTIONS, A. S. Besicovitch. This unique and important summary by a well-known mathematician covers in detail the two stages of development in Bohr's theory of almost periodic functions: (1) as a generalization of pure periodicity, with results and proofs; (2) the work done by Stepanoff, Wiener, Weyl, and Bohr in generalizing the theory. Bibliography. xi + 180pp. 5⅜ x 8.
S18 Paperbound **$1.75**

THEORY OF FUNCTIONALS AND OF INTEGRAL AND INTEGRO-DIFFERENTIAL EQUATIONS, Vito Volterra. Unabridged republication of the only English translation. An exposition of the general theory of the functions depending on a continuous set of values of another function, based on the author's fundamental notion of the transition from a finite number of variables to a continually infinite number. Though dealing primarily with integral equations, much material on calculus of variations is included. The work makes no assumption of previous knowledge on the part of the reader. It begins with fundamental material and proceeds to Generalization of Analytic Functions, Integro-Differential Equations, Functional Derivative Equations, Applications, Other Directions of Theory of Functionals, etc. New introduction by G. C. Evans. Bibliography and criticism of Volterra's work by E. Whittaker. Bibliography. Index of authors cited. Index of subjects. xxxx + 226pp. 5⅜ x 8. S502 Paperbound **$1.75**

AN ELEMENTARY TREATISE ON ELLIPTIC FUNCTIONS, A. Cayley. Still the fullest and clearest text on the theories of Jacobi and Legendre for the advanced student (and an excellent supplement for the beginner). A masterpiece of exposition by the great 19th century British mathematician (creator of the theory of matrices and abstract geometry), it covers the addition-theory, Landen's theorem, the 3 kinds of elliptic integrals, transformations, the q-functions, reduction of a differential expression, and much more. Index. xii + 386pp. 5⅜ x 8.
S728 Paperbound **$2.00**

THE APPLICATIONS OF ELLIPTIC FUNCTIONS, A. G. Greenhill. Modern books forgo detail for sake of brevity—this book offers complete exposition necessary for proper understanding, use of elliptic integrals. Formulas developed from definite physical, geometric problems; examples representative enough to offer basic information in widely useable form. Elliptic integrals, addition theorem, algebraical form of addition theorem, elliptic integrals of 2nd, 3rd kind, double periodicity, resolution into factors, series, transformation, etc. Introduction. Index. 25 illus. xi + 357pp. 5⅜ x 8. S603 Paperbound **$1.75**

THE THEORY OF FUNCTIONS OF REAL VARIABLES, James Pierpont. A 2-volume authoritative exposition, by one of the foremost mathematicians of his time. Each theorem stated with all conditions, then followed by proof. No need to go through complicated reasoning to discover conditions added without specific mention. Includes a particularly complete, rigorous presentation of theory of measure; and Pierpont's own work on a theory of Lebesgue integrals, and treatment of area of a curved surface. Partial contents, Vol. 1: rational numbers, exponentials, logarithms, point aggregates, maxima, minima, proper integrals, improper integrals, multiple proper integrals, continuity, discontinuity, indeterminate forms. Vol. 2: point sets, proper integrals, series, power series, aggregates, ordinal numbers, discontinuous functions, sub-, infra-uniform convergence, much more. Index. 95 illustrations. 1229pp. 5⅜ x 8. S558-9, 2 volume set, paperbound **$4.90**

FUNCTIONS OF A COMPLEX VARIABLE, James Pierpont. Long one of best in the field. A thorough treatment of fundamental elements, concepts, theorems. A complete study, rigorous, detailed, with carefully selected problems worked out to illustrate each topic. Partial contents: arithmetic operations, real term series, positive term series, exponential functions, integration, analytic functions, asymptotic expansions, functions of Weierstrass, Legendre, etc. Index. List of symbols. 122 illus. 597pp. 5⅜ x 8. S560 Paperbound **$2.45**

ELEMENTS OF THE THEORY OF REAL FUNCTIONS, J. E. Littlewood. Based on lectures given at Trinity College, Cambridge, this book has proved to be extremely successful in introducing graduate students to the modern theory of functions. It offers a full and concise coverage of classes and cardinal numbers, well-ordered series, other types of series, and elements of the theory of sets of points. 3rd revised edition. vii + 71pp. 5⅜ x 8.
S171 Clothbound **$2.85**
S172 Paperbound **$1.25**

TRANSCENDENTAL AND ALGEBRAIC NUMBERS, A. O. Gelfond. First English translation of work by leading Soviet mathematician. Thue-Siegel theorem, its p-adic analogue, on approximation of algebraic numbers by numbers in fixed algebraic field; Hermite-Lindemann theorem on transcendency of Bessel functions, solutions of other differential equations; Gelfond-Schneider theorem on transcendency of alpha to power beta; Schneider's work on elliptic functions, with method developed by Gelfond. Translated by L. F. Boron. Index. Bibliography. 200pp. 5⅜ x 8. S615 Paperbound **$1.75**

THEORY OF MAXIMA AND MINIMA, H. Hancock. Fullest treatment ever written; only work in English with extended discussion of maxima and minima for functions of 1, 2, or n variables, problems with subsidiary constraints, and relevant quadratic forms. Detailed proof of each important theorem. Covers the Scheeffer and von Dantscher theories, homogeneous quadratic forms, reversion of series, fallacious establishment of maxima and minima, etc. Unsurpassed treatise for advanced students of calculus, mathematicians, economists, statisticians. Index. 24 diagrams. 39 problems, many examples. 193pp. 5⅜ x 8. S665 Paperbound **$1.50**

DICTIONARY OF CONFORMAL REPRESENTATIONS, H. Kober. Laplace's equation in 2 dimensions solved in this unique book developed by the British Admiralty. Scores of geometrical forms & their transformations for electrical engineers, Joukowski aerofoil for aerodynamists. Schwartz-Christoffel transformations for hydrodynamics, transcendental functions. Contents classified according to analytical functions describing transformation. Twin diagrams show curves of most transformations with corresponding regions. Glossary. Topological index. 447 diagrams. 244pp. 6⅛ x 9¼. S160 Paperbound **$2.00**

THE TAYLOR SERIES, AN INTRODUCTION TO THE THEORY OF FUNCTIONS OF A COMPLEX VARIABLE, P. Dienes. This book investigates the entire realm of analytic functions. Only ordinary calculus is needed, except in the last two chapters. Starting with an introduction to real variables and complex algebra, the properties of infinite series, elementary functions, complex differentiation and integration are carefully derived. Also biuniform mapping, a thorough two part discussion of representation and singularities of analytic functions, overconvergence and gap theorems, divergent series, Taylor series on its circle of convergence, divergence and singularities, etc. Unabridged, corrected reissue of first edition. Preface and index. 186 examples, many fully worked out. 67 figures. xii + 555pp. 5⅜ x 8.
S391 Paperbound **$2.75**

INTRODUCTION TO BESSEL FUNCTIONS, Frank Bowman. A rigorous self-contained exposition providing all necessary material during the development, which requires only some knowledge of calculus and acquaintance with differential equations. A balanced presentation including applications and practical use. Discusses Bessel Functions of Zero Order, of Any Real Order; Modified Bessel Functions of Zero Order; Definite Integrals; Asymptotic Expansions; Bessel's Solution to Kepler's Problem; Circular Membranes; much more. "Clear and straightforward . . . useful not only to students of physics and engineering, but to mathematical students in general," Nature. 226 problems. Short tables of Bessel functions. 27 figures. Index. x + 135pp. 5⅜ x 8.
S462 Paperbound **$1.35**

MODERN THEORIES OF INTEGRATION, H. Kestelman. Connected and concrete coverage, with fully-worked-out proofs for every step. Ranges from elementary definitions through theory of aggregates, sets of points, Riemann and Lebesgue integration, and much more. This new revised and enlarged edition contains a new chapter on Riemann-Stieltjes integration, as well as a supplementary section of 186 exercises. Ideal for the mathematician, student, teacher, or self-studier. Index of Definitions and Symbols. General Index. Bibliography. x + 310pp. 5⅜ x 8⅜.
S572 Paperbound **$2.00**

A TREATISE ON THE THEORY OF DETERMINANTS, T. Muir. Unequalled as an exhaustive compilation of nearly all the known facts about determinants up to the early 1930's. Covers notation and general properties, row and column transformation, symmetry, compound determinants, adjugates, rectangular arrays and matrices, linear dependence, gradients, Jacobians, Hessians, Wronskians, and much more. Invaluable for libraries of industrial and research organizations as well as for student, teacher, and mathematician; very useful in the field of computing machines. Revised and enlarged by W. H. Metzler. Index. 485 problems and scores of numerical examples. iv + 766pp. 5⅜ x 8.
S670 Paperbound **$2.95**

THEORY OF DETERMINANTS IN THE HISTORICAL ORDER OF DEVELOPMENT, Sir Thomas Muir. Unabridged reprinting of this complete study of 1,859 papers on determinant theory written between 1693 and 1900. Most important and original sections reproduced, valuable commentary on each. No other work is necessary for determinant research: all types are covered— each subdivision of the theory treated separately; all papers dealing with each type are covered; you are told exactly what each paper is about and how important its contribution is. Each result, theory, extension, or modification is assigned its own identifying numeral so that the full history may be more easily followed. Includes papers on determinants in general, determinants and linear equations, symmetric determinants, alternants, recurrents, determinants having invariant factors, and all other major types. "A model of what such histories ought to be," NATURE. "Mathematicians must ever be grateful to Sir Thomas for his monumental work," AMERICAN MATH MONTHLY. Four volumes bound as two. Indices. Bibliographies. Total of lxxxiv + 1977pp. 5⅜ x 8.
S672-3 The set, Clothbound **$10.00**

A COURSE IN MATHEMATICAL ANALYSIS, Edouard Goursat. Trans. by E. R. Hedrick, O. Dunkel. Classic study of fundamental material thoroughly treated. Exceptionally lucid exposition of wide range of subject matter for student with 1 year of calculus. Vol. 1: Derivatives and Differentials, Definite Integrals, Expansion in Series, Applications to Geometry. Problems. Index. 52 illus. 556pp. Vol. 2, Part I: Functions of a Complex Variable, Conformal Representations, Doubly Periodic Functions, Natural Boundaries, etc. Problems. Index. 38 illus. 269pp. Vol. 2, Part 2: Differential Equations, Cauchy-Lipschitz Method, Non-linear Differential Equations, Simultaneous Equations, etc. Problems. Index. 308pp. 5⅜ x 8.
Vol. 1 S554 Paperbound **$2.25**
Vol. 2 part 1 S555 Paperbound **$1.65**
Vol. 2 part 2 S556 Paperbound **$1.65**
3 vol. set **$5.00**

INFINITE SEQUENCES AND SERIES, Konrad Knopp. First publication in any language! Excellent introduction to 2 topics of modern mathematics, designed to give the student background to penetrate farther by himself. Sequences & sets, real & complex numbers, etc. Functions of a real & complex variable. Sequences & series. Infinite series. Convergent power series. Expansion of elementary functions. Numerical evaluation of series. Bibliography. v + 186pp. 5⅜ x 8.
S152 Clothbound **$3.50**
S153 Paperbound **$1.75**

TRIGONOMETRICAL SERIES, Antoni Zygmund. Unique in any language on modern advanced level. Contains carefully organized analyses of trigonometric, orthogonal, Fourier systems of functions, with clear adequate descriptions of summability of Fourier series, proximation theory, conjugate series, convergence, divergence of Fourier series. Especially valuable for Russian, Eastern European coverage. Bibliography. 329pp. 5⅜ x 8.
S290 Paperbound **$1.50**

COLLECTED WORKS OF BERNHARD RIEMANN. This important source book is the first to contain the complete text of both 1892 Werke and the 1902 supplement, unabridged. It contains 31 monographs, 3 complete lecture courses, 15 miscellaneous papers, which have been of enormous importance in relativity, topology, theory of complex variables, and other areas of mathematics. Edited by R. Dedekind, H. Weber, M. Noether, W. Wirtinger. German text. English introduction by Hans Lewy. 690pp. 5⅜ x 8.   S226 Paperbound **$2.85**

See also: **A HISTORY OF THE CALCULUS,** C. B. Boyer; **CALCULUS REFRESHER FOR TECHNICAL MEN,** A. A. Klaf; **MONOGRAPHS ON TOPICS OF MODERN MATHEMATICS,** ed. by J. W. A. Young; **THE CONTINUUM AND OTHER TYPES OF SERIAL ORDER,** E. V. Huntington.

Symbolic logic

AN INTRODUCTION TO SYMBOLIC LOGIC, Susanne K. Langer. Probably the clearest book ever written on symbolic logic for the philosopher, general scientist and layman. It will be particularly appreciated by those who have been rebuffed by other introductory works because of insufficient mathematical training. No special knowledge of mathematics is required. Starting with the simplest symbols and conventions, you are led to a remarkable grasp of the Boole-Schroeder and Russell-Whitehead systems clearly and quickly. PARTIAL CONTENTS: Study of forms, Essentials of logical structure, Generalization, Classes, The deductive system of classes, The algebra of logic, Abstraction of interpretation, Calculus of propositions, Assumptions of PRINCIPIA MATHEMATICA, Logistics, Logic of the syllogism, Proofs of theorems. "One of the clearest and simplest introductions to a subject which is very much alive. The style is easy, symbolism is introduced gradually, and the intelligent non-mathematician should have no difficulty in following the argument," MATHEMATICS GAZETTE. Revised, expanded second edition. Truth-value tables. 368pp. 5⅜ x 8.
S164 Paperbound **$1.75**

THE ELEMENTS OF MATHEMATICAL LOGIC, Paul Rosenbloom. First publication in any language. This book is intended for readers who are mature mathematically, but have no previous training in symbolic logic. It does not limit itself to a single system, but covers the field as a whole. It is a development of lectures given at Lund University, Sweden, in 1948. Partial contents: Logic of classes, fundamental theorems, Boolean algebra, logic of propositions, logic of propositional functions, expressive languages, combinatory logics, development of mathematics within an object language, paradoxes, theorems of Post and Goedel, Church's theorem, and similar topics. iv + 214pp. 5⅜ x 8.   S227 Paperbound **$1.45**

A SURVEY OF SYMBOLIC LOGIC: THE CLASSIC ALGEBRA OF LOGIC, C. I. Lewis. Classic survey of the field, comprehensive and thorough. Indicates content of major systems, alternative methods of procedure, and relation of these to the Boole-Schroeder algebra and to one another. Contains historical summary, as well as full proofs and applications of the classic, or Boole-Schroeder, algebra of logic. Discusses diagrams for the logical relations of classes, the two-valued algebra, propositional functions of two or more variables, etc. Chapters 5 and 6 of the original edition, which contained material not directly pertinent, have been omitted in this edition at the author's request. Appendix. Bibliography. Index. viii + 352pp. 5⅝ x 8⅜.
S643 Paperbound **$2.00**

INTRODUCTION TO SYMBOLIC LOGIC AND ITS APPLICATIONS, R. Carnap. One of the clearest, most comprehensive, and rigorous introductions to modern symbolic logic by perhaps its greatest living master. Symbolic languages are analyzed and one constructed. Applications to math (symbolic representation of axiom systems for set theory, natural numbers, real numbers, topology, Dedekind and Cantor explanations of continuity), physics (the general analysis of concepts of determination, causality, space-time-topology, based on Einstein), biology (symbolic representation of an axiom system for basic concepts). "A masterpiece," Zentralblatt für Mathematik und ihre Grenzgebiete. Over 300 exercises. 5 figures. Bibliography. Index. xvi + 241pp. 5⅜ x 8.   S453 Paperbound **$1.85**
Clothbound **$4.00**

SYMBOLIC LOGIC, C. I. Lewis, C. H. Langford. Probably the most cited book in symbolic logic, this is one of the fullest treatments of paradoxes. A wide coverage of the entire field of symbolic logic, plus considerable material that has not appeared elsewhere. Basic to the entire volume is the distinction between the logic of extensions and of intensions. Considerable emphasis is placed on converse substitution, while the matrix system presents the supposition of a variety of non-Aristotelian logics. It has especially valuable sections on strict limitations, existence of terms, 2-valued algebra and its extension to propositional functions, truth value systems, the matrix method, implication and deductibility, general theory of propositions, propositions of ordinary discourse, and similar topics. "Authoritative, most valuable," TIMES, London. Bibliography. 506pp. 5⅜ x 8.   S170 Paperbound **$2.00**

THE LAWS OF THOUGHT, George Boole. This book founded symbolic logic some hundred years ago. It is the 1st significant attempt to apply logic to all aspects of human endeavour. Partial contents: derivation of laws, signs & laws, interpretations, eliminations, conditions of a perfect method, analysis, Aristotelian logic, probability, and similar topics. xviii + 424pp. 5⅜ x 8.   S28 Paperbound **$2.00**

THE PRINCIPLES OF SCIENCE, A TREATISE ON LOGIC AND THE SCIENTIFIC METHOD, W. S. Jevons. Treating such topics as Inductive and Deductive Logic, the Theory of Number, Probability, and the Limits of Scientific Method, this milestone in the development of symbolic logic remains a stimulating contribution to the investigation of inferential validity in the natural and social sciences. It significantly advances Boole's logic, and contains a detailed introduction to the nature and methods of probability in physics, astronomy, everyday affairs, etc. In his introduction, Ernest Nagel of Columbia University says, "[Jevons] continues to be of interest as an attempt to articulate the logic of scientific inquiry." Index. liii + 786pp. 5⅜ x 8.   S446 Paperbound **$2.98**

Group theory, algebra, sets

LECTURES ON THE ICOSAHEDRON AND THE SOLUTION OF EQUATIONS OF THE FIFTH DEGREE, Felix Klein. The solution of quintics in terms of rotation of a regular icosahedron around its axes of symmetry. A classic & indispensable source for those interested in higher algebra, geometry, crystallography. Considerable explanatory material included. 230 footnotes, mostly bibliographic. 2nd edition, xvi + 289pp. 5⅜ x 8.   S314 Paperbound **$1.85**

LINEAR GROUPS, WITH AN EXPOSITION OF THE GALOIS FIELD THEORY, L. E. Dickson. The classic exposition of the theory of groups, well within the range of the graduate student. Part I contains the most extensive and thorough presentation of the theory of Galois Fields available, with a wealth of examples and theorems. Part II is a full discussion of linear groups of finite order. Much material in this work is based on Dickson's own contributions. Also includes expositions of Jordan, Lie, Abel, Betti-Mathieu, Hermite, etc. "A milestone in the development of modern algebra," W. Magnus, in his historical introduction to this edition. Index. xv + 312pp. 5⅜ x 8.   S482 Paperbound **$1.95**

INTRODUCTION TO THE THEORY OF GROUPS OF FINITE ORDER, R. Carmichael. Examines fundamental theorems and their application. Beginning with sets, systems, permutations, etc., it progresses in easy stages through important types of groups: Abelian, prime power, permutation, etc. Except 1 chapter where matrices are desirable, no higher math needed. 783 exercises, problems. Index. xvi + 447pp. 5⅜ x 8.   S299 Clothbound **$3.95**
                                                                              S300 Paperbound **$2.00**

THEORY OF GROUPS OF FINITE ORDER, W. Burnside. First published some 40 years ago, this is still one of the clearest introductory texts. Partial contents: permutations, groups independent of representation, composition series of a group, isomorphism of a group with itself, Abelian groups, prime power groups, permutation groups, invariants of groups of linear substitution graphical representation, etc. 45pp. of notes. Indexes. xxiv + 512pp. 5⅜ x 8. S38 Paperbound **$2.45**

THEORY AND APPLICATIONS OF FINITE GROUPS, G. A. Miller, H. F. Blichfeldt, L. E. Dickson. Unusually accurate and authoritative work, each section prepared by a leading specialist: Miller on substitution and abstract groups, Blichfeldt on finite groups of linear homogeneous transformations, Dickson on applications of finite groups. Unlike more modern works, this gives the concrete basis from which abstract group theory arose. Includes Abelian groups, prime-power groups, isomorphisms, matrix forms of linear transformations, Sylow groups, Galois' theory of algebraic equations, duplication of a cube, trisection of an angle, etc. 2 Indexes. 267 problems. xvii + 390pp. 5⅜ x 8.   S216 Paperbound **$2.00**

CONTINUOUS GROUPS OF TRANSFORMATIONS, L. P. Eisenhart. Intensive study of the theory and geometrical applications of continuous groups of transformations; a standard work on the subject, called forth by the revolution in physics in the 1920's. Covers tensor analysis, Riemannian geometry, canonical parameters, transitivity, imprimitivity, differential invariants, the algebra of constants of structure, differential geometry, contact transformations, etc. "Likely to remain one of the standard works on the subject for many years . . . principal theorems are proved clearly and concisely, and the arrangement of the whole is coherent," MATHEMATICAL GAZETTE. Index. 72-item bibliography. 185 exercises. ix + 301pp. 5⅜ x 8.
                                                                              S781 Paperbound **$1.85**

THE THEORY OF GROUPS AND QUANTUM MECHANICS, H. Weyl. Discussions of Schroedinger's wave equation, de Broglie's waves of a particle, Jordan-Hoelder theorem, Lie's continuous groups of transformations, Pauli exclusion principle, quantization of Maxwell-Dirac field equations, etc. Unitary geometry, quantum theory, groups, application of groups to quantum mechanics, symmetry permutation group, algebra of symmetric transformation, etc. 2nd revised edition. Bibliography. Index. xxii + 422pp. 5⅜ x 8.   S268 Clothbound **$4.50**
                                                                              S269 Paperbound **$1.95**

ALGEBRAIC THEORIES, L. E. Dickson. Best thorough introduction to classical topics in higher algebra develops theories centering around matrices, invariants, groups. Higher algebra, Galois theory, finite linear groups, Klein's icosahedron, algebraic invariants, linear transformations, elementary divisors, invariant factors; quadratic, bi-linear, Hermitian forms, singly and in pairs. Proofs rigorous, detailed; topics developed lucidly, in close connection with their most frequent mathematical applications. Formerly "Modern Algebraic Theories." 155 problems. Bibliography. 2 indexes. 285pp. 5⅜ x 8.   S547 Paperbound **$1.50**

ALGEBRAS AND THEIR ARITHMETICS, L. E. Dickson. Provides the foundation and background necessary to any advanced undergraduate or graduate student studying abstract algebra. Begins with elementary introduction to linear transformations, matrices, field of complex numbers; proceeds to order, basal units, modulus, quaternions, etc.; develops calculus of linear sets, describes various examples of algebras including invariant, difference, nilpotent, semi-simple. "Makes the reader marvel at his genius for clear and profound analysis," Amer. Mathematical Monthly. Index. xii + 241pp. 5⅜ x 8.   S616 Paperbound **$1.35**

THE THEORY OF EQUATIONS WITH AN INTRODUCTION TO THE THEORY OF BINARY ALGEBRAIC FORMS, W. S. Burnside and A. W. Panton. Extremely thorough and concrete discussion of the theory of equations, with extensive detailed treatment of many topics curtailed in later texts. Covers theory of algebraic equations, properties of polynomials, symmetric functions, derived functions, Horner's process, complex numbers and the complex variable, determinants and methods of elimination, invariant theory (nearly 100 pages), transformations, introduction to Galois theory, Abelian equations, and much more. Invaluable supplementary work for modern students and teachers. 759 examples and exercises. Index in each volume. Two volume set. Total of xxiv + 604pp. 5⅜ x 8.   S714 Vol I Paperbound **$1.85**
S715 Vol II Paperbound **$1.85**
The set **$3.70**

COMPUTATIONAL METHODS OF LINEAR ALGEBRA, V. N. Faddeeva, translated by **C. D. Benster.** First English translation of a unique and valuable work, the only work in English presenting a systematic exposition of the most important methods of linear algebra—classical and contemporary. Shows in detail how to derive numerical solutions of problems in mathematical physics which are frequently connected with those of linear algebra. Theory as well as individual practice. Part I surveys the mathematical background that is indispensable to what follows. Parts II and III, the conclusion, set forth the most important methods of solution, for both exact and iterative groups. One of the most outstanding and valuable features of this work is the 23 tables, double and triple checked for accuracy. These tables will not be found elsewhere. Author's preface. Translator's note. New bibliography and index. x + 252pp. 5⅜ x 8.   S424 Paperbound **$1.95**

ALGEBRAIC EQUATIONS, E. Dehn. Careful and complete presentation of Galois' theory of algebraic equations; theories of Lagrange and Galois developed in logical rather than historical form, with a more thorough exposition than in most modern books. Many concrete applications and fully-worked-out examples. Discusses basic theory (very clear exposition of the symmetric group); isomorphic, transitive, and Abelian groups; applications of Lagrange's and Galois' theories; and much more. Newly revised by the author. Index. List of Theorems. xi + 208pp. 5⅜ x 8.   S697 Paperbound **$1.45**

THEORY OF SETS, E. Kamke. Clearest, amplest introduction in English, well suited for independent study. Subdivision of main theory, such as theory of sets of points, are discussed, but emphasis is on general theory. Partial contents: rudiments of set theory, arbitrary sets and their cardinal numbers, ordered sets and their order types, well-ordered sets and their cardinal numbers. Bibliography. Key to symbols. Index. vii + 144pp. 5⅜ x 8.
S141 Paperbound **$1.35**

Number theory

INTRODUCTION TO THE THEORY OF NUMBERS, L. E. Dickson. Thorough, comprehensive approach with adequate coverage of classical literature, an introductory volume beginners can follow. Chapters on divisibility, congruences, quadratic residues & reciprocity, Diophantine equations, etc. Full treatment of binary quadratic forms without usual restriction to integral coefficients. Covers infinitude of primes, least residues, Fermat's theorem, Euler's phi function, Legendre's symbol, Gauss's lemma, automorphs, reduced forms, recent theorems of Thue & Siegel, many more. Much material not readily available elsewhere. 239 problems. Index. J figure. viii + 183pp. 5⅜ x 8.   S342 Paperbound **$1.65**

ELEMENTS OF NUMBER THEORY, I. M. Vinogradov. Detailed 1st course for persons without advanced mathematics; 95% of this book can be understood by readers who have gone no farther than high school algebra. Partial contents: divisibility theory, important number theoretical functions, congruences, primitive roots and indices, etc. Solutions to both problems and exercises. Tables of primes, indices, etc. Covers almost every essential formula in elementary number theory! Translated from Russian. 233 problems, 104 exercises. viii + 227pp. 5⅜ x 8.   S259 Paperbound **$1.60**

THEORY OF NUMBERS and DIOPHANTINE ANALYSIS, R. D. Carmichael. These two complete works in one volume form one of the most lucid introductions to number theory, requiring only a firm foundation in high school mathematics. "Theory of Numbers," partial contents: Eratosthenes' sieve, Euclid's fundamental theorem, G.C.F. and L.C.M. of two or more integers, linear congruences, etc "Diophantine Analysis": rational triangles, Pythagorean triangles, equations of third, fourth, higher degrees, method of functional equations, much more. "Theory of Numbers": 76 problems. Index. 94pp. "Diophantine Analysis": 222 problems. Index. 118pp. 5⅜ x 8.   S529 Paperbound **$1.35**

CONTRIBUTIONS TO THE FOUNDING OF THE THEORY OF TRANSFINITE NUMBERS, Georg Cantor. These papers founded a new branch of mathematics. The famous articles of 1895-7 are translated, with an 82-page introduction by P. E. B. Jourdain dealing with Cantor, the background of his discoveries, their results, future possibilities. Bibliography. Index. Notes. ix + 211 pp. 5⅜ x 8. S45 Paperbound **$1.25**

See also: **TRANSCENDENTAL AND ALGEBRAIC NUMBERS, A. O. Gelfond.**

Probability theory and information theory

A PHILOSOPHICAL ESSAY ON PROBABILITIES, Marquis de Laplace. This famous essay explains without recourse to mathematics the principle of probability, and the application of probability to games of chance, natural philosophy, astronomy, many other fields. Translated from the 6th French edition by F. W. Truscott, F. L. Emory, with new introduction for this edition by E. T. Bell. 204pp. 5⅜ x 8. S166 Paperbound **$1.35**

MATHEMATICAL FOUNDATIONS OF INFORMATION THEORY, A. I. Khinchin. For the first time mathematicians, statisticians, physicists, cyberneticists, and communications engineers are offered a complete and exact introduction to this relatively new field. Entropy as a measure of a finite scheme, applications to coding theory, study of sources, channels and codes, detailed proofs of both Shannon theorems for any ergodic source and any stationary channel with finite memory, and much more are covered. Bibliography. vii + 120pp. 5⅜ x 8. S434 Paperbound **$1.35**

SELECTED PAPERS ON NOISE AND STOCHASTIC PROCESS, edited by Prof. Nelson Wax, U. of Illinois. 6 basic papers for newcomers in the field, for those whose work involves noise characteristics. Chandrasekhar, Uhlenbeck & Ornstein, Uhlenbeck & Ming, Rice, Doob. Included is Kac's Chauvenet-Prize winning Random Walk. Extensive bibliography lists 200 articles, up through 1953. 21 figures. 337pp. 6⅛ x 9¼. S262 Paperbound **$2.35**

THEORY OF PROBABILITY, William Burnside. Synthesis, expansion of individual papers presents numerous problems in classical probability, offering many original views succinctly, effectively. Game theory, cards, selections from groups; geometrical probability in such areas as suppositions as to probability of position of point on a line, points on surface of sphere, etc. Includes methods of approximation, theory of errors, direct calculation of probabilities, etc. Index. 136pp. 5⅜ x 8. S567 Paperbound **$1.00**

Vector and tensor analysis, matrix theory

VECTOR AND TENSOR ANALYSIS, A. P. Wills. Covers the entire field of vector and tensor analysis from elementary notions to dyads and non-Euclidean manifolds (especially detailed), absolute differentiation, the Lamé operator, the Riemann-Christoffel and Ricci-Einstein tensors, and the calculation of the Gaussian curvature of a surface. Many illustrations from electrical engineering, relativity theory, astro-physics, quantum mechanics. Presupposes only a good working knowledge of calculus. Exercises at end of each chapter. Intended for physicists and engineers as well as pure mathematicians. 44 diagrams. 114 problems. Bibliography. Index. xxxii + 285pp. 5⅜ x 8. S454 Paperbound **$1.75**

APPLICATIONS OF TENSOR ANALYSIS, A. J. McConnell. (Formerly APPLICATIONS OF THE ABSOLUTE DIFFERENTIAL CALCULUS.) An excellent text for understanding the application of tensor methods to familiar subjects such as dynamics, electricity, elasticity, and hydrodynamics. Explains the fundamental ideas and notation of tensor theory, the geometrical treatment of tensor algebra, the theory of differentiation of tensors, and includes a wealth of practical material. Bibliography. Index. 43 illustrations. 685 problems. xii + 381pp. 5⅜ x 8. S373 Paperbound **$1.85**

VECTOR AND TENSOR ANALYSIS, G. E. Hay. One of the clearest introductions to this increasingly important subject. Start with simple definitions, finish the book with a sure mastery of oriented Cartesian vectors, Christoffel symbols, solenoidal tensors, and their applications. Complete breakdown of plane, solid, analytical, differential geometry. Separate chapters on application. All fundamental formulae listed & demonstrated. 195 problems, 66 figures. viii + 193pp. 5⅜ x 8. S109 Paperbound **$1.75**

VECTOR ANALYSIS, FOUNDED UPON THE LECTURES OF J. WILLARD GIBBS, by E. B. Wilson. Still a first-rate introduction and supplementary text for students of mathematics and physics. Based on the pioneering lectures of Yale's great J. Willard Gibbs, can be followed by anyone who has had some calculus. Practical approach, stressing efficient use of combinations and functions of vectors. Worked examples from geometry, mechanics, hydrodynamics, gas theory, etc., as well as practice examples. Covers basic vector processes, differential and integral calculus in relation to vector functions, and theory of linear vector functions, forming an introduction to the study of multiple algebra and matrix theory. While the notation is not always modern, it is easily followed. xviii + 436pp. 5⅜ x 8. S656 Paperbound **$2.00**

Say It Correctly Records

These are the best inexpensive pronunciation aids on the market. Spoken by native linguists associated with major American universities, each record contains:

14 minutes of speech—12 minutes of normal but relatively slow speech, 2 minutes at normal conversational speed

120 basic phrases and sentences covering nearly every aspect of everyday life and travel—introducing yourself, travel in autos, buses, taxis, etc., walking, sightseeing, hotels, restaurants, money, shopping, etc.

32 page booklet containing everything on the record plus English translations and an easy-to-follow phonetic guide

Clear, high fidelity quality recordings

Unique bracketing system and selection of basic sentences enabling you to expand the use of your SAY IT CORRECTLY records with a dictionary so as to fit thousands of additional situations and needs.

Use this record to supplement any course or text. All sounds in each language are illustrated perfectly for you. Imitate the speaker in the pause which follows each foreign phrase in the slow section and you will be amazed at the increased ease and accuracy of your pronunciation. Available, one language per record, for

French	Modern Greek	Swedish
Italian	Japanese	Hebrew
Spanish	Russian	English (for German-speaking people)
Dutch	Portuguese	English (for Spanish-speaking people)
German	Serbo-Croatian	
Turkish		

7" (33⅓ rpm) record, album, booklet. $1.00 each.

FREE! All you do is ask for it!

96 MOST USEFUL PHRASES FOR TOURISTS AND STUDENTS: FRENCH, SPANISH, GERMAN, ITALIAN. A booklet with the equivalents for such important everyday phrases as "Excuse me," "Can you help me?" "Write it down, please," "Take me to this address," and "Do you speak English?"

Say It phrase books

"SAY IT" in the foreign language of your choice! We have sold over ½ million copies of these popular, useful language books. They will not make you an expert linguist overnight, but they do cover most practical matters of everyday life abroad.

Over 1000 useful phrases, expressions, with additional variants, substitutions.

Modern! Useful! Hundreds of phrases not available in other texts: "Nylon," "air-conditioned," etc.

The ONLY inexpensive phrase book **completely indexed.** Everything is available at a flip of your finger, ready for use.

Prepared by native linguists, travel experts.

Based on years of travel experience abroad.

This handy phrase book may be used by itself, or it may supplement any other text or course; it provides a living element. Used by many colleges and institutions: Hunter College; Barnard College; Army Ordnance School, Aberdeen; and many others. Available, 1 book per language:

Danish (T818) 75¢
Dutch (T817) 75¢
English (for German-speaking people) (T801) 60¢
English (for Italian-speaking people) (T816) 60¢
English (for Spanish-speaking people) (T802) 60¢
Esperanto (T820) 75¢
French (T803) 60¢
German (T804) 60¢
Modern Greek (T813) 75¢
Hebrew (T805) 75¢

Italian (T806) 60¢
Japanese (T807) 75¢
Norwegian (T814) 75¢
Russian (T810) 75¢
Spanish (T811) 60¢
Turkish (T821) 75¢
Yiddish (T815) 75¢
Swedish (T812) 75¢
Polish (T808) 75¢
Portuguese (T809) 75¢

Listen and Learn

LISTEN & LEARN is the only language record course designed especially to meet your travel and everyday needs. It is available in separate sets for FRENCH, SPANISH, GERMAN, PORTUGUESE, MODERN GREEK, ITALIAN, RUSSIAN, or JAPANESE, and each set contains three 33⅓ rpm long-playing records—1½ hours of recorded speech by eminent native speakers who are professors at Columbia, New York University, Queens College.

Check the following special features found only in LISTEN & LEARN.

Dual-language recording. 812 selected phrases and sentences, over 3200 words, spoken first in English, then in their foreign language equivalents. A suitable pause follows each foreign phrase, allowing you time to repeat the expression. You learn by unconscious assimilation.

128- to 206-page manual contains everything on the records, plus a simple phonetic pronounciation guide.

Indexed for convenience. The only set on the market that is completely indexed. No more puzzling over where to find the phrase you need. Just look in the rear of the manual.

Practical. No time wasted on material you can find in any grammar. LISTEN & LEARN covers central core material with phrase approach. Ideal for the person with limited learning time.

Living, modern expressions, not found in other courses. Hygienic products, modern equipment, shopping—expressions used every day, like "nylon" and "air-conditioned."

Limited objective. Everything you learn, no matter where you stop, is immediately useful. You have to finish other courses, wade through grammar and vocabulary drill, before they help you.

High-fidelity recording. LISTEN & LEARN records equal in clarity and surface-silence any record on the market costing up to $6 per record.

"Excellent . . . the spoken records . . . impress me as being among the very best on the market," **Prof. Mario Pei**, Dept. of Romance Languages, Columbia University." "Inexpensive and well-done . . . it would make an ideal present," CHICAGO SUNDAY TRIBUNE. "More genuinely helpful than anything of its kind which I have previously encountered," **Sidney Clark**, well-known author of "ALL THE BEST" travel books.

UNCONDITIONAL GUARANTEE. Try LISTEN & LEARN, then return it within 10 days for full refund, if you are not satisfied. It is guaranteed after you actually use it.

LISTEN & LEARN comes in 6 useful modern languages—FRENCH, SPANISH, GERMAN, ITALIAN, PORTUGUESE, MODERN GREEK, RUSSIAN or JAPANESE—one language to each set of three 33⅓ rpm records. 128- to 206-page manual. Album.

Spanish	the set **$5.95**	**German**	the set **$5.95**	**Japanese**	the set **$5.95**
French	the set **$5.95**	**Italian**	the set **$5.95**	**Russian**	the set **$5.95**
Modern Greek	the set **$5.95**	**Portuguese**	the set **$5.95**		

Dover publishes books on art, music, philosophy, literature, languages, history, social sciences, psychology, handcrafts, orientalia, puzzles and entertainments, chess, pets and gardens, books explaining science, intermediate and higher mathematics, mathematical physics, engineering, biological sciences, earth sciences, classics of science, etc. Write to:

Dept. catrr.
Dover Publications, Inc.
180 Varick Street, N. Y. 14, N. Y.